GENIUS in AMERICA

The Story of C. Harry Knowles, Inventor

GENIUS in AMERICA

The Story of C. Harry Knowles, Inventor

Mary Ellen Hendrix

THE
DONNELL
GROUP

Montgomery, Alabama

The Donnell Group
3514 Lansdowne Drive
Montgomery, AL 36111
(334) 303-2355
www.thedonnellgroup.com

Book design by Mike DeMent

C. Harry Knowles Collection compiled by Al Barrett

Printing: Wells Printing, Montgomery, Alabama

Library of Congress Control Number: 2014930110
ISBN 978-0-9884165-4-3

First Edition

10 9 8 7 6 5 4 3 2 1

For my husband, Sam, and our daughter, Kelsey,
for their unfailing support and love

and

for my parents,
Mary and Bill Hughes,
who taught me to love books
and work honorably

Contents

Author's Note

Technological wizardry often goes unnoticed in the lightning pace of daily living. However, the inventions that make our lives hum begin within insatiably curious and canny minds—such as that of C. Harry Knowles. Coming of age in the glow of post-World War II United States scientific superiority, Knowles joined a melting pot of discovery at Bell Telephone Laboratories on his way to roughly 400 patents in transistors, lasers, and bar code scanning technology. Those inventions have revolutionized and shaped us as a society.

Still, Knowles' story is not told by reviewing patents. Rather, his tale is rooted in the triumphs and failures of his personal life and nearly 40 years as shepherd of the company he founded, Metrologic Instruments, Inc. Early in the interview process, I realized that Harry Knowles also reflects the grander, perhaps more profound story of genius in America: what genius looks like when U.S. ingenuity flourishes and how entrepreneurship flails when learning lags. To that end of better learning, Knowles established his greatest legacy, the Knowles Science Teaching Foundation, to foster excellent high school science and math teaching for thousands of students each year.

The journey of underdog Harry Knowles is a pointedly human one. The telling is forthright, because the reader can rejoice in the triumphs only if he knows the obstacles. Many of the photos are from Knowles' personal collection, including Auburn aerials taken during his college days (from his brother's war surplus plane) and as editor of the *Glomerata*, the student yearbook.

Included are three sidebars of text shaded in gray (one in Chapter 7 and two in Chapter 9) written by Knowles on matters of technology dear to his heart. Also, this biography abounds in sources that are numbered within the text to correspond to the numbering within the "Notes" section at the back of the book. This approach to endnotes provides more accurate reference points and is employed for the die-hard researcher. However, the story is best served by ignoring the numbering while reading. I hope my words do justice to the life.

Chapter 1

Birmingham Boy

(1928-1945)

Within a few miles of Tuxedo Junction in Birmingham, Alabama, Carl Harry Knowles made his early-morning debut on August 15, 1928, in the bed of his grandmother, Effie Edwards, affectionately known as Big Mama.[1]

History deemed the decade the Roaring Twenties in the U.S., a Jazz Age of flappers, talking movies, automobiles and airplanes. Charles Lindbergh's successful trans-Atlantic flight from New York to Paris in 1927 added an exclamation point to America's prosperous mood, as did the falsely inflated stock market, all helping fuel Republican Herbert Hoover's election as president in 1928.

The boarding house in Birmingham where C. Harry Knowles was born August 15, 1928

In the Magic City of Birmingham, however, fissures in the economy had already appeared, especially for farmers, miners, mill workers and the unemployed.[2] Birmingham's post-agrarian, industrial foundation was made of iron, steel and coal, with U.S. Steel's Tennessee Coal, Iron and Railroad Company providing livelihoods for more workers than any other business in the county.[3] A little more than a year later, stock prices would plummet and the Great Depression would begin. In Birmingham's Jefferson County, more than 120,000 people would lose their jobs, later prompting Franklin Roosevelt, newly elected president in 1932, to label Birmingham "the worst hit town in the country."[4]

But in the dawning hours of that August day in 1928, eight-year-old

William Wallace Penn, Jr., knew nothing of his country's impending economic downslide. Young Bill only knew that his half-brother Harry had been born to his mother, Ruby, and his step-father, Harry Holmes Knowles. Bill had waited all night for news on the huge front porch swing of his grandmother's boarding house, where three floors of boarders and family lived. "It was before the Depression, but times were hard," Bill remembered. "We all lived with Big Mama."[5]

Harry's grandmother, Effie Edwards, known as "Big Mama"

"All" included Big Mama; her second husband, Dancy Edwards, an Englishman and noted brick mason known for the architecture of his arches; Ruby; Big Harry; Bill; and the new addition, C. Harry. The boarding house contained a full-size pipe organ, carved marble statues, tapestries and a beautiful wooden staircase and banister that Bill and Harry would slide down as boys. Harry was born on the first floor of the sprawling house in Big Mama's bedroom, the only bedroom with its own bath, allowing ample privacy that night for Ruby and the probably mid-wife-attended birth.

It was still dark when Big Mama told Bill the baby had arrived. "I was so excited to have a baby brother," Bill said. "I can remember the very room where he was born." Big brother got his first glimpse of Harry as Bill entered the double French doors into Effie's bedroom, where he saw the large bed with a cedar chest at its foot. "I remember going in and seeing Harry lying in that big bed. I was sure one proud brother. Being proud of him has never diminished."[6]

Although Big Mama's house would serve as a welcome haven for many years, the young family moved out soon after C. Harry's birth, at least within a year or two. Despite the arrival of the Depression, father Big Harry had a solid job as an engineer with Southern States Equipment Company designing electrical substations. Later, C. Harry would recall visiting his father's plant: "The wood and metal chips were flying. There was an excitement at being around a real working shop. I thought, 'This is me.'"[7] The family was fortunate compared to others in the city who lost their jobs as many of the town's industry smokestacks stilled.

The Knowles family's move deposited them at 436 West 5th Street, a 25-minute, seven-cent streetcar ride from Big Mama

Knowles home, 436 W. 5th Street, Birmingham

within view of the Legion Field football stadium. "I could look out the window of our house and see Legion Field," C. Harry said.[8] The modest one-story, one-bath house sat on the corner of 5th and a side alley down which one accessed the family's garage. At the end of the street, the transit track split into a side track; and the streetcars could turn around (but rarely did). Fans heading to Legion Field would come here at the end of 5th Street, get off the streetcar, and walk the sidewalk to the stadium. They also could stop at the drug store there to get some of the five-cent ice cream the neighborhood children coveted.[9]

C. Harry remembered his room at 5th Street and said he never felt lacking for anything—materially, that is.[10] However, the emotional well-being of the family sorely ached. The blended Knowles brood bore the scars of Ruby's and Big Harry's complex pasts.

Ruby and Harry probably met at the boarding house; the elder Harry was no doubt attracted to Ruby's flapper-style beauty. She was reported to be popular, pretty, energetic and organized. Ruby, born Ruby Genevieve Smith in 1902 in Macon, Georgia, had married her first husband, William Wallace Penn, in 1918 in Birmingham, but they had divorced while Bill Jr. was still an infant.[11]

She became Harry's third wife September 15, 1926.[12] Harry, born in 1881 in Illinois the third son and one of eleven children of Ianthus Shaler and Mary Dodge Knowles, grew up mostly in Kingsley, Iowa, where he met his first wife, Marguerite (later known as Margaret) Heacock.[13] Harry graduated in engineering from Iowa State having raised at least a small portion of his first term's tuition via sales of an Iowa tornado

Harry Holmes Knowles (C. Harry's father) and his first wife, Margaret

photo he snapped with his glass plate camera. This shot became, according to author Susan Goodwillie, "one of the first known photographs of the eerily funnel-shaped cyclone cloud. Using a bedroom closet as his darkroom, Harry produced several prints, which he sold for 25 cents apiece to build up his college fund."[14] This penchant for photography must have carried to Harry's sons, as two of them later became quite enamored with photography.

Barely a year after they married, Harry and Margaret had a son, Hugh Shaler, on September 23, 1904.[15] Harry had been working in mining and followed that industry to new opportunity in Mexico in 1906. An adventurer and a bit of a wanderer, Harry thrived in Mexico, becoming engineer to a 100,000-acre cotton plantation there in 1907.[16] Harry's family grew there, with Ralph Holmes joining brother Hugh May 7, 1909.[17] By 1910, however, the Knowles world was unraveling as intense unrest in Mexico led to revolution against dictator Porfirio Diaz, with politician Francisco Madero (who would be Mexico's president from 1911 until he was killed in 1913) declaring rebellion aided by the notorious general and bandit Pancho Villa.

Due to the civil turmoil, in 1912, at age eight, Hugh was sent to San Antonio, Texas, to live and study in safety.[18] Margaret and Ralph followed in 1915, but Harry, reluctant to leave the Mexico plantation, didn't head for Texas until 1917. By then, an untraversable divide had developed between Margaret and Harry. Margaret couldn't understand Harry's delays and was openly seen in the company of other men. The marriage didn't recover. Soon after Harry returned to the U.S., he and Margaret divorced in January 1918.

The children remained with Margaret, and Harry married again that same year to a woman, Florence, who was barely more than half Harry's age. Within a few years, Harry and Florence divorced. In Susan Goodwillie's biography of Hugh Knowles, *Now Hear This*, Harry is described as "poetic, sensitive, deeply feeling—perhaps above all, lusty," someone who "never really knew what to make of women, except that when he loved one, he felt duty bound to marry her. Thereafter, his extraordinary jealousy held his other emotions hostage."[19]

Harry had left Texas and eventually found his way to Birmingham, after various employment stops in between, including in Atlanta and New Orleans. His contact with sons Hugh and Ralph was extremely limited, a fact Hugh resented and for which Hugh held his father responsible.[20] When 47-year-old Harry and third wife Ruby had a child, perhaps Harry belatedly realized his fathering mistakes with his first two sons. Possibly age had calmed some of Harry's wandering spirit. Whatever the case, Harry poured his fathering energies into his new progeny—his third biological son, Carl Harry.

In fact, C. Harry analyzed his father saying he "never thoroughly loved anyone except me in the most open, warm sense." One of the younger Harry's earliest memories is of his father tucking C. Harry into his coat and looking at the stars together. A fascination toward astronomy remained, for the child carried that love for star-gazing into his adulthood.[21]

The father also immersed his son in reading. "Dad would put me in his lap every night and read to me," C. Harry said. "I remember the Big Little Books. He had an adoration of books and would encourage me to play with them and all kinds of toys." Indeed, the elder Harry, who had several patents to his name, inspired a sense of curiosity. When C. Harry would take his toys or a bicycle apart to see how they worked, even when he couldn't get them back together, his father never angered.[22]

"Big Harry doted on little Harry," Bill said. "I should have been resentful, but I wasn't. Big Harry was good to me." Bill recalled how excited his step-father was for him when Bill appeared in the newspaper for his high school pole vaulting prowess. Even so, Bill was sensitive to the fact that, although his mother Ruby had married Harry, "I still was a Penn and not a Knowles."[23]

As effusively warm as Harry was toward his son, Ruby maintained an opposite parenting style toward both her children. Bill and C. Harry had no memories of their mother ever hugging or holding them or telling her sons she loved them. Charming, efficient and a superb cook, she nonetheless seemed incapable of expressing love.[24] C. Harry, almost always referring to his mother as "Ruby" in his remembrances and

Harry at about age 2 with Ruby, his mother

rarely as "Mom or Mother," characterized her as an extraordinarily cold woman.[25] This sentiment, cemented and expressed in C. Harry's later years, is understandable when one takes into account the child's subsequent experiences with his mother.

Ruby called her younger son "Carl Harry" but C. Harry's dad always called him "Harry," disliking the uncle for whom his son was named. Uncle Carl, an undertaker, was Ruby's brother, an ex-Marine boxing champion, and more than a mild drinker.[26]

Care of the house and children was shared with a black nanny named Liza, who, along with Big Mama, provided Bill and C. Harry some of the mothering their lives lacked. The children also received hugs and love from friends of their parents, "Uncle Luke and Aunt Jean," a childless couple who doted on the children. "Jean took us in her lap and dumped all her love on Harry and me," Bill said.

The Knowles household bore a veneer of normalcy, with certain routines firmly planted in the children's memories, such as Big Harry listening to the news on the radio and on Saturdays, during the "Texaco hour," the father conscripting the boys to listen to opera.[27]

Dinner was a formal event, with good silverware and napkins. Father Harry was a wizard with cuts and cooking of meats and often assumed a chef's role on the weekends. The children were expected to appear at the table with themselves and their clothes clean—a feat that could be challenging for C. Harry, who confessed to being a "dirty kid" who enjoyed a good romp in the mud. C. Harry's favorite food growing up was fried chicken.[28]

As well intentioned as the order of the dinner table may have been, however, Harry and Ruby could not prevent their problems from breaking the family surface. Ruby was neither stable nor tranquil and Harry, although matured, carried his own emotional baggage from his past.

The marriage floundered. "I remember stormy meals between Ruby and Dad," C. Harry said.

Bill recalled waking up in the night to the sound of his parents arguing. "I never saw Big Harry and Mother kiss or hold hands," he said. "They didn't get along. Mother was a hard woman but could be a loyal friend. She did not have a capacity to have that feeling—to love someone. She came as close to it with me as anyone. She could care but not love; it was almost a defense."[29]

Tolerating a tie, six-year-old Harry in his back-yard, October 1934

Ruby's lack of maternal warmth can be seen in one of the children's successes. Bill and several classmates in his Graymont Elementary School were double-promoted one year. "I was *so proud*," Bill said. The young boy rushed home, where he found his mother tending laundry in the big wash tub on the enclosed back porch. After sharing his big news, Bill said, "she didn't even look up. That's how cold and uncaring she was. I know it was because she was unhappy with Big Harry."

Ruby was unhappy enough that she abandoned her home time and again. When C. Harry was quite young, with no warning, according to Bill, Ruby fled to New York City, where she worked in a department store as a floor-walker watching for shoplifters. During the first five years of C. Harry's life, Ruby, with only Bill in tow, bounced back and forth to Big Mama's house, while C. Harry remained with his father.[30]

Finally, the turmoil climaxed in 1934.[31] The marriage was over and Ruby was leaving for good. Harry, not even a first-grader yet, had to be told. His father sent him down to the corner drugstore. "Dad primed me for her leaving," C. Harry said. "In the store there were a toy gun and a sailor cap. I wanted those so bad. Dad sent me down with a quarter and told me to buy them."

When the child returned, the parents sat him down and told him Ruby and Bill were leaving. His father asked him, "Do you want to go with her or stay here?" The young child looked down at the toys he clutched in his small hands. "I'll stay here," he answered quietly.

That the elder Harry placed such a weighty decision on a six-year-

Graymont Elementary School photo of Harry

old is remarkable. "If I'd gone with Mom," C. Harry said, recalling the incident as a 79-year-old, "it would have killed Dad. It would have been unthinkable to not stay with Dad. Dad would put me in his lap every night and read to me."[32] Ruby and Big Harry's divorce became final in 1935.[33]

"I was probably a junior in high school when Harry and Ruby broke up for good," Bill said. Separating the brothers apparently posed little issue as they were already separated by their eight-year age gulf and their differing parental experiences. Bill seemed remote to young Harry. "He was so much younger, we didn't have that close a relationship," Bill said. "He was such a neat, sharp little kid…more quiet with his dad's intelligence. We both lacked for a mom. He felt that [deeply, as he was] much younger and more impressionable. I guess he was happy but not as happy as he could have been with a loving mother."[34]

Following young Harry's declaration that he would remain with his father, Ruby and her first son moved out. Their residence was somewhat fluid, but C. Harry did visit Bill at Big Mama's. Harry recalled tagging along with Bill to an air field within walking distance of the boarding house. There, the older brother would fly his model airplanes, marvels to Harry who was awed by the working parts. "Bill was into airplanes; he always wanted to fly," Harry said. One of Bill's models was a bi-plane with moveable controls, ailerons and rudder. "I would go with him to the air field and touch a real airplane." Thus, despite no longer living together and a gulf brought on by circumstance, the two brothers did share a bond. As Harry said, Bill was "quite a hero in my eyes—my first hero." Bill's love for airplanes foreshadowed a later time in his life when he would become a true hero during wartime service.[35]

At one point, Bill and mother Ruby lived in a downtown Birmingham apartment near the courthouse before moving to Big Mama's again. Ruby was working as secretary to the president of the Tutwiler Hotel,[36] where she met Joe Torbron, a traveling salesman for a nuts and bolts company. Joe became Ruby's third husband in 1935 and moved them to Houston, Texas, a sizeable sales area for hardware accounts at the time. Bill, who said he remembers more times without his mother than with her, stayed at Big Mama's until the couple found an apartment. After Bill joined them, they moved again, this time to Pasadena, Texas.[37]

Meanwhile, the two Harrys (with help from nanny Liza) were on their own back in Birmingham. With Ruby gone, the elder Harry concentrated on his son even more. Books and music were always encouraged. C. Harry started school a year late with Graymont Elementary's first grade. Harry felt "out of place because I had no mom." His first-grade teacher, Mrs. Barnes, figured out her pupil's situation quickly. "She was always sweet to me," Harry said.[38]

Young Harry, who walked to Graymont, loved school and excelled, earning double promotions in grammar school. Thus, he started out as one of the oldest students in his grade school class and ended up one of the youngest.

Fifth Street was "loaded with kids" and Harry enjoyed playing with Jack, Sue, Frank Harrison (who many years later came to Ruby's funeral), Pauline Whaley next door, and others from the neighborhood. Birmingham's Judge Bonner lived across the street from the Knowles residence. Nanny Liza kept tabs on her charge until Harry's father came home from work on the streetcar. C. Harry's life—occupied with his dad, Liza, school, and friends—settled into a more consistent rhythm without the constant tension Ruby's presence had caused.

Early in this period, when C. Harry was about seven, the elder Harry's first son Hugh, who was in his early 30s, visited at the urging of Hugh's wife, Jo.[39] Hugh, who felt more abandoned by his father than even C. Harry did by Ruby, had a tough, scarred history with his father. However, Hugh acquiesced to Jo who, following the death of Margaret (Hugh's mother and Harry's first wife) a few years earlier in 1932,[40] decided their son needed a grandparent in his life.

Big Harry, left, and his first son, Hugh, C. Harry's half-brother, circa 1935

Hugh, though not likely to admit it, owed at least some of his career

C. Harry, right, with his dad at the L&N Railroad

success to the inventive gene he must have inherited from Harry Knowles. Hugh was destined to make a huge name for himself in the hearing aid industry, inventing many of the first smaller, transistor-based hearing aids, revolutionizing acoustical theory and standards and providing critical sound experience for wartime application.[41] He would be named president of the Acoustical Society of America in 1944[42] and later his equipment would go to the moon and Mars. The company he founded, Knowles Electronics, remained a global acoustical leader into the next century.[43]

Even at this early juncture in his career, Hugh provided another hero-sized big brother to little Harry. Thus, it was with great excitement that, in 1937, nine-year-old Harry visited Hugh and Jo and their children in their Chicago apartment. Hugh, 35mm camera in hand, took Harry to the circus, where Hugh snapped pictures of their day together.[44] More amazing to Harry, Hugh then went to his home darkroom and developed the film and printed the pictures that allowed reliving the wonderful day.[45]

The incident is recounted in *Now Hear This*: "Harry was spellbound as Hugh reproduced the miracle of the circus from his mysterious elixir of chemicals, liquid and paper. It was a magical, life-changing experience for Harry....Hugh became an inspiring, though distant, role model for Harry, whose interest and subsequent skill in photography earned him his way through college."[46]

"I had an instant attraction to photography," C. Harry said. "I thought maybe I could do this. To me Hugh was an absolute giant." Not only did Hugh show Harry how to take pictures and unlock the mysteries of developing film, but Harry said Hugh was "charming, multi-linguistic... this tower of intellectual strength." The impression on the nine-year-old boy was deep and forecast a near-constant attachment between Harry and a camera. Again, the brothers need only to have looked to their father for the first hint of a Knowles knack for photography, languages, and scientific discovery.[47]

C. Harry not only bonded with Hugh during his visit but Jo, who "poured time and attention into me," he said. That loving attention was an anchor to Harry for many years, especially later during the normal frustrations of high school.

In contrast, Ruby was anything but an anchor to C. Harry during his youth, providing a sort of drifting, ever-elusive compass to his life. She did write to her second son, and Harry spent at least two summers in Pasadena. During a vacation to Camp Warnecke in New Braunfels, Texas, with the Torbrons, Harry learned to swim after he accidentally jumped off the wrong side of a tree straight into the water, at which point he decided he "better start swimming."[48]

In 1938, C. Harry told his father he wanted his mother. Texas was calling on a more permanent basis. No doubt key to the drama was the fact that, at the same time, the elder Harry had become serious about a woman in his life, Thelma Villines Ramsey, and married her on June 22 that year in Gulfport, Mississippi.[49] At age 36, Thelma was 20 years younger than Harry and a divorced mother of a son, Jim, two months and a day older than C. Harry. Harry and Thelma had started out just friends, introduced through a mutual friend a couple of years earlier.[50] Neither of the boys attended the wedding, after which Big Harry moved Thelma and Jim into the 5th Street house. One can imagine how

C. Harry's step-mother, Thelma, and his father, Harry Holmes Knowles

the 10-year-old Harry felt when, for the first time since Ruby left, the father's attention was not completely focused on his son.

Looking back, C. Harry said he felt "strong guilt pains for plucking my dad's heartstrings, saying 'I want my mother.'"[51] Considering how the elder Harry had revolved his life around his son, it must have been difficult to tell C. Harry that he could go live with his mother—a mother who had paid little attention to her offspring in his earliest years. Perhaps the elder Harry realized on some level a need for the father and son to place a little distance between themselves. As painful as it is for any parent, Harry had to let his son find his own way.

Young Harry moved soon after to Houston, where the Torbrons had relocated, to live with Ruby and her husband, Joe. In 1938, Bill had enrolled in (Auburn's) Alabama Polytechnic's cooperative education tion program, which alternated schooling with work experience; so he came home to Texas periodically.

Jim Ramsey, left, and Harry, right, at age 9, with neighborhood friend Frank Harrison

Life in Texas and with Joe had provided Ruby a good lifestyle, complete with a nice home and garden clubs. She'd always hungered for an active social life and organized a local Pilot Club.[52] She signed Harry up for piano lessons and Boy Scouts and gave Harry a wide berth of freedom for friends and exploring the local woods, even making her second son a Robin Hood outfit.[53]

Harry attended Pershing Junior High where he was recognized for his talent for debate and hung out with his best friend, Billy Shoemaker. Constant companions, Harry and Billy rode bikes together, practiced piano, gazed into microscopes, experimented with their chemistry sets, went to Boy Scouts, or even shared girlfriends. For fun, sometimes they would "do encyclopedia lookups" or build model airplanes. Brother Bill, with his passion for airplanes, may have inspired some of the boys' interest.

"Bill was mostly at Auburn," Harry said. "But when he was around, he was a wonderful big brother."

All was not wonderful with Ruby, however. "Life with Ruby was disorderly," Harry remembered. "I always needed a haircut. My school

Harry, left, and step-brother Jim at their Birmingham home

towels were always dirty. My grades with Dad were good, but with Ruby, my grades were a problem. It was the result of being upset." Harry recalled one time when he saw Ruby hit her husband, Joe, in the head with a vacuum cleaner nozzle, Joe's thank you for writing Ruby a check for Christmas instead of buying her a present.[51]

The tensions of the Torbron household in some ways reflected the tension in the U.S. with most families feeling the strain of a struggling economy. Back in Birmingham, the elder Harry's fourth wife Thelma worked at Liberty National Insurance Company while her new husband continued his work as an electrical engineer. "Mom had to work and Dad worked, so I came home to an empty house," Thelma's son Jim commented. "But times were bad in 1938. It took the war to bring the economy up."[55]

While President Roosevelt's New Deal had helped many areas of the country such as Birmingham with various work programs and although railroads placed several large orders for Birmingham steel in the mid-1930s[56] easing some of the fiscal crisis, the national recession of 1937 left citizens uneasy. Those feelings would only increase during the next several years as eyes turned to war in Europe.

Pershing Junior High student Harry, 1941

Following the absorption of Austria by Germany in 1938, Adolph Hitler completed his takeover of Czechoslovakia in 1939 as part of his

Bomber pilot William Penn, Harry's half-brother, would lead 29 missions over Germany before his Army Air Corps tenure ended.

devastating march through Europe. With the German leader's invasion of Poland that same year, Great Britain and France formally declared war. The U.S., hunkered in an isolationist mentality, proclaimed neutrality despite Roosevelt's attempts to supply the Allies. 1940 saw the defeat of Norway, Denmark, Luxembourg, Belgium and the Netherlands by Germany before spring was out. Then, Hitler invaded France June 5, and Roosevelt shifted the country from its formally neutral stance to "non-belligerency."

Freedom-lovers were horrified as Paris fell on June 15 and less than a month later the Battle of Britain brought Germany's first aerial attack on England. Americans found it increasingly difficult to maintain a hands-off approach. When Roosevelt was re-elected in November to an unprecedented third term, he converted many factories for war production. As historian Kenneth Davis stated, this "shift to a wartime economy [shook] off the last effects of the Great Depression. During the war, America [would] produce 297,000 planes, 86,000 tanks, 12,000 ships, and enormous quantities of other vehicles, arms, and munitions."[57]

A war-ready nation meant jobs, especially in Birmingham where steel and iron were king. The country and the Knowles and Torbron families entered 1941 with many changes on the horizon. Most realized the U.S. would be drawn into the war. After Japan, as part of the German-Italian Axis, invaded French Indochina in July 1941, Roosevelt cut off trade with Japan, froze U.S. assets and cut off oil supplies. By the fall, *The Birmingham News* saw war with Japan as imminent.[58]

This era of escalating world war did not immediately affect young Harry, busy as he was with his junior high life and friends and coping with an erratic mother. But, as war became inevitable, Ruby and Joe's marriage became a casualty of the times. Bill remembered he was home on a college co-op cycle working at a local air base in December 1941. "I was staying with Mother and Joe in Houston," he said, "and I was out driving Sunday afternoon, December 7, when I heard the announcement of the attack on Pearl Harbor. The next day I went down to the recruiting office and within two weeks I was in Army Air Corps pilot training."[59] Also on December 8, the U.S. declared war on Japan. Europe's war had hit home.

Harry, as a 13-year-old, knew how tiny Japan looked on the map. He remembered his reaction to Pearl Harbor as shock and thinking "How can the Japanese even think of attacking us?"[60]

Subsequently, Joe, a reservist, entered the service, as did Ruby who enlisted in the Women's Army Auxiliary Corps, effectively ending their marriage and Harry's life in Texas.[61] "I had no doubt Ruby wanted me out," Harry said. "She saw the end of her marriage. So I moved back to live with Dad." Harry did finish out the school year in Texas the spring of 1942, however, before heading home to Birmingham.

Before Harry left, Ruby filled his head with one overwhelming thought—that Thelma "is not your mother." Thus, the teenage Harry arrived back in the Magic City with plenty of attitude for armor.[62]

But Thelma was no Ruby. Rather, she was full of warmth and guided by her complete loyalty to family. In fact, when her first husband left while Jim was still a baby until marrying the elder Harry, she had served as the primary breadwinner for 12 family members, including her parents and siblings.[63] A lovely redhead with a good figure and an even better personality, Thelma would not be undone by the newly arrived C. Harry.

C. Harry was shocked when

When Ruby enlisted in the Women's Army Auxiliary Corps, Harry's life in Texas ended.

Harry with Viola, the Knowles family maid

he found Jim in his—Harry's—room. As Harry recalled, "I swaggered into the house asking myself 'who is this woman?' I called her Thelma. I came back and it wasn't my room; it was Jim's room. This boy had taken over *my* room."[64]

Thelma gave the young Harry about two weeks before adjusting his attitude. "I remember the day Thelma sat me down and said 'I am your mother and you are my son and Jim is your brother.' She laid the law down."

C. Harry's defenses fell away. "She was everything Ruby was not—loving, huggy, squeezy, kissy. Jim and I were equals. I could not in my wildest imagination have asked for a better mother."

Meanwhile, the elder Harry provided Jim a father. "He was a dad for me like Mom was a mom for Harry," Jim said. "Neither of them made a difference between the two of us. We lived as brothers."[65]

Jim and C. Harry shared a small bedroom with twin beds. Harry's bed rested against a wall and, three feet away, Jim's bed was tucked against a window. The boys spent more time on the back porch, where they could keep warm by the wood stove and where they typically studied for their classes at Ensley High School, a 10-mile streetcar ride away from home. Because Harry had been double promoted, he was a grade ahead of Jim. It took a long time for the boys to become comfortable with each other, perhaps a remaining effect of Ruby's influence. Then, they weren't that close, Jim said, because Harry was a year ahead in school.

But family life on 5th Street was good for the boys and stable with parents who loved each other. Liza, who had left while C. Harry resided in Texas, had been replaced by another black maid, one victimized at least once by the two teenagers. While C. Harry and Jim played in a tree in the yard, they came upon and captured a small, harmless snake. When the maid walked underneath the tree, the opportunity proved too tempting for the boys, who let the snake fall. Of course, the snake landed on the maid.

The maid didn't bother giving a two-week notice. When the boys' father got home, he was minus one caregiver. Big Harry deployed the boys to Ensley's black neighborhood to apologize and bring the poor woman back to work.[66]

The elder Harry, although he didn't look to be in his late 50s and was reported to be "strong as an ox,"[67] missed the wartime draft because of his age. Harry's typical jealousy concerning his wife was allayed by the fact that Thelma truly loved him. Her loving nature created a nurturing home and compensated for Harry's idiosyncrasies.

"Dad kept to himself and was a little distant," Jim said. "He couldn't get along with people sometimes because he was aloof. But that was his personality; he lived within himself. Dad would have the most horrible nightmares about Mexico—you didn't dare touch him then.

"Mom had everything to do with his mellowing; she made life warm and loving. He never raised a hand to me and only scolded me once. He was a good dad and husband. I don't remember

With her loving ways, Thelma, shown kissing Big Harry, became "Mom" to C. Harry.

any real arguments. I have nothing but pleasant memories of my whole childhood."[68]

Big Harry's habits were entrenched, still listening to the Texaco hour on Saturday. He would sit in his chair, smoke, and listen to Mexi-

The Knowles farmhouse, located on 65 acres near Helena on the Cahaba River, provided a fresh-air retreat for the family.

can music and opera. But the family broke away from 5th Street for fun at times, especially during warm weather.

Harry owned a 65-acre farm outside the city, near Helena, on a bend of the Cahaba River; the land was spectacular in that it hugged river on three sides.[69] Citizens of Birmingham, where smokestacks often left the city with a fine layer of industrial dust, had a long tradition of retreating to the country for fresh air. The boys enjoyed the chance to swim and fish, and the family was able to visit with Thelma's parents, who lived on the farm.

Jim remembered one day on the farm vividly when he and C. Harry and their parents were swimming. Leeches latched onto Jim, whose terrified reaction was the "closest to walking on water" one could see. Jim, who described his childhood physique as "short, fat and blond" and C. Harry as the opposite, said his brother found the incident hilarious. The normally intense, serious C. Harry laughed long and hard.[70]

Another time on the farm, Jim triumphantly returned from the water with a five-pound fish he'd caught. So his brother went down and caught a bigger one. Not to be out-done, Jim headed to the water again. Thus went the brotherly competition.

On the way back from another vacation—this one to Panama City

Teenager Harry, an avid reader, had a natural penchant for math and science.

on the Gulf of Mexico—Big Harry let the two 16-year-olds take turns driving the family Plymouth. At one point, Harry told the younger Harry to turn right; instead, C. Harry turned left through a gas station lot. "He didn't even slow down," Jim said. "I giggled for 100 miles."[71] Panama City was a regular summer destination, where the Knowles family rented the same cottage by the pier each year.[72]

Sunday's schedule included church for the boys, who attended McCoy Memorial Methodist Church with several friends. Big Harry did not attend but had a firm opinion his children should go there because the church had given the boys Bibles on which their names were inscribed.[73] Thelma usually caught up with her work at home on weekends, since she worked during the week.[74]

McCoy Memorial Methodist Church retreat, 1940s

"I went but not with any great conviction," C. Harry said. Jim, on the other hand, at one point in his teenage years contemplated becoming a minister. "I even went to Sunday school fairly regularly," Harry continued, "but it didn't stick. I asked all the hard questions."[75]

Young Harry had witnessed his share of religious cycles with Ruby and Effie as a youngster. When he was born, they were in a "Christian Science mode," which Harry said had been fairly constructive, while later Ruby and Big Mama were involved in a Birmingham non-mainstream religious group called the "I AM" movement. (This movement, a New Age predecessor founded in Chicago in the 1930s, got the acronym from its philosophy of "Ascended Masters.") As a teenager, Harry's experiences thus far had left him lukewarm toward religion; although he participated in McCoy Methodist's activities and described himself as "not rebellious."[76]

C. Harry, a more secure young man with the new-found comfort of a loving mother—she provided a "wonderful, even structure," Harry said—gravitated toward his natural talents. He loved school, but math and science were his favorites, as were his studies of the Latin and French languages. One of C. Harry's favorite places was the Birmingham Public Library. "I would go down on Saturday or Sunday and read," he said. "Life was discovering things and making things."[77] His interest in chemistry led him to build his own lab at one end of the garage.

"I had a friend who was into explosives," Harry said. "Fascinating kid. We built a pipe bomb in our garage. We mixed it, put the cap on… and put a big hole in the side of the garage."[78]

The garage survived and eventually served as C. Harry's darkroom. By the summer of '43 or '44, Harry had garnered a job at Lollar's, one of the largest mail-order film processing outfits in the South. With his salary, he bought a sequence of cameras, his first one being a fold-up three-and-a-quarter format Kodak. He obtained his first serious camera, he said, by 1944—a Leica IIIa which cost him $240. Harry carried it everywhere.

Harry quickly learned every job at Lollar's under the tutelage of the founder's son Bill Lollar, who took Harry under his wing. Lollar's occu-

Harry's first boss, Bill Lollar

pied the third floor of a building on 3rd Avenue that also contained the Lyric Theatre, a 1,300-seat vaudeville-era (opening in 1914) theater diagonally across from the Alabama Theatre.[79] With war raging, male employees were hard to find. Men not at war often worked one of three shifts at the mines and factories. Harry usually ended his day with the final developing stage of about 100 rolls of film, all of which had to be run under water before hanging to dry overnight.

One morning in the summer of 1945, as he got off the streetcar at 17th and 3rd and walked to 18th headed to work, he looked up and saw fire engines. Harry remembered thinking, "What's going on at the Lyric? Then I saw the water."[80]

Birmingham's 3rd Avenue, with the Lyric Theatre, left, two floors above which sat film processor Lollar's

Water was flowing down the steps onto the street. Bill Lollar, spotting Harry, said, "Harry, I think you forgot to turn off the water." Actually, an errant roll of film had backed up the drain, causing water to not

Cameraman Harry, from top left, clockwise: with Speed Graphic at age 17; with his Leica as Ensley High photographer in 1945; first camera, a fold-up Kodak; setting up an outside shot, April 1945; and Harry facing a mirror, 1945

only flood Lollar's but the furrier on the second floor and the Lyric Theatre lobby. Lollar's had to close down and move. Harry was much impressed by how Bill never raised his voice; the two remained close friends.

"It was an era that will never be reproduced again," Harry said of the unique job possibilities wartime brought to the youth of the day. "The opportunities for a teenage kid to flood a downtown theatre—what rich experiences came during the war."

The money Harry earned at Lollar's often was spent on camera equipment or supplies, much to the chagrin of Jim, who couldn't under-

Harry and his father, 1945

stand ignoring an opportunity to buy a car instead.[81] But Harry could hide behind his camera, a trick the self-proclaimed introvert said always eased

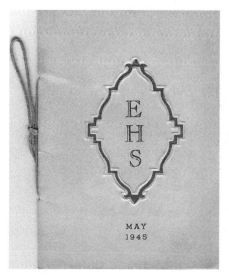

Harry's Ensley High School graduation program, May 30, 1945

social stresses.[82] The prop must have worked because Harry was voted the fourth most popular senior at Ensley High, which also recognized him for his service as an assistant in the science department. His high school senior yearbook was full of photographs he snapped.[83] In addition, before Harry graduated in 1945, he won two Alabama Junior Academy of Science Awards, one for building a working table-top sulphuric acid plant and the other for a paper on photographic emulsion. The youth envisioned working one day for Kodak Research in Rochester, New York.

Despite C. Harry's academic success, high school graduation came with unwanted drama.[84] Two renegade publications—mimeographed sheets—defamatory about the Ensley principal had surfaced amongst the student population. The principal accused Harry of authoring them. "When the principal came to my name, he set my [diploma] aside and said, 'Harry, come see me.' It was an ironic accusation since I'd never been in trouble," Harry said. The principal wasn't convinced of Harry's innocence until the high schooler's father conversed with him. "I went and got Dad. I'd never seen him so angry. I don't think he said five words, but by the time Dad came out it was settled."

Harry left hometown Birmingham in 1945 to pursue a degree in Auburn.

That spring, May 8, the U.S. celebrated with all Allies V-E Day, Victory in Europe Day, following the surrender of Germany to General Eisenhower. Victory over Japan would not come until summer and after the dropping of two atomic bombs.

Thus, as the country celebrated with the world the end of the war, 17-year-old Harry headed (at that time) three-and-a-half hours southeast from Birmingham to Auburn for college at Alabama Polytechnic Institute, where his brother Bill was finishing up his last year after a hiatus for military service. C. Harry arrived armed with his camera, money saved from his job at Lollar's, and a scientific mind ready for the shaping. Harry was about to discover a whole new world.

Chapter 2

Auburn

(1945-1953)

This aerial view of the API campus was shot in 1946 by Harry from his brother Bill's Stearman biplane.

Alabama Polytechnic Institute, API, referred to casually as Auburn, was 5,484 students strong during the 1945-46 school year—its largest enrollment in the land-grant college's near-90-year history.[1] The small East Alabama town, which received its name from the Oliver Goldsmith poem "The Deserted Village"—"...sweet Auburn, loveliest village of the plain"—existed for the most part in support of the college and boasted around 5,000 non-student citizens.[2] That fall, Auburn, along with the nation, welcomed home its boys and men from war and adjusted to the swelling populace. Female students, who, during war, had taken up residence in fraternity houses, moved back to their dorms.

The 1946 *Glomerata*, API's yearbook, commented on the school year's many changes: "...students, crowding the Auburn campus, go to college under the first peace-time conditions we have known in five years. Veterans, returning with their families, bring housing problems and mature evaluation of college that sets a new pace in and out of classes for all of us."[3]

Naïve Harry arrived on campus eager to plow his way in the world. By spring of 1946, nearly 3,000 freshmen would be classmates with him as increasing numbers of veterans arrived.[4] His gravitation toward Auburn resulted from half-brother Bill's presence there. "I thought if Bill's there, then it must be wonderful. So it was natural to go to Auburn," Harry said.[5]

Another family connection existed via Harry's half-brother Hugh

who had attended Auburn for most of a year from September 1920 until July 1921, when the financially strapped Hugh lied about his age—he was just shy of 17 at the time—and joined the merchant marines. Although Hugh was in Auburn but a short time, he'd already been impressed by his professors whom he called "some of the best in the South." In turn, Hugh left his mark on Auburn, breaking an underwater swimming record at the school his first month there.[6] Harry, however, in September 1945, was oblivious to this particular family tie with API.

Hugh Knowles on Auburn's Samford lawn, 1921

During the 1945-46 academic year, Luther N. Duncan led API in his 11th year as president of the college. He would serve just one more year before his death in office July 26, 1947. Alabama Governor Chauncey Sparks presided over the API board of trustees which included Paul S. Haley, T.D. Samford, and S.L. Toomer, whose last names either already adorned or later would appear on Auburn landmarks. The *Glomerata* spoke of the Auburn administration saying it had "made an effort to expand its scope, influencing its students to live intelligently and courageously in a world which many of them have helped to make free and in which many of them will be leaders. With the largest enrollment and faculty on record, the school has shown marked advancement and progress under the years of Dr. L. N. Duncan's presidency, and promises to show even more. Renewed vigor in the cause of liberal and democratic education is the aim of the administration."[7]

Although Auburn tuition and supplies costs were minimal, Harry said his father couldn't help with expenses because he no longer had

Harry, left, and brother Bill Penn at Auburn, 1945

a steady job. "Before the war he had a solid engineering job with Southern States," C. Harry said. In fact, the elder Harry had at least six patents to his name for electrical equipment, such as switches and circuits.[8] "Something prompted Dad to set up his own company in competition with Southern States, which in turn sued Dad for patent infringement and won."[9] The son was living with Ruby in Texas at the time. Thus, during the war and after, C. Harry's father struggled financially. At one point, he was a sales representative of electrical equipment; by the late 1940s, he worked as an engineering draftsman. The bottom line was college man Harry was on his own when it came to tuition and living expenses.

Harry lived on Gay Street in Garden Courts, dorm-style residences for 40 to 50 students behind a duplex where brother Bill, his wife Cathy, and their baby girl Hope lived on one side.[10] The duplex and the dorm apartments were all owned by Professor and Mrs. Ware whose large family home sat just south of the duplex. Harry paid $30-$35 a month for room and board; he ate mostly at the boarding house up the street from the Wares.[11]

About a third of the Ware apartment dwellers were war veterans, including Harry's first roommate, Henry, who "had a shoulder blown off in the

Harry's second API roommate, Frank Liberato, studying at their Ware apartment in Spring 1946. Liberato would become a Naval captain, aviator, and officer in charge of the **USS Enterprise** *photo detachment, completing 4,200 flight hours and 28 photo missions during the Cuban Missile Crisis. In 1962, President Kennedy issued Liberato a "Blue Moon" order asking Liberato to determine the ranks of the Cuban soldiers. The Auburn man flew over the missile site during mealtime to take the needed photos.*

Harry sporting his freshman "rat" cap

war," Harry recalled. "He didn't like me. He was neat; I was sloppy. Very quickly, I found another roommate." Indeed, many war stories were traded in the Garden Courts community. Wide-eyed Harry found it "glamorous and scary at the same time. People had chunks missing. The ones who were injured didn't talk as much; the guys who came back unscathed were the big talkers."[12]

In fact, the unpresuming Bill, nicknamed "Coony" (from cocoon) as a child, had a dramatic wartime history of his own. Not only had he been busy in the intervening years since Pearl Harbor marrying and starting a family, but he led 29 bomber pilot missions over Germany during his Army Air Corps tenure. He'd turned his childhood love of airplanes into a selfless service for his country. As the war ended, he returned to Auburn for his last year toward an aeronautical engineering degree.

Bill's time with brother Harry was mostly limited to an occasional meal or babysitting session with Hope; although Bill did fly his war

API life included mandatory ROTC.

surplus biplane with re-stitched wings over Auburn, so Harry could take aerial photos. "We didn't see Harry a great deal," Bill said. "He was very involved. He always had a camera around his neck and a smile on his face. It seemed easy for Harry to become involved because that was just Harry."[13]

Harry managed to build a darkroom in his apartment amidst settling into his life at Auburn. As a freshman, he wore the required "rat" cap, a beanie-type hat designating the first-year students, and took classes in mandatory ROTC and physical education. He attended football games only because everyone went. For Harry it was a "love-hate activity. I didn't get it."[14] He also attended baseball games (where fellow-Ensley graduate Dick Webb would play second base his senior year).

With the war over and the GI Bill running at full throttle, male

API chemistry class, 1946

students once again overwhelmingly outnumbered females, 4,021 to 1,463.[15] The coeds, most of whom sported shoulder-length hair popular at the time, could accompany their dates to Chewacla State Park for picnics, attend the dance and athletic events of the given season, partake in sorority teas or meet at the student center for a good bridge game. Energetic youth spilled over campus to fill downtown eateries such as The Pastry Shop and The Grille.[16]

However, soon Harry would not have the luxury of spending time even contemplating a social life. His hours wouldn't be taken by studies either. Academic success freshman year came easily to Harry, who arrived in Auburn with a solid math and science foundation from

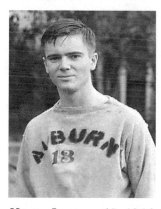

Ensley High and a plan of studying chemical engineering. "To me, the scholastic part was easy," Harry remembered. "I spent more time helping others academically."[17]

Instead, Harry's schedule would be ruled by newly hired coach Swede Umbach, who targeted Harry during physical education class for Auburn's first wrestling team. By winter quarter of 1946, Harry was essentially on the team and practicing several hours a day. It was an unfamiliar venture for Harry, whose comfort zone role was more the bookish shutterbug than the athlete.

Harry, January 10, 1946, as a member of Swede Umbach's first wrestling team

Harry recalled dropping eight pounds at

one point, down from his normal 136-pound wrestling weight. "It was the day before we went to Appalachian State for a match," Harry said. "The coach said, 'Harry, you look weak. Take a pound of sugar.' So I took a pound of sugar on the trip and showed it to the coach. He said, 'I meant to ingest it not take it!'"[18]

"I was not a good wrestler. You could earn a letter if you won a match with a pin, won two matches with points, or if you wrestled in all the matches. I did get to wrestle in all four matches by beating out others in my weight class, so I got a letter."

Step-brother Jim Ramsey, who still had a year left of high school back in Birmingham when Harry left for Auburn, said he "didn't remember Harry ever playing sports [before college]. Like his dad, he was somewhat of a loner. [But] whatever Harry did, he did well." Harry invited Jim to visit Auburn. "The thing that got me was how friendly Auburn was," said Jim, who later attended arch-rival University of Alabama for its pre-med program. "At Auburn, Harry blossomed out. The atmosphere of the students there did that."[19]

Harry didn't own a car, but caught rides back and forth to Birmingham during breaks. His father and step-mother didn't visit Auburn. "Mom [step-mother Thelma] wrote loving letters. Dad was badly beaten down at the time [with his job situation] so he didn't. I wish I'd known then to pay more attention."[20]

As Harry's first year of college came to a close, his funds came precariously close to an end, too. Spending so much time wrestling, especially in Coach Umbach's daily practices, prevented Harry from holding a job during the

Margaret Brown, circa 1946

season. Thus, he returned to Birmingham for the summer with good grades and a wrestling letter in hand and uncertainty about the future. Of one thing he was certain: he would finish college. "We didn't have money, but I never worried about it or had that stark terror about where money would come from. I figured things would work out somehow."[21]

What was a poor college student to do? Head to the beach, of course. When C. Harry got home for summer break, he joined the family for its usual summer vacation to Panama City Beach, where they rented their normal cottage for $50 and where Harry promptly met and fell in love with Margaret Brown from the north-Alabama town of Guntersville. "At age 17, I was all hormones," said Harry.

Meanwhile, Harry's mother Ruby had returned as a captain from military service that year and bought and set about remodeling a small hotel, The Durango Hotel, in Durango, Colorado.[22] Ruby had not played a significant role in her son's first year of college, writing some letters that held little meaning for Harry. Still, when Ruby painted Colorado as picturesque and offered work, Harry fell into his normal pattern of spending summertime with his mother. For his

Brothers Jim, on left, and Harry in uniform, Christmas 1946

summer of work at the hotel, Ruby paid him a total of $25 before he headed home.[23]

Harry, who had dated different girls in high school, had fallen hard enough for Margaret he drove to Guntersville that summer to see her. She rejected him. Heart-broken, Harry was convinced he'd been spurned in favor of one of the many young uniform-clad men home from military service.

Adding to the mixture of emotions was the fact that brother Jim had joined the Navy that June following high school graduation. Harry determined he would get himself a uniform and, at age 17, walked into the Navy recruiting office in Birmingham. In the corner sat a Marine with crisp red stripes running down the pants legs propped up on a table.[24]

"Excuse me, sir," stammered Harry. "Is the Navy recruiter here?"

"Nah, buddy," the Marine answered. Then as Harry turned quickly to leave, the Marine added, "What's the matter, buddy, are you chicken?"

Marine Private Knowles, 1946

Harry at boot camp, Parris Island, 1946

"He called me chicken," Harry recalled years later. "I went home and thought about that for three weeks and then went back and signed up for the Marines."

The Marine uniform Harry received August 1946 didn't garner Margaret Brown's affection, but it did solve another problem—college tuition. Whatever was in store for Harry in the military, he knew that on the other side of it was a GI Bill ride for finishing his education.

For training, the Marine Corps sent Harry to South Carolina's Parris Island, an 8,000-acre land mass made mostly of salt marsh with two other islands between it and the Atlantic Ocean. Located a dozen miles south of the town of Beaufort and across the Beaufort River from Port Royal, Parris Island did boast close to 3,300 habitable acres used for molding Marines since 1915 when enlisted men began training there.[25]

During World War II, Parris Island shaped 205,000 recruits. In 1944, a 16-week training cycle had been adopted; half the time was spent on basics, half on field training. (Training would later run about 13 weeks total.) When Harry arrived for boot camp, Parris Island was in transition following the end of the war.

"The sudden collapse of the Japanese Empire in August 1945," said a Marine Corps history of the depot, "caused...drastic changes at Parris Island. Along with the anticipated reduction in strength, the depot was forced to assume the extra task of aiding in the rapid discharge of Marine combat veterans. The almost unanimous desire to 'bring the boys home' led to the establishment at Parris Island of a Separation Company which functioned from 16 October to 9 November."[26] December 1945 saw the abolishing of two of the recruit training battalions as Parris Island adjusted to shrinking numbers.

Thus, by September 1946, Marine Corps Headquarters had decided to restructure the Parris Island post to reflect post-war needs. The Marine Barracks officially became the Marine Corps Recruit Depot in December of that year. Parris Island's purpose would focus on the sometimes torturous process of making recruits Marines.

The bookish Harry found himself a fish out of water in the Marines. He was glad to have Swede Umbach's wrestling team experience under his belt, for Harry discovered that Marines liked to fight and drink. Harry wasn't big on either.

Still, brother Jim, the Navy man, said that the Marines suited Harry's personality better than the Navy, because the Marines required more physical and mental stamina and dedication.[27] What Harry may have lacked in natural physical prowess, he made up for with a good mind and dogged determination. He and Jim both had solid family encouragement from mother Thelma, who, every month, loyally sent her boys each a box of Mary Ball candies, rich white nougat and caramel rolled in pecans.

During boot camp, Harry and his platoon believed they were training to go fight Chinese as part of the 2nd Division, according to Harry. Instead of his rifle, his camera was Harry's companion, chronicling the weeks Harry and his fellow recruits spent laboriously learning the art of being Marines. (In fact, when Harry's platoon gathered 50 years later for a reunion, they had Harry's boot camp pictures as a nostalgia resource but no Harry, who, having no real attachment to his past military life, didn't attend.)[28]

Drills and orders and field training finally ended that fall of 1946, and the platoon members were sent home to anticipate a move to the Orient at the end of their brief leave. While home, word reached the new Marines that the 2nd Division had moved out of China, so when the platoon came back from leave to the awaiting transfer area, Harry and the others waited in anticipation for their new assignments.

"The 2nd Division was assigned to protect American property," Harry recalled. "Finally, we were sent to do guard duty at

Harry at one of his Henderson Hall posts

Harry, left, with fellow Marines at the Casablanca restaurant in D.C.

Henderson Hall at the Arlington Cemetery for the Navy. There's no duty worse than guard duty."

The Henderson Hall complex, located on 22 acres of land on the southern edge of Arlington National Cemetery in Arlington, Virginia, sheltered and provided support for the Marines assigned to Corps headquarters, which had moved to the nearby Navy Annex in 1941 during wartime expansion.[29] Guarding Henderson Hall proved a boring task for the Marines, several of whom found themselves punished for sleeping while on duty. Harry said he "kept his nose clean— mainly by knowing how not to get caught sleeping" and, after a couple of months, was picked for Special Services.[30]

Brother Jim years later joked about the luck of Harry's new assignment, running a "swimming pool and bowling alley with all the WRs" (Marine Corps Women's Reserve members).[31] Indeed, Harry was assigned to two of Henderson Hall's recreational areas, the bowling alley in the winter and the pool in the summer. Harry remembered that, from the bowling alley, one could see the caissons arriving at Arlington Cemetery. "Every day there seemed to be another funeral."[32]

Harry was an oddball in the rowdy Marine brotherhood, occasionally joining his colleagues at the local beer joint for a 50-cent pitcher of beer but viewing as incomprehensible those who would intentionally get drunk. Harry found more enjoyment with a few of the fellow "nerdy

Harry's mother, Ruby, outside the National Gallery while visiting her son, 1946

types," as he described them, on jaunts to nearby D.C., where they would visit the museums on the mall. The National Gallery of Art was a favorite. Although he didn't know it then, Harry would later find his own handiwork—a transistor—displayed as part of Project Vanguard in the Air & Space Museum.

One day in the latter part of his near-two-year tenure in the Marines, Harry met Marianne Schurdak while lifeguarding at the

Harry Knowles and Marianne Schurdak, 1948

Henderson Hall swimming pool. A Cleveland native, Marianne lived in Arlington and was a guest on base that day. She and Harry began to date. The relationship soon blossomed to serious.

"My dad and I had never had any father-son talks," Harry said. "Dad was never very comfortable around women. His comments about them when I was a child were not realistic or healthy perceptions. [My relationships with women were rooted] in this fantasy Dad built about women."[33]

Like his father, son Harry loved female company but didn't know quite what to do with that company once attracted. It's no wonder then that when in doubt, like his father, Harry's thoughts jumped to marriage. Thus, after only a few months of dating, Harry and Marianne were engaged.

Already weighing on Harry's mind were his departure from the military and a decision about where to finish college. Engagement, Harry said, seemed to fill his "need to hang on to something."[34] Harry felt uncertain about life after the Marines, but he knew that the military was not his niche; he couldn't fathom re-enlisting.

"I thought the Marines were a waste of time but it got me the GI Bill," Harry said. "It never crossed my mind not to complete college." With Harry's good grades from his freshman year and the GI Bill, he could finish his degree anywhere. He considered Columbia and Case Western Reserve University in Cleveland, Marianne's hometown. But following his discharge as a Marine corporal and his temporary return to Birmingham that July 1948, Harry would find the ease of returning to Auburn too great.

Harry went to Cleveland and visited his presumptive future in-laws

Harry working on his transportation

and invited Marianne to come to Alabama. As Harry sorted out his feelings, he tinkered with a used Chevy he bought for $220 while in the Marines. With money he had saved from his military duty, he spent another $400 and part of a summer rebuilding it and getting it running.

With the beginning of fall term looming at API, Harry set out for Auburn to finish the higher education he had begun three years prior. On the way from Birmingham that September, the Chevy blew a cylinder. Harry ended up selling the car for junk and catching a train to Auburn. Things weren't going exactly as planned.

Plans changed further when Harry got back to the collegiate familiarity of Auburn and decided he didn't need to "get wrapped up in getting married." His next problem was how to tell the "sweet kid," Marianne, who was headed to town to iron out plans for her life with Harry.[35]

When Marianne arrived in Auburn, she took lodging in the Pitts Hotel downtown. Harry recalled sneaking up the back steps to see her and break off their engagement. Not surprisingly, she "took it badly," Harry said. "But I knew I did the right thing."

With Marianne gone, the 20-year-old Harry turned his attention to college life. He rushed and was accepted into a fraternity, Pi Kappa Alpha, or the Pikes, one of the oldest fraternities on campus known for its student leader members and several unique social

Toomer's Corner, downtown Auburn, circa 1948

Harry, seated, second from right, with the 1948 Pi Kappa Alpha fraternity pledge class in front of the Pike house

events such as the Bohemian Ball in the fall and its Dream Girl formal. Harry's brother Bill also had been a Pike as an Auburn student.

Auburn, while still a familiar home to Harry, had undergone many changes during the former Marine's absence. Following Dr. Duncan's death in July 1947, Dr. Ralph Brown Draughon took over as interim president of the college.[36] A 16-year veteran of the campus, he was unanimously voted to the permanent post October 1948.[37] Dr. Draughon, a former history professor, would prove to be a popular president, eventually having Auburn's library named in his honor and remaining as president until 1965. Fifty buildings would be erected on campus during his tenure; and Dr. Draughon reorganized academic departments and schools, resulting in a broader mission for API. Thus, by 1960, API's name officially became Auburn University.[38]

But in fall of 1948, some of the other notable changes addressed serving the ever-growing post-war student population. As the 1949 API yearbook, the *Glomerata*, explained: "With its 2,085 acres of campus crowded to almost every corner by the record enrollment of the post-war period, building took a spurt which far surpassed the 1938-39 era of expansion. Albeit much of the work in the 1945-48 period was of a temporary nature hastily erected to alleviate the swollen enrollment, the campus gained many needed and necessary buildings which will survive the boom following the war. Highlights in this march of progress were climaxed with the construction of permanent structures such as

1946 aerial view of Auburn (from brother Bill's plane) looking southwest toward Magnolia Ave. Note downtown Auburn bottom left, stadium top right quadrant, and the campus core in the middle.

the Wilmore Engineering Laboratory, the new Men's Dormitory, and the Agricultural Engineering Annex."[39]

The $1 million men's dorm opened that fall of 1948 as home for 431 students—but not for Harry, who lived behind the area known as Ag Hill in one of the temporary converted barracks.[40] The Wilmore lab was due to open July 1949. Also set for completion summer 1949 was a 13,000-seat eastside addition to the recently named Hare Stadium, which would bring capacity to 21,000. When Harry left Auburn a little more than two years earlier, a park existed where a new forestry building now stood. Also underway was a new administration facility for the API-owned Auburn-Opelika Airport.[41]

It was a time of new challenges for Harry, who, as a fresh fraternity member, began to venture out of his usual reticent social style. Coach Umbach invited Harry to return to the wrestling team, but after one day of tryouts, Harry decided he was too busy. During that one day of wrestling he also happened to accidentally break fellow student John Hembree's rib.[42]

At his small student abode, Harry witnessed a strange phenomenon at the end of every month, when the student veterans received their

GI checks. It seems Harry's roommate was a professional poker player. Checks would arrive and for the next 72 hours the roommate would sit around a poker table. "It was insane," Harry recalled. "He'd come back with a roll of money from his winnings. I'd watch but I didn't play. One time he came home with a guy's car."[43]

Harry placed his concentration elsewhere. Unlike his roommate, Harry had begun to see his intellect enticed by his sophomore classes, especially Physics 201, a beginning physics course taught by a new associate professor, Howard Carr, who had arrived in Auburn September 3 from teaching at the U.S. Naval Academy in Annapolis, Maryland.[44] Howard was no stranger to Auburn, having received a bachelor's degree from API and having served as a physics instructor in Auburn the summers of 1937, 1938, and 1941.[45] A protégé of physics department head Fred Allison, Dr. Carr had been trying to return to Auburn permanently almost his whole career, which included receiving his master's and Ph.D. from the University of Virginia, teaching at the University of South Carolina, and serving in the military.

Harry sat in the back of the huge physics class of about 125 students in Tichenor Hall,[46] which was completed in 1940 with specific space for teaching and research of physics.[47] On the first day of the Physics 201 class, Dr. Carr walked into the room and opened with "This is what you're going to learn...." Then he rolled a ball down an incline and exhibited other processes, electrical and of motion, and said, "You're going to learn how to describe what happened."[48]

"I was hooked," Harry remembered years later. "He was a fabulous teacher." Harry excelled in the class, often thwarting the grading curve that might have saved some of the struggling students. By the end of his sophomore year, Harry's major had changed from chemical engineering to engineering physics.[49] Before he would graduate in 1951, Harry's major would change again to straight physics.[50] The serious, spectacled student Harry had found his niche. From his childhood days of taking toys apart and visiting the manufacturing floor with his father, Harry had loved seeing how things worked and how they were put together. Now, he had found an academic pursuit to satisfy those bents.

In Harry, the new associate professor saw a rare individual. In fact, Howard Carr said decades later that when Harry was a student, "there was no stopping him. He was always fascinated by how things work." Then, with a grin, Dr. Carr added, "He was revved up. He was interested

Harry spoke often in later years of how Auburn shaped him as a person.

in how and if things would sell in this country."[51]

But Harry's relationship with his new favorite teacher and physics was only just beginning. During the rest of Harry's time at Auburn, Howard Carr and his wife, Carolyn, would become surrogate parents and an over-whelming guiding influence to the young man with such a tumultuous upbringing.

Carolyn, both an Auburn graduate and an Emory master's chemistry graduate herself,[52] stayed involved in her husband's academic life, helping Howard host faculty and students for meals and what turned into challenging life discussions.[53] The Carrs' house on Auburn's Payne Street became a welcome home for Harry, who—like most college students—navigated the sometimes painful turns of self-discovery toward adulthood. In the Carrs, Harry found a safe haven to ask questions; along the way, Harry felt he also found some answers.

In a 1999 interview for the alumni magazine, Harry talked about this unique time in his life: "When I was at Auburn, what Howard and Carolyn Carr were to me...I didn't realize until many years later how absolutely, incredibly formative they were in shaping me as a whole person. Teaching's not just formulas out of the books. That's interesting, but the side comments of 'Yeah, but *this* is what life is about' become so much more overpowering and important. Those like the Carrs are the people who make Auburn what it is. What is a good education? Is it only reading, writing, and arithmetic, or is there something else?"[54]

"We didn't realize we had such an effect on him," Dr. Carr commented. But, in retrospect, Harry said he found a new life philosophy during this formative time, although he didn't always recognize it while a college student. "The whole question of what is truth became, during my time at Auburn, very important. Physics was the magnificent lucky stroke that led me to that," Harry said.

"What I learned to develop at Auburn," he continued, "was a passion for truth and a passion for understanding underlying factors that drive any situation." The tenacity Harry honed at Auburn would contribute signifi-

API Physics Professor Howard Carr inspired Harry to study physics and became a lifelong guiding influence.

cantly to business success in later years. At the same time, this character trait of constantly turning situations inside out to examine them could be an exhausting exercise for his personal relationships.

By the end of his sophomore year, Harry had earned a 4.0 grade point with one exception: a B+ in typing, a result of his typewriter breaking during the final.[55] The teacher wasn't persuaded that the catastrophe justified an A.

Nonetheless, Harry had survived several transformations during this first year back at Auburn. He went from being a Marine in the nation's capital to a second-year student in a small southern town; an engaged man to an unattached single man; an outsider in his own platoon to fraternal brotherhood on campus; and he changed from a young man without a specific plan to one who had discovered the beginnings of a possible life's work in the realm of physics.

Harry started the fall 1949 term at Auburn with a different living arrangement. He left behind his previous poker-playing roommate and moved into the Pi Kappa Alpha fraternity house on Gay Street, two blocks from Toomer's Corner, the heart of downtown Auburn and the beginning of the most historic end of campus.

He also began the academic year with a different mindset, albeit forced, as he was swept into a fast-moving current of activities. The Pikes were joiners. Members of the fraternity were encouraged to get and stay involved.

"It was a painful time for me," Harry recalled in later years. "The introverted bookworm nerd was learning to interact with other people.

Harry joined the **Tiger Cub** *staff in 1949 and rose to editor of the handbook.*

With Joy Love at a student formal

Harry pinning Dean Allen's daughter, Patsy

I was becoming dependent on others."[56] Harry's family disappointments had taught him to avoid dependency and emotion. The rush of friends and relationships overwhelmed Harry at times, but the strength of Auburn, he said, was it taught him "a sensitivity to people on a personal level" he had lacked in the past.

Harry's campus involvement swelled, as he joined the student handbook *Tiger Cub* staff, becoming the 1950 editor, and served as vice president of the student body. His counterpart on the Women's Student Government Association side was Patsy Allen, who served as vice president for the female students.[57] Patsy was daughter of Dean Roger Allen, head of the School of Science and Literature—home of the physics department. Patsy and Harry dated some while at Auburn, but Harry was "in a trance" over Joy Love, the Women's SGA representative to the executive cabinet that year and who, Harry said, "didn't know I existed. Women were foreign territory and a frustration to me."[58]

Harry's awkwardness with women, however, didn't keep him from rising in the ranks of campus prestige positions. Several fraternity friends, such as Jim Haygood, Ralph Jennings and Crawford Nevins, mentored and encouraged Harry. Jim was already serving as business manager of the student newspaper, *The Auburn Plainsman*, under editor Ed Crawford and alongside assistant business manager Crawford Nevins (who would be business manager the following year).[59]

Of course, also encouraging Harry his

This 1950 photo depicting charter members of Auburn's Sigma Pi Sigma chapter included front row, starting fourth from left: Howard Carr, Harry, Ray Brannon, Fred Allison, and Gordon Hughes. Front row, far left, is Vanderbilt's physics department head Robert Lagemann, who gave the keynote address.

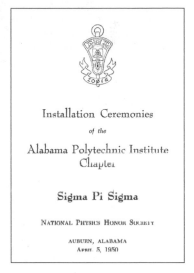

Installation Ceremonies

of the

Alabama Polytechnic Institute Chapter

Sigma Pi Sigma

NATIONAL PHYSICS HONOR SOCIETY

AUBURN, ALABAMA
APRIL 5, 1950

junior year were the Carrs. Harry had developed a true rapport with his physics professor by the end of his sophomore year, and that continued as Harry progressed through more of the physics curriculum.[60] Despite his involvement in student government and fraternity life, Harry maintained a good grade point average the 1949-50 school year and even organized Sigma Pi Sigma, a national honor society for physics to recognize outstanding academic achievement by physics students.[61] The Auburn chapter was inaugurated into the national society April 5, 1950;[62] Harry was its first president.[63]

Harry also was chosen a member of Blue Key, a men's national honor fraternity.[64] One of his more notable achievements, however, came the end of his junior year when that year's Spades chose 10 rising seniors to replace them the following year. Being tapped a Spade was supposedly the highest honor an Auburn man could attain. The secretive group, according to its constitution, sought out the "most prominent and influential men of the class and of the institution." The idea was to pick

In Spring 1950, Harry was recognized as a top campus leader when he and nine fellow rising seniors were tapped as Spades. Members of his Spades class were, front row, from left: Graham Everidge, Ed Crawford, Milton Blount, and Herman Blagg. Standing: Dick Webb, Joe Pilcher, Crawford Nevins, Harry, and Bruce Greenhill. Not pictured: Ellwood Burkhardt.

the campus' top male leaders, crossing all organizational and fraternity barriers. Harry's Spades group included friends Ed Crawford, Crawford Nevins, Herman Blagg, Milton Blount, incoming student body president Joe Pilcher, and baseball captain Dick Webb.[65]

Harry's high involvement on campus kept his mind on Auburn even as his junior year ended and his summer began. As vice president of the students, he was already a member of the executive cabinet and chair of the ring committee for sales of class rings. Also, he stepped in as acting president of the student body that summer.[66] As ring chair, Harry earned the amazing amount of $3600, part of which he spent on an AM/FM record player for the fraternity house.

With school out, mother Ruby was back on Harry's radar screen. Ruby had sold her hotel in Colorado and returned south after the death of her mother and Harry's grandmother, Effie—Big Mama. By the summer of 1950 Ruby was managing a hotel on the Gulf coast in Destin, Florida.[67]

Harry and two of his fraternity brothers, Charlie "Oodoo" Mathews of Andalusia, Alabama, and Jim Raulston of McMinnville, Tennessee, thought the beach would be a perfect place for summer employment and joined Ruby at the new Silver Beach Hotel.[68] Once again, Harry was working for Ruby.

The Silver Beach Hotel on the Gulf coast, Destin, Florida

The hotel, the only nice resort between Pensacola and Panama City on a long strip of beautiful, white sandy beach, was partly owned by Roger Clary, a longtime developer of the area.[69] Clary also owned the Shalimar Club about 10 miles west of Destin, known for good night club acts and gambling. After a week of working, the boys would sometimes sneak in to catch the acts such as big band artist Tommy Dorsey.

Harry, Charlie and Jim worked and played hard and enjoyed the respite of beachside living. All was well until a couple of months into hurricane season.

On August 20, a tropical storm which was churning east of the Lesser Antilles intensified into a 115-mile-per-hour hurricane before hitting Antigua.[70] By the time it reached Puerto Rico three days later it had weakened to a tropical storm. Then, passing north of Cuba, the system dissipated to less than storm status. The college boys, far away in Florida's panhandle, paid little if any attention as they exhausted the last of their summer days before returning to Auburn.

After the storm reached the Caribbean Sea on August 26 and re-formed into a tropical storm, the Gulf of Mexico's warm waters fed the system further as it moved northward. Hurricane Baker reached peak winds of 110 miles per hour on August 30 while churning on a path in the general direction of New Orleans. The entire Gulf coast was on alert, including the Silver Beach Hotel.

Owner Roger Clary had wisely chosen to evacuate the hotel and staff. Indeed, virtually all of Destin evacuated. Charlie, Jim, and Harry convinced Roger to leave them there to look after things. Roger, perhaps not so wisely, agreed. Ruby evacuated without the boys. After Roger and the others left, Charlie recalled, the three "went to the refrigerator and removed the largest steaks and proceeded to have a hurricane party."[71]

The power was out and the surf was already seeping under the lobby doors as the boys listened to WWL Radio out of New Orleans that night on Harry's portable, vacuum-tube Motorola radio.[72] At about midnight, Charlie said, WWL announced that New Orleans could "rest easy because the storm had turned east and would strike halfway between Fort Walton Beach and Panama City with its full fury at about 2 a.m. About that time a foamy wave crossed the lobby."

With Destin in the prime predicted target area, the vigil continued. When Hurricane Baker made landfall on August 31 in Mobile, it had lessened to a Category 1 hurricane.[73] Since Destin was northeast of the eye, though, some of the worst winds were felt in the Silver Beach Hotel's vicinity before the storm continued north over land and dissipated the next day. Although a minimal hurricane, Baker caused $2.5 million in damage and one death.

In Destin the next morning, the boys found sand piled across the door and a few shingles off but little damage. They waited for returning staff, but no one came. Phones weren't working and they wondered what had happened elsewhere. They discovered the next day that the road between Fort Walton Beach and Destin had been washed out.[74]

However, the waves were spectacular and, despite the danger of rip tides from high surf, Harry, the former Marine Corps swimming instructor, and his friends hit the deserted waters. While Harry called the complete void of caution "stupid" in retrospect, the hurricane watch and enjoyment of their storm-induced private beach provided a dramatic end to summer break.[75]

Harry taking to the skies again for aerial photos, 1950

Auburn life in the fraternity house was pleasant for Harry his junior and senior years. He had his music, and there was always a bridge game afoot. But Auburn became more complicated for the Birmingham native at the end of his junior year and after his senior year began fall 1950. As Harry's organizational activities escalated, his grades began to slide. He remembered a theoretical

Harry served as editor and photographer of the 1951 **Glomerata,** *API's yearbook.*

mechanics class that was fantastic except for the fact that he was so distracted.

Distraction came full force that October when the editor of the yearbook, the *Glomerata*, was called into military service and the executive cabinet searched for a responsible replacement. Harry volunteered for the job with no background in assembling a yearbook. Howard and Carolyn Carr warned Harry, telling him, "Are you crazy? You're getting in way over your head."[76]

Harry figured he'd already taken so many pictures of campus life, he might as well give it a try. "I had a lot of friends I tapped to help," he said. His pictures would fill the 1951 *Glomerata* by publication time. Harry even took more aerial shots with help from a yearbook staffer pilot who owned a Piper Cub.

With spending his time on the challenge of assembling a yearbook, Harry put studies at the bottom of his priorities. He stopped going to class; as a result, he went on academic probation that fall. Still, somehow Harry was selected as a Rhodes Scholar representative and went to Birmingham to compete with five others at the Tutwiler Hotel. A West Point student won. "I was amazed I got that far," Harry said. "I was in the middle of the *Glom* stuff and almost failing. I wanted someone to talk to, but Dad was not very relational. I talked with [Hugh's wife] Josephine and the Carrs. I was one messed-up kid."[77]

Carolyn Carr was especially supportive, having become Harry's on-site surrogate mother. She gave Harry "little dollops of love," he said. "Carolyn was so influential. You need somebody like that to say, 'Harry, you're wonderful. Everything's going to be alright.'"[78]

Other influences affected Harry during his final year of college.

Harry on one of his many modes of transportation

Some were subtle, such as API President Ralph Draughon, who met with student leaders on occasion. Harry, who took *Glomerata* pictures in the president's office and met privately with him about the Rhodes Scholar process, found Dr. Draughon open and close to his students.

Some influences, on the other hand, were intense, such as the powerful relationships among the Spades and the strong ties of the fraternity. "I was forced into tight social relationships," Harry said. "Dad was never very social. But I'm not a loner. I hand that to Spades."

During the school year, Harry attended the wedding of fellow Spade Joe Pilcher and Joe's sweetheart Anne in their hometown of Selma, Alabama. As he witnessed the spectacle, Harry felt out of place in his pink "wash-and-wear" shirt. But the larger emotion he felt was amazement at the grand network of relationships present via all of Joe and Anne's friends and family. Harry had not grown up with that kind of network, but with a little help, he cast off his isolationist ways during his time at Auburn.

The 1951 *Glomerata* continued to wreak havoc on Harry. When the staff reached a milestone deadline, finishing up all the organizational pictures by Christmas 1950, Harry threw a party. "Inebriation was not my thing," Harry said. "I was not interested in losing control. I got bombed." In fact, Harry was so drunk he threw records, "Frisbee style," he said, from the second floor of the Pike fraternity house.[79]

In the pressure cooker Harry had placed himself, something was bound to blow. For the most part he ignored classes and concentrated on his *Glomerata* editor tasks. At some point his senior year, he lived with horticulture professor Dr. Charles L. Isbell in his house and rode a motor scooter to campus.

Even amidst the chaos, Harry managed to hold a campus job as an instructor in the sophomore physics laboratory from September 1950 to June 1951. In a 1953 reference letter to Bell Telephone Laboratories, Howard Carr (by then physics department head following Dr. Allison's retirement) reported that Harry's services were satisfactory and that

"Mr. Knowles is a most enthusiastic worker with more than usual ability."[80]

"The ingestion of everything my senior year," Harry said, "was almost more than I could cope with emotionally. My senior year was a tough time."[81]

With the successful publication of the yearbook in the spring of 1951, Harry was left to deal with his sinking grade point average and his future. He had fallen in love with physics more than two years earlier and knew he wanted to pursue a career applying what he'd learned.

His brother Hugh had told him about a new invention—the transistor—being worked on at New Jersey's Bell Labs. When General Motors and Bell Labs came to Auburn recruiting, Harry signed up for visits. He found GM's research lab primitive but was impressed with Bell Labs. "I told Bell I wanted to work on the transistor," Harry said. But Bell told the eager college student no; only Ph.D.s worked on transistors. Bell Labs then offered Harry another job and a chance to participate in their training program. At first, Harry accepted, but Hugh encouraged Harry to concentrate on his interest in an advanced degree first and offered financial assistance (although Harry didn't accept it). Thus, Harry ultimately told Bell, "No. I'll go to grad school."[82]

With rock-bottom grades senior year, however, graduate school offers weren't pouring in. Harry was already looking at staying in Auburn the summer of 1951 to finish up his degree requirements. He would not graduate until August. That time gave mentor Howard Carr an opportunity to work some magic with the Vanderbilt physics department.

Harry had already met Robert P. Lagemann, head of Nashville's Vanderbilt University physics department, when Dr. Lagemann came to Auburn to give the keynote speech for Sigma Pi Sigma physics honorary.[83] Since Harry had founded the chapter in Auburn, Dr. Lagemann had an initial good impression of the young physics student. Dr. Carr's letter of recommendation provided reassurance, however:

> Mr. Knowles has taken three physics courses under me at Alabama Polytechnic Institute. He began his sophomore physics work under me two years ago and I have known him well since. There have been many occasions under my observation when his moral code underwent serious tests, and I have never seen him retreat or compromise from

his high standards. Although his ethics are clean cut they are not so strict as to make him appear prudish. He appears to be a well rounded and mature young man.

One finds Mr. Knowles affable and pleasant. He is well liked by all our staff and by his fellow students. Mr. Knowles entered into many extra-curricular activities here, and in his last year his scholastic endeavors lessened to such an extent that his grades suffered. Coincident with his extra-curricular activities was a broad expansion of his social-fraternal-organizational activities. Some few students here have expressed the opinion that he just became a joiner for the prestige that might ensue. However, I am of the opinion that he became a member of most of the organizations and groups because he was interested in their programs.

Mr. Knowles rates as one of the best students I have ever taught although his transcript is not imposing for reasons cited above. The physics staff believes that Mr. Knowles will make a superior graduate student.

I am sure Mr. Knowles would rank in the top ten percent of students I have had in recent years.[84]

That 1951 Auburn summer cemented admittance to Vanderbilt's graduate school for Harry as well as Harry's total devotion to the Carrs.[85] With his final classwork completed at API, all Harry had left to do in Auburn was graduate.

"I was Dad's life distilled. For months, if not years, Dad was looking forward to my college graduation," Harry explained. "Graduation was the fulfillment in his mind of everything he poured into me. There was no question he was going to be there. It was to be our day."[86]

Ruby had other plans. As Harry recalled, the day before commencement, Ruby phoned and told Harry how happy she was; she was coming to his graduation. Young Harry was flabbergasted; he wasn't prepared to tell her to stay away.

Harry called his father immediately, saying, "Dad, Mother is coming to graduation." Harry's father simply said, "Well, that's

Harry, center, graduation day at Auburn, August 1951

API Executive Vice President David Mullins congratulates Harry at commencement.

okay, we'll see you when you come back to Birmingham."

Father and son were crushed they wouldn't share the special day. But the elder Knowles could not bring himself to face Ruby.

About two hours before the afternoon commencement ceremony in which Harry was to receive his bachelor's degree in physics, Ruby called to say she couldn't make it to Auburn after all. "I remember thinking Dad would not have time to get in the car and come down here," Harry said. "I can't help but think she planned it. You don't think your mother is going to treat her child that way. That was a pivotal moment in realizing how calculatingly callous she could be.

"Neither Thelma nor Dad ever said a word about Ruby when I got back to Birmingham. Dad was probably ashamed he didn't come anyway. I felt so bad for him and I felt some degree of guilt. What could I have done differently?"[87]

A chapter of Harry's life closed with the end of his time in Auburn. In some ways, Auburn had made a man out of Harry more than the Marines, especially in the arena of personal relationships. He learned not only physics at API but how to be and have close friends and how to function as a leader and in social situations. He also observed closely how families and interactions worked for others. He realized his early childhood was not a normal one. While he felt and accepted his father's love and was thankful for the warmth of his step-mother Thelma, he could not reconcile his feelings about his mother Ruby. There would be no more summer jobs with Ruby and little time spent with her in coming years.

The 23-year-old had a bachelor's degree in hand, however, and a dream of one day holding a Ph.D. His first stop on that journey was Nashville, where Vanderbilt's graduate school awaited him.

Harry as a graduate student in the physics department at Vanderbilt

Life at Vanderbilt stoked Harry's studious side, which had all but lain dormant his senior year at Auburn. Gone were the distractions of campus positions and activities. In graduate school, the academic bar was higher. "Vandy was almost a reversal of the Auburn experience, moving from people back into [focusing on] academics," Harry said.[88]

At first Harry lived in a dorm. He remembered his dorm mate had a good record collection. Harry enjoyed the appreciation of good music in Nashville and on the Vanderbilt campus.

His graduate school experience not only exposed him to good music but, of course, a different faculty. One of his favorite professors was an atheist. Students would spend occasional evenings at his house and brood over the question of what is truth. "He was bald, studious, wore thick lenses," Harry remembered. "He scared the hell out of me. Fundamentally, science says you believe only things that can be repeated. Later on, I became comfortable *not* following the sterility of the scientific atheist. There is a mystical side to the human spirit. I believe in a higher structure and that prayer works."

Whereas Harry felt the need to attend church during his time at Auburn, sporadically going to the Methodist and Presbyterian churches, he didn't attend while at Vandy, instead immersing himself in his graduate school existence. It would be several years before he settled upon a spiritual approach that he felt fit his view of life.

But as 1951 turned into 1952, his mind was busy building his technical and mathematical foundation. He was taken under wing by Dr. Sherwood Haynes, who was working on infrared research (and later served as president of the American Association of Physics Teachers). Another professor, Dr. David Hill, gave Harry an assistantship to help with his project. Harry's job was to build a vacuum station for a chamber which would measure the spectrum of the neutron emissions of one of the isotopes of the element cadmium.

Dr. Hill told Harry to design the vacuum station and build it. Harry, who'd chosen to employ glass (rather than metal) for its perceived cleaner qualities, was able to enlist the aid of the glass blower from

Glass blowing became a valued skill in Vanderbilt's physics laboratory. This vacuum station included a neutron spectrometer (the round drum at bottom right) for measuring the energy spectrum of cadmium neutrons.

the chemistry department. One night in the lab, a supporting metal structure fell and destroyed a large section of the fragile glass vacuum station. Harry wasn't about to admit defeat. Instead of calling the glass blower back in, Harry stopped going to class for two weeks, learned how to blow glass and rebuilt the station. Harry didn't know it at the time, but that glass-blowing skill would serve him well later in his career.[89]

Near catastrophe struck the vacuum station again another day. Harry cleaned the station's several-liter, round, glass flask—used for storage of gas samples—with acetone. Eager to join his colleagues for the always enjoyable, discussion-filled dinner hour, he then turned his flask upside down to dry and went to dinner.

After dinner he returned to the lab, put on his goggles, and lifted the flask to join it to the vacuum station. Since acetone is lighter than air, however, the acetone had not dissipated by turning it upside down. Instead, acetone had mixed with air. The instant the flask hit the vacuum tubing's mouth, the glass flask exploded. "People from all over the building came running into our laboratory," Harry said. "Thank goodness I had on goggles."[90] Harry luckily only suffered a few cuts, although windows and lights were destroyed.

Harry traveled to Birmingham occasionally to see the family.

Harry built this equipment as part of his thesis to measure the ultrasonic speed of liquid hydrogen fluoride.

During his time at Vanderbilt from 1951 to 1953, he met his brother Jim's future wife, Ruth, during a visit home.[91] For the most part, though, Harry remained in Nashville during this time. He moved from the dorm to an apartment early in his graduate school days.

While in Nashville the summer of 1952, Harry started spending time with a friend, Judy Cassidy, who was also captive in graduate physics at Vanderbilt that summer, and fell in love with her.[92] The problem was they both were dating other people, although neither Judy's boyfriend nor Harry's girlfriend was in town that summer. Harry threw caution to the wind and asked Judy to marry him. She declined. She was committed to her boyfriend. They remained friends and, amazingly, the unexpected proposal did not cause awkwardness.

What was difficult, however, was Harry's financial need, despite his graduate fellowship. While Harry had hoped to pursue his Ph.D. toward a future teaching college physics, he was growing weary of Vanderbilt. Short on money, Harry was eager to work. His brother Hugh had written Harry while at Vanderbilt and advised him that a Ph.D. was not essential for a career in applied physics and talked again of the work at Bell Labs on the innovative technological wonder, the transistor. Remaining long enough to earn a Ph.D. no longer held appeal for Harry, compared to the excitement of actually working on Bell Labs' newly developed junction transistors. "I recognized what was coming in the transistor," Harry said. "So did Hugh."[93] Harry wrote to Bell Labs and learned opportunity remained for the program called Kelly College in which cohort members were recruited and trained by Bell. It seemed a good option.

However, Harry was in the midst of a two-year experiment under Dr. Lagemann which would result in a thesis and the completion of his master's degree requirements. He could not leave that undone. He pressed on with his thesis experiment—measuring the ultrasonic speed of liquid hydrogen fluoride.

Liquid hydrogen fluoride had the slowest ultrasonic speed of any material known at that time and, while caustic and extremely dangerous if not handled properly, can be worked with if one has the right equipment. Harry built the equipment for handling and making the measurements. By June of 1953, the experiment was complete and the thesis written. (The work was published under Lagemann's and Harry's names in a 1960 issue of the *Journal of Chemical Physics* and cited repeatedly in subsequent years.)[94] Harry accepted a position within Bell Laboratories' Kelly College training program; but, first, another graduation ceremony awaited.

Although Harry's father was ill, he was not going to miss this commencement. Thelma drove the two of them to Nashville, where on the Vanderbilt campus June 7, 1953, the elder Knowles watched his son receive his master's degree. That the father thoroughly enjoyed the trip is evident from a note he wrote to Howard Carr a month later:

This is secretarial duty Harry Knowles should have performed

Harry's step-mother, Thelma, and father, Harry, proudly joined their son at his June 1953 Vanderbilt graduation.

though he has reported to me that you were away from API when he looked you up.

Harry received his M.S. at Vandy June 7th. My wife and I were at the lawn tea June 6th and met the [faculty] of the Physics Department as well as dean of graduate school. They were quite as observant as I was interested in them.

H had also completed more than half the work required for his Ph.D. His grades and finals have been very good mostly As. It has not been easy as he taught undergrad classes around the clock on the fellowship allotted him. He left the next day for N.J. Bell Labs.

Bell increased his paper salary nearly $100 a month each year he was at Vandy, which makes him feel quite respectable. They also put him in the field he asked for.

He is undecided whether to return to Vandy or go to Columbia. Columbia would be the longer drag.[95]

Mr. Knowles then provided Harry's address in New Jersey and signed off, "Very Truly, H.H. Knowles."

The circle was complete for the proud father, who knew his son was ready to face the working world. For the 25-year-old Harry, the career journey was just beginning and he felt there was no better place to start than technological powerhouse Bell Laboratories.

Chapter 3

Bell Labs

(1953-1958)

The ink on his master's degree barely dry, Harry arrived in Murray Hill, New Jersey, eager to join the melting pot of discovery at American Telephone and Telegraph's research arm, Bell Telephone Laboratories. Bell Labs served as a mecca for inventive minds, having already produced Nobel Prize winners and countless patents. It was a heady era of invention in America amidst war-driven innovation.

World War II had inspired many technological breakthroughs, especially in aircraft, radar, and communications. With Allied victory came a sense that there was nothing Yankee moxie couldn't accomplish. As Harry landed in New Jersey, the U.S. was a little more than a month away from the end of another war—this one between North and South Korea. Republican and former general Dwight D. Eisenhower had taken office as president that January 1953, succeeding Harry S. Truman and ending 20 years of Democratic rule. America's military antennae were heightened in the country's efforts to fight the monster of communism.

Bell Labs, of course, was a key player in U.S. military advancements. With its rich history, the AT&T research branch was a magnet for genius. AT&T had been born out of its predecessor American Bell Telephone Company following Alexander Graham Bell's invention of the telephone in 1875. One of American Bell's subsidiaries since 1881, Western Electric Company became the manufacturing arm for the telephone giant. Western Electric's engineering department, in turn, birthed Bell Labs, formed in 1925 to handle AT&T's sprawling research and development work and to, as author Jeremy

1939

Courtesy of AT&T Archives and History Center

Bernstein said in *Three Degrees Above Zero*, "feed directly to Western Electric potential products for manufacture and sale."[1] In fact, Bell Labs' first patent came the next year, in 1926, for a clamping and support-

Harry's fellow Kelly College members, front, Dave Favin and, back, Don Kissel, left, and Dick Small

ing device. The first Nobel Prize awarded to Bell Labs researchers occurred in 1937 for Clinton Davisson and Lester Germer's detection of the electron's wave nature. These early accomplishments marked the beginning of a steady stream of patents and recognitions for Bell Labs scientists.

Harry joined his new science community as a fresh-faced member of Bell Labs' Communications Development Training Program, popularly known as "Kelly College," a training program for promising minds straight out of college. Most of the 150 to 200 members of each new Kelly College class were among the country's top new recipients of science and engineering degrees. The Bell Labs norm assigned each incoming employee a home department. The near-25-year-old Knowles, however, gained a position without a sponsoring department. Although self-conscious and thinking himself under-educated because he had no Ph.D., the bright Southern transplant would discover no hindrance in advancement.

Without a pre-set department, Harry worked for Kenneth D. Smith, known as K.D. or Ken. A Bell Labs employee since 1930, the 48-year-old Smith had a solid research reputation, having worked on proximity fuses and radar during World War II and the TD-2 trans-continental

Bell Labs colleagues in training from left: Tom Grigsby, Phil Porter, and Costas Papaliolios

microwave relay system.[2] He would also work on the solar cell, but, during this era of the 1950s, he headed up a group of engineers and other researchers who were exploring the exciting potential of semiconductor diodes. Most other departments in the electronic technology development groups were working on various forms of transistors.

Six feet tall, strong and gray,[3]

Commuting on the ferry across the Hudson River to Manhattan

Smith, according to his son Dave, was "proud of the fact that both his degrees were in pure science," having received his bachelor's and master's degrees in physics (his graduate degree coming from Dartmouth).[4] Jim Early, one of Smith's engineers from 1951 to the mid-1950s, recalled Smith as a hands-on supervisor with his most impressive qualities being curiosity and adaptability.[5]

"On technical matters," Early said, "our relationship was that of peers working on a problem. Bell Labs was that kind of world, a world where 'I don't know,' 'I don't understand,' and 'My idea was wrong' were easily said, readily accepted, and taken as descriptive. It was a world focused on solving problems that had not been thought of before."[6]

Thus, Harry Knowles, another "pure" scientist, most likely fell into natural step with the kind, dependable Smith, who obviously fostered enthusiastic exploration in his laboratory. During his first year as a Kelly College member, Harry spent three days a week on training; the other two days Harry worked on two-terminal devices and other rotating assignments.[7] Although Harry was based in New Jersey in the Murray Hill labs, he traveled about 30 miles via train to Hoboken and ferry across the Hudson River to Manhattan for his Kelly College coursework. Joining him for the commute was friend Phil Porter, a fellow Vanderbilt physics graduate who had, independent of Harry, also gotten a job at Bell Labs in 1953 and became a Kelly College student and, in November of that year, one of Harry's Bell Labs roommates.[8]

Bell Labs roommate Phil Porter became one of Harry's dearest friends.

Kelly College was so named because the three-year graduate study fellowship program was the brainchild of Mervin J. Kelly, third president of Bell Labs from 1951 to 1959, who knew pairing colleges' top talent with his company's top scientists resulted in an unbeatable research

Mervin J. Kelly
Reprinted with permission of Alcatel-Lucent USA Inc.

breeding ground.[9] Harry recognized the distinction of the experience. "I was with the top one percent of students in the country," he said. "Our courses were taught by Nobel laureates. The combination of theoretical and hands-on work was right down my alley. I was just soaking it all up enthusiastically."[10]

To properly understand the Bell Labs setting upon Harry's 1953 arrival, one must grasp the significance of the body of work in the preceding two decades. Kelly, a Missouri native and 1918 University of Chicago physics Ph.D. graduate, joined the Bell system right out of college as a research physicist. By 1934, he was director of research.[11] With a background in vacuum tubes, Kelly pushed for continued tube research to improve transmission of telephone signals.[12] By the mid-1930s, telephone demand was outpacing AT&T's technology; the company desperately needed a new switching system.[13]

As described in a 1997 *Washington Post Magazine* article by Ronald Kessler:

> At that time, the state of electronic technology was defined by the vacuum tube, which had been developed 30 years before by an American electrical engineer named Lee De Forest. De Forest discovered that by placing an electrified wire grid across a stream of electrons in a vacuum, he could alter or manipulate the flow of electrons in a number of ways: The current could be interrupted, reduced, stepped up or stopped entirely. Because of this, vacuum tubes could pull faint electromagnetic signals out of the air, magnify them and convert them to sound or pictures. They made commercial radio and television possible.
>
> Vacuum tubes could also act as electrical switches, but they had certain drawbacks. They wouldn't work until they warmed up. Once they did, they generated heat as high as 400 degrees. Because the filaments became so hot, they often broke.[14]

As the 1930s wore on, Kelly became convinced that vacuum tubes were not the answer after all. He looked to the new field of solid-state science, which examines how the interaction of atoms within solid matter provides the properties of that solid. In other words, instead of a vacuum tube device serving mechanically as a switch, the internal

Bell Labs headquarters in Murray Hill, New Jersey
Reprinted with permission of Alcatel-Lucent USA Inc.

workings of matter itself could, if manipulated, act as a switch. The possibilities would prove revolutionary.

With a shortage of scientists at Bell who could conduct this new solid-state research, Kelly "started a campaign to hire bright young Ph.D.s" whose education had versed them in the new field.[15] Joining Kelly's team in 1936 was a fresh physics Ph.D. from MIT, William Shockley, who worked at first with vacuum tubes before Kelly assigned him to solid-state research as a replacement potential for vacuum tubes.[16] By the end of the decade, Shockley plotted a preliminary plan for a solid-state amplifier, but the required materials were not available, and the project was deemed unfeasible.

World War II dictated Bell Labs' switch to focusing on military research, resulting in concentrated, swift advances with radar, gunfire control and bombsights. Kelly oversaw all the military research, rising to executive vice president in 1944, and, in recognition for his wartime contributions, receiving the Presidential Certificate of Merit.[17]

As the war ended, according to a PBS transistor history, Kelly "reorganized all the labs at Bell, and formed a department dedicated to solid-state science."[18] Kelly believed that crystal semiconductors would provide the alternative, more efficient technology so needed.

As Kessler explained, "Because of their atomic makeup, such crystals as germanium and silicon are normally poor carriers of electricity, but they can become conductive when they are 'doped' [loaded] with impurities and voltage is applied to them in particular ways. 'Free' electrons—those that are not attracted to and paired with other charges—will wander toward or away from electrodes as the electrode charge is changed from positive to negative. This attraction-repulsion effect would allow a semiconductor to act as a switch that alternates between a conductive state and an insulating state."[19]

Bell Labs researchers, such as chemist Russell Ohl, had been working since the 1930s to develop purer semiconductor materials. The purer the materials were, the less erratic the behavior of the semiconductor. According to David C. Brock, Chemical Heritage Foundation senior research fellow and author, when Ohl and his colleagues succeeded in 1940 in "producing high-purity silicon…[they] determined that the presence of different chemical impurities in silicon transformed its electrical behavior."[20] With precise introduction of certain chemical elements, the semiconductor material acted in predictable ways—as a rectifier, that is, restricting electrical current to one direction. "These semiconductor rectifiers, or diodes," Brock said, "served as the crucial detector components in the radar systems developed and deployed during the war. To meet this demand for high-purity silicon, DuPont developed a process for producing ultra-pure silicon in the early 1940s."[21]

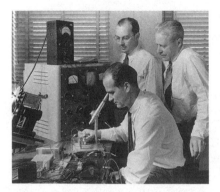

The invention of the transistor can be credited to, from left: William Shockley, John Bardeen, and Walter Brattain.
Reprinted with permission of Alcatel-Lucent USA Inc.

Thus, the stage was set for expanded electronic applications as the war ended. In 1945, Shockley was assigned to head up the solid-state physics team, most likely splitting his time half on his own research and half on supervising a dozen or so other scientists. According to journalist Kessler, Shockley designed "what was then called a field-effect amplifier (and later called a transistor), but it did not work. As he went on to other projects, two senior physicists who worked for him, John Bardeen and Walter H. Brattain, took over."[22]

Bardeen, who was hired by Shockley, was the theorist of the duo and analyzed what went wrong in Shockley's experimentation,[23] while Brattain took that theory and fiddled with the testing, adjusting earlier assumptions along the way. As the two experimented with the problem, their model short-circuited. Brattain moved the electrodes around and detected a signal. With additional tinkering, on December 16, 1947,

Brattain and Bardeen "were able to amplify sound."[24] Their apparatus, which employed polycrystalline germanium, would be known as the point-contact transistor. After improving their method further, they demonstrated the device to Bell Labs administrators (including their boss Shockley) on December 23, which became the official date of the invention of the transistor. "The scientists recorded their discovery on page 708 of Bell Labs notebook No. 21780," noted Kessler.[25]

The public did not recognize the importance of the invention, which caused barely a stir in newspapers when, on June 30, 1948, Bell Labs announced the creation of the transistor to the world. "The announcement received little public notice—one of the most restrained send-offs in recent memory, according to *Fortune* magazine—but its importance was quickly recognized by the electronics industry," Kelly stated in a 1953 look at the first five years of the transistor.[26]

Brock of the Chemical Heritage Foundation explained the significance in his book, *Understanding Moore's Law*: "Brattain and Bardeen's point-contact transistor was the first solid-state amplifier. The new semiconductor electronics was now in a position to overtake the vacuum tube. Like vacuum tubes, semiconductor devices could both rectify and amplify. Yet because of their simpler design, centered on using an appropriately fashioned piece of semiconductor material, they seemed far more reliable, were certainly far smaller, and were potentially better performing than the vacuum tube."[27]

That summer of 1948, while the transistor was being introduced to the public, Harry was preparing to return to Alabama Polytechnic (later Auburn University) after two years in the Marines. That fall he would discover Howard Carr and the wondrous world of physics. Meanwhile, fall 1948 saw Bell Labs chemist Gordon Teal's development of a crystal grower capable of producing, first, single crystals of germanium and, later, silicon. These single crystals were superior in purity to the earlier polycrystalline structures and resulted in a plethora of electronic inventions.[28]

By 1949, Shockley was advancing a theory for a different kind of transistor[29]—a junction transistor, which would work without the points of Brattain and Bardeen's original point-contact transistor.[30] But it was Morgan Sparks, a Bell Labs chemist, who actually constructed the first germanium junction transistor in 1951.[31] The new transistors were quiet, amazingly efficient, and functioned with little power compared to the vacuum tube. Later, the silicon junction transistor, introduced by Teal in 1954 after he left Bell Labs in 1952 to form Texas Instruments, would demonstrate earlier Bell work which highlighted silicon's ability to withstand higher temperatures than germanium.[32]

While it would take time for the Bell system to integrate the new technology, the transistor was destined to revolutionize telephone switching systems, radio and television communication, and countless other applications such as computers. Transistors would alter the electronics world forever with automation and faster, more reliable circuitry. Bardeen and Brattain's first transistor was the beginning, but it was Bell Labs which created opportunity for much of the early discoveries.

As Frederick Seitz and Norman Einspruch said in their book, *Electronic Genie: The Tangled History of Silicon*: "...it must also be emphasized that the subsequent follow-through by the other dozen or so members of the staff involved in the research was both imaginative and thorough. The ultimate successful development of the transistor must be regarded as a reflection of the excellent teamwork that characterized the activities of the Bell Telephone Laboratories at its peak, each member providing imaginative input to obtain greater understanding and advance the development of the transistor. In fact, the laboratories probably were the main source of technical innovation in the field for the next decade."[33]

It's no wonder the transistor tantalized the Knowles brothers. By the time Harry was in his final days as an Auburn senior in 1951, with his brother Hugh's regaling of the transistor's potential echoing in his head, Harry was already targeting Bell Labs as an employer. Harry remembered the Bell Labs glory days he entered in 1953 following his graduate study at Vanderbilt: "There was nothing we couldn't do. We were at the top of the most powerful technology in the world. Bell was so far ahead of everyone else. [Everyone felt] the euphoria of that period—the combination of technology, enormous economic thrust, and manufacturing ability."[34]

The Kelly College freshmen bore a heavy and quick learning curve. The world's experts taught a curriculum which gave one a complete command of mathematics and both practical application and theoretical approach. "I came from being technologically deprived at Auburn and uninspired at Vandy to the tremendous breadth and depth of Kelly

College's brilliant teachers," Harry said. "They made us into world-class experts and taught us so we wouldn't be cowed by concepts thrown at us."[35]

In the second year of the three-year training program, Harry and his roommate, Phil, attended classes one or two days a week and worked in their departments the other days. Phil worked with station apparatus such as dials, ringers, and other phone equipment. A physics man amidst a sea of electrical engineers, he later advanced to work in radio and cellular

Phil Porter and Louise Jett, who married in 1957

phones. He would spend his career with Bell and remain one of Harry's closest friends.[36]

"Bell was a good place to work," Phil remembered. "We had a good bit of freedom. They were tolerant of us new recruits. Our teachers had written books on the subjects we studied."[37]

Harry had settled into Ken Smith's department, working on diode devices. In his group was colleague and friend Mort Prince, who helped advance the patent Russell Ohl had secured in 1946 for the modern semiconductor solar cell. According to Harry, Prince's Bell Labs success was part of a road toward a prestigious position at the Department of Defense in Prince's future. In 1954, however, Bell Labs' research on the solar cell ushered in a modern era of taking solar cell energy potential seriously when, while testing semiconductors, researchers "accidentally found that silicon doped with certain impurities was very sensitive to light." While the energy conversion rate was only six percent, "production of the first practical solar cells" resulted. In March 1958, the U.S. would launch the first spacecraft to use solar panels in the Vanguard satellite[38]—a project on which Harry himself was destined to play a role.

One of Harry's Kelly College instructors was Art Schawlow, who came from Columbia University and taught wave physics. He was later generally recognized as the co-inventor of the laser (for his work with

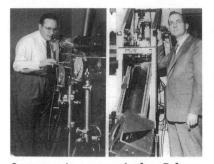

Laser co-inventors Arthur Schaw-low, left, and Charles Townes
Reprinted with permission of Alcatel-Lucent USA Inc.

Charles Townes, who would receive the Nobel Prize in 1964). Working at Bell Labs 1951 to 1961, Schawlow would go on to a distinguished professorial career at Stanford and to share the 1981 Nobel Prize for his research in laser spectroscopy.[39] Schawlow became well known for his sayings, such as, "To do successful research, you don't need to know everything, you just need to know of one thing that isn't known." Or "Anything worth doing is worth doing twice, the first time quick and dirty, and the second time the best way you can."[40] Schawlow's approach was sure to have spilled into Harry's and his Kelly College colleagues' mindsets. Schawlow's research specialty, lasers, would also prove central to Harry's future.

Thus, Harry's initial time at Bell Labs laid much groundwork for later professional achievement and prepared Harry for increasing responsibility. One such opportunity materialized when Harry attended an IRE device research conference about his second year at Bell, probably in the 1954-55 timeframe.[41] The IRE, or Institute of Radio Engineers, had centered more and more on electronics since its inception in 1912 and would become, when merged with the American Institute of Electrical Engineers (AIEE) in 1963, the Institute of Electrical and Electronics Engineers, or IEEE—today's premier electronics professional society.[42]

At the IRE meeting, Harry noticed the differing symbols used by the various companies in attendance—RCA, IBM, and Bell included— for their work. Even though research fields overlapped, there was no common symbology, or language, for the same science. In other words, no standards existed to describe a transistor or circuit. It occurred to Harry that it would be difficult to learn from one another if the principal scientists didn't even speak the same language. Bell Labs managers saw the same problem and assigned Harry to the IRE's semiconductor diode definitions committee, which became an all-encompassing international device standards committee by the time its work was done.

Because Harry was from powerhouse Bell Labs, the committee looked to Harry as its leader and named him chair. The in-charge aura of Bell lent natural credence to Harry, Bell's official representative to the committee. As far as the committee was concerned, when Harry spoke, he spoke for Bell Labs. The standards the committee formed and the IRE enacted into "law" are still in place and used by a host of scientists and engineers worldwide as part of the International Electrotechnical Commission's official standards. For Harry, the experience was yet another validation of the power of Bell Labs during the 1950s and an essential confidence builder to the young scientist.

Soon after this experience, Harry made a discovery (most likely during 1955 or 1956) while working on zener diodes for Ken Smith. Two-terminal devices, zener diodes permit current in both the forward and reverse directions and act as voltage regulators. Controlling voltage at this time was hit or miss. But Harry discovered predictable patterns for the zener diodes' performance, depending on how heavily they were doped, or loaded with impurities, and the diffusion factors. In fact, Harry plotted the pattern and published the resulting chart on diffusivity and voltages in a Bell Labs internal memo.[43]

Harry at Bell Labs explaining zener breakdown voltage

The reaction to Harry's chart was swift; the significance was not lost on his fellow scientists. Zener diodes could now be manufactured with predictable voltage results. Departmental colleagues Harold Veloric and Sol Miller, recognizing the accuracy of the chart, expanded the research and later published extensively on the subject in external publications. "I didn't worry about publishing it," Harry recalled. "I almost never published anything. To me, the discovery was the important thing. I just wanted to get the work done."[44]

Harry would carry that penchant for the work and distaste for the paperwork throughout his career. However, when engineer and researcher Bill Hittinger tapped him during his third year at Bell Labs to help teach a class on semiconductors to younger Kelly College students,

Harry wrote his own textbook for his group of students—*Theory of P-N Junctions and Function*. The text was paperwork about which Harry could get excited.

In the transistor world, impurities in crystals cause areas of varying electrical properties. A *P*-type crystal is positively charged due to holes dominating in number over free electrons, while an *N*-type crystal is negatively charged because of too many electrons that dominate over the holes.[45] When the crystal-growing process is manipulated, one can form extremely thin (one-thousandth of an inch) layers into a sandwich consisting of both a *P*-type area and an *N*-type area. Bell Labs chemist Ohl first discovered in 1939 the *P-N* barrier—or *P-N* junction—between the two areas (at the center of the "sandwich"). Shockley built on this work when he spearheaded the junction transistor. His theory was to put two *P-N* junctions back to back, creating the *P-N-P* junction or, conversely, the *N-P-N* junction. "For much of the 1950s the junction transistor persisted as the central semiconductor device," author Brock said.[46] Various types of junction transistors followed as research advances heated up, including the alloyed junction transistor; diffused junction transistor; and even, in 1955 by Bell chemist Morris Tanenbaum, the first doubly diffused silicon junction transistor.

In this frenzy of activity, Harry's grasp of the intricacies of *P-N* junctions served him and Bell Labs well. Finished with his Kelly College training, Harry presented a paper which compiled his expertise on *P-N* junctions at a device research conference in Boulder, Colorado. Specifically, Harry developed the first usable theory on hyper-abrupt *P-N* junctions for variable capacitors—which meant a new principal method for high-frequency tuning.[47] For high frequencies, diodes need to turn on and off quickly, but they don't. By heavily doping them, one can make them hyper-abrupt or fast. Harry's work defined what makes diodes fast or slow. The whole field of microwaves was built on these definitions and methodology, but Harry said he missed the microwave connection at the time.[48]

Unfortunately, Harry failed to publish his paper after a reviewer told him to rewrite the presentation. He felt he was too busy at the Laureldale, Pennsylvania, Western Electric plant (the manufacturing arm of Bell where he was following through on some of his Labs work) and couldn't spare the time. Thus, he received no credit for the paper's content. Still, Harry was as happy about his hyper-abrupt *P-N* junction

GRADUATION EXERCISES

CLASS OF 1953

COMMUNICATIONS DEVELOPMENT TRAINING PROGRAM

MURRAY HILL, JULY 2, 1956

Presiding - S. B. Ingram

INTRODUCTION . . . . F. D. Leamer

ADDRESS - "THE NEVER ENDING PROCESS" . . . . . . Dean Thorndike Saville
New York University

PRESENTATION OF C. D. T. FELLOWSHIP AWARDS . . J. B. Fisk

PRESENTATION OF CERTIFICATES . . . . E. I. Green

Students to be honored:

E. S. Anderson	G. V. Hill	P. F. Parks
H. P. Anderson	S. G. Homic	M. C. Paull
D. Baker	W. F. Howard, Jr.	R. G. Pecina
F. J. Balash	S. M. Humerick	R. Pettai
E. E. Barrett	R. F. Irby	M. Poulos
H. R. Bedell, Jr.	D. Jarett, Jr.	H. Raag
T. L. Beeler	R. D. Johnson	V. L. Ransom
E. A. Berkery	E. V. Kindberg	R. F. Rey
A. A. Binder	D. O. Kiser	F. A. Reynolds
J. W. Boyhan	D. E. Kissel	S. C. Rogers
C. E. Brady	J. R. Klauder	P. F. Sennewald
W. D. Brooks	C. H. Knowles	N. Sharko
W. B. Cagle	L. M. Kolensky	R. H. Small
C. S. Caron	T. B. Light	S. M. Smith
D. E. Colvin	D. C. Lincicome	J. H. Soderberg
W. A. Crabtree	G. C. Loeffler	C. Spector
H. Cravis	J. R. Macy	A. Stavrinaki
M. G. Davis	R. H. Mattson	D. E. Stinson
D. P. Defino	A. B. Mearns	J. L. Sullivan
L. J. Donohoe	H. J. Meinholtz, Jr.	C. P. Susen
G. H. Ebel	R. S. Menne	C. R. Swanson
H. E. Elder	M. E. Mitchell	C. J. Vincent
D. L. Favin	S. Mottel	J. B. Vreeland
P. J. Fillingham	D. W. Nast	R. D. Wiese
L. L. Fogarty	M. Nesenbergs	R. L. Wilson
L. Freimanis	E. G. Nielsen	D. A. Wolf
E. Filienakis	J. C. Null	J. G. Wood
R. L. Gault	W. G. Nutt	J. R. Woodbury
R. G. Giguere	J. W. Oomun, Jr.	F. J. Woolam
T. N. Grigsby	F. P. Pace	A. Zarouni
D. Hampel	G. Parker	

Harry and his fellow graduates of "Kelly College," Bell Labs' intense three-year training program, July 2, 1956

work as anything he accomplished at Bell because it represented an "absolute command of *P-N* junction theory."[49]

About Harry's fourth year at Bell Labs, in 1956 or 1957, toward the end of his *P-N* junction work, Jim Early, who had worked under Ken Smith and was now a departmental manager, "plucked" Harry to work for him on germanium mesa transistors, "finally making it to three-terminal devices."[50] Harry was promoted to supervisor—one of Bell Labs' youngest. "For years, I dreamed of getting a Ph.D. I had it in my head that I was thought less of because I didn't have a Ph.D., then four out of five promotions went to non-Ph.D.s. It was quite an ego boost."[51]

Jim Early, left, at an IRE semiconductor symbol committee meeting in the 1950s, picked Harry to work for him on germanium mesa transistors.

Division head Jack Morton, vice president of electronic technology who, years earlier, had been put in charge of transistor development by Bell Labs president Mervin Kelly, had switched company focus to silicon as the transistor material of choice and diffusion as the technology after Tanenbaum's 1955 silicon junction transistor success. Silicon doesn't have the same sensitivity to temperature that germanium has. Germanium transistors had a history of decreasing performance at 60 to 70 degrees Celsius and not making the best switches because they would leak current even when off. Although germanium was easier to purify, had higher frequency capabilities, and its technology was well established, silicon solidly provided better electronic switching capabilities.[52]

Still, germanium had its usefulness, such as for submarine cables, where temperature was not a problem but need was great for frequency bandwidth. Harry was one of the few researchers left at Bell Labs working with germanium. His transistor was targeted for the transmitting transistor of Project Vanguard, the United States' first satellite and a project of the Naval Research Laboratory (NRL).[53] About the same time, Harry's friend Bill Hittinger was chosen to develop the transistor for Nike Zeus, the latest installment in the Army's Nike anti-aircraft missile system.

Project Vanguard's satellite transmitter transistor needed high frequency, and silicon wasn't fast enough. As Harry worked with the germanium mesa transistor in 1957, he was aware other Bell Labs research projects, such as Nike Zeus, were employing silicon. Harry said he was "sort of off in a corner" with his germanium work.[54] On October 4, 1957, however, Harry's work took on a new urgency when the Soviet Union

The tiny, 6.4-inch TV3 satellite contained Harry's even smaller transistor launched within the nosecone of a Vanguard rocket.
Photo courtesy of NASA

launched Sputnik, man's first artificial satellite. The race was on between the United States and its communist foe.

"All of a sudden my project became extremely important," Harry said in a 2007 interview with author David Brock of the Chemical Heritage Foundation. "The transistor had to be efficient and very small. The whole project had been designed around this roughly grapefruit size. The antenna was small so it had to operate at a high frequency. The entire system was designed around a transistor that would emit at 107 megahertz and we were targeted to get 100 milliwatts of power out. The mesa transistors I was working on would do that."

Metal tungsten was used to make electrical contact with the transistors. This contact, only a thousandth of an inch wide, greatly determined performance. As one of the engineers working with Harry toiled on Project Vanguard, even before Sputnik went up, he tried gold wire instead of tungsten, using a sharp wedge to push down the gold wire and make the contact needed. The gold proved more reliable than the more fragile tungsten. In addition, Bell could mechanically automate gold wire but not the tungsten point contacts.[55]

About the time Sputnik was launched, Harry's group had samples of their new gold bonding technique ready to show the Naval Research Lab. Harry demonstrated gold's superiority to NRL representatives in dramatic fashion, shooting the transistor through a BB gun into a wall, then taking the transistor out and plugging it in. It still worked. Harry suggested to NRL that the tungsten process be switched out for gold. NRL, however, would not rewrite the project specifications. Blanketed under pressure from Russia beating the U.S. to a satel-

Vanguard rocket exploding during launch, December 6, 1957
Photo courtesy of NASA

lite launch, NRL could not take the extra time. Bell Labs' Project Vanguard transistor was sent on to Cape Canaveral.[56]

Russia launched Sputnik II in November 1957, adding to U.S. panic to compete. On December 6, 1957, a Vanguard rocket carrying America's first satellite exploded on its Florida launch pad. As the rocket had risen, however, the nosecone detached and landed clear of the fire. During the satellite recovery process, Harry's transistor was found still beeping inside the radio beacon. (That transistor can be seen today in the Project Vanguard display at the nation's Air and Space Museum in Washington, D.C.)

Meanwhile, Bill Hittinger, according to Harry, was struggling with developing a silicon version of

On the Vanguard the window-like Solar Batteries turn sunlight into power for a radio.

What's the news from outer space?

Scientists want a lot of information from the Explorer and Vanguard space satellites—information about temperature, cosmic ray activity, meteorite density and other matters.

Radios in the satellites send back this useful "news" from outer space. Since every cubic inch and every ounce in a satellite is precious, these radio transmitters must be quite small. Bulky vacuum tubes, such as you find in most radios at home, would be too large and heavy for them.

So, instead of vacuum tubes, the radios use tiny transistors, an invention of the Bell System. These do the same job as vacuum tubes, but require much less power as well as room.

There's another Bell System invention in the Vanguards—the Solar Battery, which converts sunlight directly into power for a radio. Those in the satellites were made by Hoffman Electronics Corp., Evanston, Illinois.

The Bell System is proud that its inventions are helping man to explore and understand outer space. We're equally proud, though, to serve you, your family and your community with good, dependable telephone service right here on earth!

 **BELL TELEPHONE SYSTEM**

Tiny Bell System transistors like this one help the satellites radio vital information back to earth.

This Boys' Life *magazine ad boasts of the 1958 successful* Vanguard I *satellite (at top) transmitting data back to Earth thanks to tiny transistors (such as held at lower left) developed by Harry and his colleagues at Bell Labs and manufactured at Western Electric.*
Photo courtesy of Jack Ward, Transistor Museum

the transistors for Nike Zeus' computer, which needed speed equivalent to Harry's Vanguard mesa transistors. As Harry recalled, another member of the Zeus military project team, a former Kelly College classmate of Harry's, said to Harry, "We're just not getting the speed and the whole Nike program is going to fold up unless we can do something."[57]

Harry was busy at the Western Electric Laureldale plant (one of Bell's manufacturing facilities), continuing his work on mesa transistor production. But he did some quick, napkin-type calculations for his

Mesa transistor production at Western Electric's Laureldale plant. Note C.H. Knowles nameplate on desk, lower left.

friend, saying, "You know, if I take low-resistivity germanium, make it thin, and then dope up the base like hell, I think we'll make a pretty good switching transistor. We can't do 100 degrees Celsius, but maybe 85 or so." (The Air Force, which took over all longer-range systems from the Army, had set the criterion for 100 degrees Celsius.)

Because Harry had worked at such an in-depth level with practical application of junction theory, he knew how to adjust the doping level of the germa-

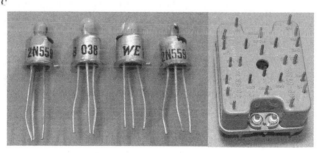

On left, Harry's 2N559 germanium transistors such as those in the Nike Zeus missile system. Right is a Nike Zeus circuit pack containing multiple 2N559s. Photos courtesy of Jack Ward, Transistor Museum

nium such that it maintained its characteristics almost to 100 degrees Celsius. That, teamed with the 100 megahertz frequency, was enough.[58] "That would be fabulous," Harry's friend responded.[59]

The 1957 Western Electric Christmas party at Laureldale, which celebrated the huge success of the 2N559, proved to be Harry's last formal gathering at Bell Labs.

"The U.S. was concerned about Russian bombs," Harry said. "So there were missile systems all over our country. They wanted computers in missiles and needed transistors to go in them. I thought I could build a germanium transistor that would work."[60] Harry was right; he had the first sample in two-and-a-half weeks. "The damned thing was perfect," Harry said.

While the design was different for the Zeus transistor (and employed gold instead of tungsten), it fit the manufacturing process that Harry had developed for Vanguard's 107 MHz oscillator.[61] Harry was in charge of manufacturing as well as research and development at Laureldale, so he was able to tinker with processes on the production floor—thus taking his "napkin" calculations from theory straight into reality.

"Nike Zeus was dumb in that it was easy to do," Harry said.[62] "What was significant was what we did at Laureldale to make the mechanics work. We switched transistors, and the production facilities were ready at the same time."

When the engineers working with the Air Force sampled the transistors, they said, "These are perfect."

"All hell broke loose," Harry said, "because all of a sudden [the Zeus transistor] made the whole next generation of computers feasible [via] the mesa transistor. That *P-N-P* germanium made Nike Zeus feasible and we began to talk outside of Bell Labs.[63] We became a sudden top priority. Western Electric built a new plant in Reading, mainly to produce adequate quantities of the new switching version of the mesa transistor for Nike Zeus.[64] That mesa transistor pushed into manufacturing a whole industry of new computers."[65] Indeed, the germanium mesa transistor served every significant computer of the late 1950s and 1960s, such as the Minuteman computers and IBM's 7000 series. "The timing of the technology was such that almost anything you picked up was productive, fruitful," Harry said. "We were developing an industry that now represents billions of dollars."[66]

For Harry, the Nike Zeus experience was pivotal. There, on the Laureldale manufacturing floor, and then, solving the nuances of need and production, Harry decided he loved manufacturing. "The emotional high of going on the floor—it just clicked," Harry said.[67] "I loved the speed; I loved the need for what I could do on the floor, making decisions on the floor, sequential process changes to get incredible increases in yield and performance.[68]

"Here I was just a young kid, yet I was in command, responsible for good and bad decisions. It was technical heaven. When you get funny electro-characteristics, it allows you, right there on the production floor, to say 'change the doping level.' I knew what I was talking about. You get this aura of invincibility. I discovered the incredible power of having a manufacturing facility—the ability to solve problems, the responsivity. You could see the results fast."[69]

One reason Harry saw such swift results is that he violated Western Electric protocol, which normally dictated that one change at a time be made on the line, with results then documented and analyzed. Never one to bother with workplace politics, Harry's shoot-from-the-hip style meant design changes were often made on the floor where Harry observed the results as they were happening.

"What I found was there was a *huge* gap between guys who understand theory and those on the floor," Harry said. "I loved R&D. I was happiest on the floor in total command. I found I loved it and was the best in the world at that time.[70] Design and production in one person made for a powerful combination."[71]

Full of confidence, Harry knew he was a valuable commodity but felt frustrated by his $7200 annual salary at Bell. The Ph.D.s who worked under him made more money than he did. Don Dickson with National Semiconductor in Chicago offered Harry twice his salary to work for them on zener diodes, so Harry told his bosses. Bell Labs' Jack Morton assured Harry there were three raises in the works for him if he stayed with Bell. Harry, however, was tired of Western Electric's all-procedures approach and explained to Morton he liked manufacturing and wanted to go where his talents could flourish. Morton suggested Harry talk with Dan Noble, the executive vice president who ran R&D at Motorola in Phoenix, Arizona.[72]

A new year had begun—January 1958 in cold New Jersey and Pennsylvania. It was time for Harry to spread his wings beyond the institution of Bell Labs. Much had happened since his arrival in Murray Hill in 1953—including getting married and starting a family. As his career prospered, however, his home life suffered. Perhaps Arizona would offer both warmth and a new beginning.

Chapter 4

Phoebe

(1953-1958)

Harry's garage apartment in Summit

Harry had been intent on finding a wife since his time at Vanderbilt.[1] Upon arriving at Bell Labs in June 1953 and beginning his professional life, Harry felt that need for marriage even more. After his roommate left in November of that year, Phil Porter shared Harry's garage apartment in Summit, New Jersey.[2] Casual friends when they both studied physics at Vanderbilt, Harry and Phil became true buddies when they roomed and attended Bell Labs' Kelly College together.

When they weren't working, the two Bell Labs boys were busy socially, hosting parties in their apartment, taking dates to the Metropolitan Opera in New York City, or occasionally traveling. For Easter of 1954, the two visited Washington, D.C., where Phil's aunt and uncle lived. They also went to car rallies with Phil's Austin Healy sports car. Despite Harry's claim to the contrary, Phil said Harry was not shy, liked to joke, and had a good sense of humor.[3]

One of Phil's dates, Phoebe Hall Barrett, worked at Bell as a chemical technician and lived with her parents in New Jersey. A 1951 Vassar chemistry graduate, Phoebe didn't first date until college.[4] After college she thought she'd work for Swiss pharmaceutical giant Ciba-Geigy, but her overprotective parents wouldn't let her have a car or move into her own apartment, so she took a job at Bell Labs. Phil remembered that, when he picked Phoebe up for their first date, her father challenged him to a game of croquet.[5]

BELL TELEPHONE LABORATORIES   APRIL, 1953

Phoebe Barrett, right, at the Murray Hill main entrance on the cover of Bell Labs' monthly magazine, The Reporter, *April 1953*

Phil had only dated Phoebe a couple of times when Harry saw Phoebe at a dance and she blew in Harry's ear. After that, Harry and Phoebe became a couple.[6] Since Harry was of a mindset to find a wife, only a few months passed before the two were informally engaged. A year younger than Harry, Phoebe seemed a natural match for him; with her chemistry background, the two already had science in common. Harry found her "attractive, athletic, extremely well-read [she had originally wanted to be a writer], and bright."

Phoebe had been engaged to several others in the past before breaking off the relationships.[7] She intently wanted to move out of her parents' home. But she figured the only way she would be able to leave would be via marriage. When

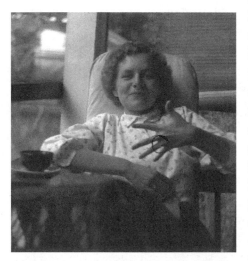

Phoebe showing off (with circled-finger photo) her engagement ring

she and Harry became engaged, before a date was set, her parents pushed the union forward by—unknown to her or Harry—publishing a notice of their upcoming September marriage in the *New York Times.* Thus, at the age of 25, Phoebe married Harry, age 26, on September 25, 1954, in South Orange, New Jersey. Phoebe was free of her parents' home, and Harry had found a wife. Not one of Harry's parents was present for the ceremony—in fact, they were not invited by Phoebe or her family—but Harry's half-brother Hugh and his wife, Jo, did attend.

The newlyweds headed to the Poconos for their honeymoon. The day after the wedding, Harry thought, "'This is a mistake.' It was a very unhappy honeymoon. I didn't know anything about love."[8] Harry felt he should be able to talk im-

Hugh and Jo Knowles, late 1950s

mediately on the deepest, most private levels with his wife. She would have none of that. Conversely, Phoebe said that the day after they were married, Harry "laid down the rules" about what he expected of a wife.[9] In addition, she said Harry wouldn't buy her shorts in which to play tennis in the hot September weather. Whatever actually happened, the result was clear: the Knowles marriage was off to a rocky start.

Phoebe and Harry lived in the garage apartment in Summit in which Harry and Phil had lived.[10] Phil, meanwhile, housesat for a couple of weeks in the main house for the owners before moving in with other Bell Labs colleagues in nearby Berkeley Heights. Before the year was

Honeymooning Phoebe at Skytop in the Poconos

out, Phoebe was pregnant ("unexpectedly and unhappily pregnant,"[11] according to Harry). The pregnancy did not bring the couple closer as they began a new year.

By summer of 1955, the newlyweds were penning letters of complaint to each other in an attempt to address their struggling marriage.[12] Harry's complaints stemmed from what he saw as Phoebe's uncooperative attitude toward closeness—both physically and emotionally. Phoebe, on the other hand, had a litany of complaints, including Harry favoring friends' feelings over his wife's and her husband's insistence that she stop wearing earrings, makeup, and

Phoebe and Harry strike a happy pose at the dinner table.

bath powder—apparently in an attempt to keep a budget. But Phoebe's biggest hurt was rooted in the constant criticism she said Harry delivered. That year, Phoebe quit her job at Bell Labs, where she had worked since 1951.[13] Harry Holmes, II, named after Harry's father, was born September 12, 1955, in Summit.

While Phoebe was home with their infant son, new father Harry was busy building his career at Bell Labs. The two were not communicating in any productive way. Harry thought intellect might overcome the marital obstacles; since he and Phoebe were both intellectual people, he reasoned that the marriage could be fixed.[14] But Harry had no deep well of emotional understanding from which to draw. His father before him did nothing to unlock the mysteries of relationships for his son. Mother

Within a year, the newlyweds were parents to Harry Holmes, II

Ruby had been a poor, mostly absent, role model of parenting when Harry was young. Only his relationships with step-mother Thelma and sister-in-law Jo provided any hope of insight.

Still, when baby Harry cried during the night and Phoebe failed to seem to care, Harry had no sympathy for his wife's listlessness. According to Harry, Phoebe showed the baby little love; but, in later years, Harry theorized they might have used the baby's discomfort as a lever with each other. In retrospect, Harry said he "didn't possess much, if any, paternal instinct."[15]

Judging his wife to be a cold mother, Harry probably was haunted quickly by flashbacks of his own mother—a mother who never held him or told him she loved him. The mixture of past with present and feelings of anger and rejection were surely manifested.

Harry's brothers, in retrospect and from afar, made their own judgments. "Harry married Phoebe not for love but as a helpmate. But she wasn't strong enough mentally to handle it," step-brother Jim Ramsey said.[16] Half-brother Bill Penn, Ruby's son by her first marriage, said the marriage never should have happened. "Harry had a terrible mother," he said, "and he married his mother."[17] Harry agreed that, in some ways at least, he did marry his mother.[18]

Harry feeding the baby

Phoebe's recollections of those early days of marriage reflected a woman overwhelmed. She admitted there was no great love before the marriage; but, during the dating days, Harry seemed "decent, pleasant, and smarter than everyone else."[19] One can imagine that, as a 1950s housewife, this Vassar chemistry graduate measured her success by her accomplishments as a wife and mother. What Phoebe saw as Harry's harshness after the wedding shook her; the strains of motherhood left her exhausted. Phoe-

Phoebe at the Vassar campus, where she earned a degree in chemistry

be felt pulled between the baby and trying to please Harry. She said Harry was jealous whenever she was holding the baby. Phoebe, who'd never lived independently, knew little about motherly responsibilities. Her behavior resembled that of a classic postpartum depression case.

Indeed, a private journal penned by Phoebe when Harry II was a baby, most likely in 1955, wove a story of an extremely lonely and depressed woman.

It is time for me to put down how I feel about our marriage and what is to become of Harry, Harry II, and me. I don't feel like a per-

Enjoying some down time with his son away from the challenges of his Bell Labs duties

son anymore, just a thing. I have no desire to eat, dress, wash myself or anything. I know that no matter what I do or accomplish during any day or week, Harry will find some devastating criticism. If the meals are good and everything clean, Harry says I am too fat…. The whole situation is driving me into a very peculiar and abnormal state. I don't feel free to make friends and have social contacts because I am so afraid that people will find out what a horrible fiasco our marriage is….

I am afraid to do anything. Before I move, I stop and decide whether or not Harry will fly into a temper…. The only way I seem to be able to deal with him is to criticize him back, which only makes matters worse….

I can't enjoy anything!! The books I read are trash. Anything I say or opinion I express is either "illogical" or a lie…. If it is my fault, I really can't see any way out of the situation. If it is not my fault, there is no way out of the situation either except separation or divorce. Would that ruin my life, Harry's and Harry II's or would it be better? Can I accept Harry the way he is, stick it out and keep hoping desperately that "tomorrow" things will be better?

I really don't feel like a wife and mother. I can't plan to do anything (or at least don't dare to). Because we can't have a baby sitter and because we quarrel all the time I would prefer not to even know the neighbors….

Every phase of our relationship is a vicious circle. I think Harry feels that if he did anything I suggest and it worked out, I would win! That would make him, in his mind, less of a man than he thinks he is and he doesn't think he is much. However, he thinks going away, getting a Ph.D. will change things. I don't think they will, but I do think that if we could change things first and have a pleasant relationship with confidence in each other and just gentle affection between us, then we could accomplish all the other things and have a fine life. I am very unhappy. I have never been more unhappy than in the last six months in my whole life. The terrible hemmed-in way we live—is it too much to stand?

I think Harry really hates me. He is only pleasant when he thinks

I have done some great thing for him and yet he doesn't want to do anything for me. The greatest thing I did for him was produce a son, but even that doesn't begin to satisfy him. It is very strange indeed the way he thinks.

Everything is his—the car, the furniture, the baby, me. He hates me if I'm tired or sick and doesn't seem to consider me a person worthy of respect or capable of having any free will of my own. I feel sorry for myself. I could cry all day every day if it weren't for little Harry. Since we have had night feedings, night and day are one to me; it doesn't make any difference anymore whether I sleep or stay awake.

Phoebe with baby Harry sharing a peaceful moment in the Knowles nursery

I just turn the same old things around in my mind all the time until I am slowly driving myself insane. I certainly must get a grip on myself. I can't go on toadying to someone who may not be worth the trouble. I must face the facts. Harry's background is not good, with each of his parents having been married [several] times and lies and recriminations flung between all the various parties to all the marriages. It often seems to me that Harry doesn't know what a pleasant life is or have any respect for women.

Too young to swing alone, Harry, II, gets a little help from his dad.

Am I throwing myself away staying in a situation that seems hopeless? Can I have a better life and a more useful life apart from him, feeling that I have more control over my own destiny and free to act as I see fit? I am beginning to think I can.[20]

The journal thoughts admit self-pity, deep unhappiness, and a maddening sense of loss of self. Phoebe did get some help from a homemaker, who showed her how to care for the baby after he was born. Her husband, meanwhile, had sought assistance even before Harry, II, was born via a psychotherapist. "With all the problems that Phoebe and I had, I perceived I should be doing something about them," Harry said. "I had this tremendous dissatisfaction with myself."[21]

After his son's birth, Harry saw a second therapist, Dr. Kinley, and proclaimed, "This is all my fault."[22] He also looked to Hugh's wife, Jo, for guidance, trading correspondence with one of the few females in his life who had consistently offered wise counsel. Phoebe and Harry pushed on, both tense when together. Harry usually arrived home from work about 6:30 for dinner. He went to bed at 8; she retired at 10 before getting up in the night with the baby.

On December 3, 1955, after 14 months of marriage, Phoebe left Harry and went home to her mother and father with the baby.[23] She tried talking with them about her marriage struggles, but her parents

Marriage and motherhood could be overwhelming at times.

told her it was not polite to talk about unpleasant things.[24] Christmas, then into the new year, found mother and baby still with the Barretts. A January 22, 1956, letter from Harry to his therapist, Dr. Kinley, indicated a possible breakthrough, however.[25] Phoebe and Harry had a "free-for-all complaint session" one evening over coffee that ended with Harry concluding that his wife loved him after all, he loved her, and that he was intensely jealous about sharing Phoebe with her mother. Phoebe admitted being torn between her two homes; but, according to Harry's letter, she had decided she wanted to come back to her husband.

"…[B]elieving that Phoebe really loves me wrought the most remarkable change of heart," Harry wrote to Dr. Kinley. "…[I]t is not healthy to need someone as I need her. Needless to say, I should have had this during childhood—however, it is not too late with your help and hers…. When she returns, I believe I know at least some of my responsibilities…of showing a kindness I had not heretofore…."[26]

Harry's hope for an immediate homecoming was not realized. Correspondence from Phoebe to Harry dated February 7, 1956, portrays a woman still undecided about what to do. However, she went on to list the many details of her grievances with Harry and left the door open for reconciliation, saying that if Harry "just lent a hand now and then and [tried] to enjoy the fruits of my labors and stop asking for more all the time we might have a successful marriage....When I left you, marriage to me meant endless drudgery, no rest, no fun....I just couldn't go on another day thinking...maybe someday I can dance again."[27]

Phoebe preparing a meal in the kitchen of the garage apartment

Phoebe did return home, most likely soon after. An undated letter to Jo from Harry giddily tells of Phoebe moving back with a completely different attitude toward their marriage. Harry described his wife as "the picture of the dedicated, proud, hard-working wife and mother...her expressions of love...unselfish."[28] Therapist Kinley encouraged Phoebe to come in and talk about her and her husband's problems. She went once. Harry, on the other hand, decided he "rather liked psychotherapy" and continued with it in subsequent years.[29] Given his upbringing, therapy was a logical way to attempt to piece together the huge relational gaps he had suffered as a child.

Harry's idyllic description of his wife when she first returned was not a lasting impression. In later years, Harry said, "I don't remember anything but pain. I don't recall her ever being joyful."[30]

Perhaps both husband and wife were on their best behavior for a while, but marriage strains continued to surface. Harry sought solace in his Bell Labs accomplishments. In 1956 or 1957, Harry was promoted to supervisor—despite not having a Ph.D.

Success followed with increasing work hours and importance of projects, such as Project Vanguard and Nike Zeus. Phoebe didn't share in her husband's enthusiasm. She said Harry had tried to explain his

Phoebe keeps a watchful eye on her child.

work when they had first married and she didn't understand.

Harry, with little support from home, found validation of his worth from work. Harry's achievements at the lab and on Western Electric's manufacturing floor "made the relationship with Phoebe worse," Harry said.[31] "I *loved* my work. It was very exciting. Home was awful. So work was my escape.

"We were building mass production techniques, starting with [quantities in the] hundreds. Then, when we saw the transistors met the needs, the numbers moved to the thousands and grew to more from there."

The command Harry held on the production floor was difficult to turn off. "I'm not naturally an extrovert or leader," he said. "I lead only by knowing what to do and saying, 'This is what we're going to do.' When you're very authoritative at work, you tend to take it home with you."[32]

In 1957, with his reputation growing, Harry was recruited by Bill Shockley to join a new subsidiary of Beckman Instruments—Shockley

Harry's fourth Christmas with Phoebe in Summit

Semiconductor Laboratory in Palo Alto, California.[33] Shockley had left Bell Labs for the west coast in 1955 following years of groundbreaking transistor work. In fact, Shockley, John Bardeen, and Walter Brattain received the Nobel Prize in physics in 1956 for the invention of the transistor. (Bardeen and Brattain's point-contact transistor was built in 1947; Shockley's junction transistor debuted in 1951.) Shockley had already succeeded in attracting chem-

Phoebe at home in 1957

ist Gordon Moore and physicist Robert Noyce, but they left Shockley in 1957 to start Fairchild Semiconductor. Names well known in the electronics industry were flocking west in what would result in the birth of Silicon Valley. Thus, it was quite an honor for Harry to be recruited by the brilliant, well-known Shockley.

Harry and Phoebe had lunch with Shockley to discuss Harry's career future, but Phoebe concluded the venerated Shockley was unstable; she also had no desire to move to California.[34] Shockley actually did have a reputation of being a difficult, erratic boss; so Phoebe's protests may have saved Harry from that particular angst. Phoebe recalled saying, "I will go nowhere with William Shockley."[35] Harry, although he had great respect for Shockley's group, had no desire for another marital roadblock and declined the job offer.

Mounting discomfort with Western Electric's production con-

The young Knowles family in 1957

straints kept Harry seeking change.[36] After Bell Labs' Jack Morton suggested to Harry that he consider Motorola instead of leaving the Bell system to work at National Semiconductor, Harry, with Phoebe, interviewed with Motorola executive vice president Dan Noble at the Phoenix facility. Noble promised Harry that, at Motorola, Harry could run his own group making germanium mesa transistors and liberally exercise his manufacturing talents. "I jumped at the chance of this new challenge," Harry recalled. "And, on a personal level, we probably felt the change would be good for our ailing marriage."[37] Thus, in January 1958, Harry and Phoebe moved their family to much warmer Arizona.

Harry in November 1957 as he was winding down his time at Bell Labs and preparing to move his family

Harry's Bell Labs era had ended. What began as the simple desire to work on the transistor had resulted in a complex web of events. While his marriage limped along, his career soared. On the Kelly College bedrock of incredible learning and spurred on by a host of inspiring colleagues, Harry became an inventor. From the intoxicating power of the production floor, Harry emerged as a confident builder of groundbreaking new technologies not merely theorized but manufactured en masse.

Chapter 5

Motorola

(1958-1962)

The Knowles family lived in a rental house (top) before moving into their home at 6015 Calle Del Media.

Phoenix, known as the Valley of the Sun for its 300 days of sunshine a year, provided the Knowles family a definite change of scenery, as they traded the Garden State for desert landscape. Perhaps the added sunshine and distance from Phoebe's family helped the marital situation—even if only a little.

"Arizona was fine," Phoebe said. "We started out in a cinder-block rental house in the desert."[1] After Phoebe became pregnant that February of 1958, however, Harry bought his growing family a new home on Calle Del Media on the northeast edge of Phoenix near neighboring Scottsdale.

89

Harry as he began his new job at Motorola
Arizona Photographic Associates

Motorola announced the addition of Harry to the team in a news release out of the corporate office in Chicago: "C. Harry Knowles has joined the Semiconductor Division of Motorola Inc., according to an announcement from Daniel E. Noble, Executive Vice President of the company's communications and Industrial Electronics, Military Electronics and Semiconductor Divisions.

"In his new post Knowles's [sic] responsibility will be for development and exploratory production of video VHF and UHF transistors."[2]

The news release continued with a description of his Bell Labs experience, saying that, at Bell, "he supervised exploratory developmental efforts in high frequency transistors. He was also responsible for the Bell Laboratories production engineering in high frequency transistors at the Western Electric Company, Laureldale, Pennsylvania." The announcement ended with a mention of his educational credentials.

Harry found his first months at Motorola exhilarating but frustrating. The operation in Phoenix originally had been set up to build germanium audio transistors for car radios.[3]

Dan Noble, Motorola's executive vice president who had hired Harry, had a team in Phoenix including a general manager and chief engineer.[4] "Dan was a nice fella but he had a group of people there who didn't know much about high-volume manufacturing," Harry said.[5] "They wanted me to fill out all this paper. I said, 'If you want transistors, I can make you transistors, but don't bog me down with paperwork.' I was very unreasonable—a stupid kid like myself making

Harry as Motorola's mesa transistor product manager

demands." But, as mesa transistor product manager there in Phoenix, Harry didn't expect to be faced with a barrage of paperwork. Bureaucracy was what Harry fled at Western Electric.

Because the team didn't mirror Harry's semiconductor understanding, his arrival "knowing theory and practice," Harry said, upset the status quo.[6] Dan Noble needed to make major adjustments in the company dynamics to utilize his new talent—Harry. He did just that. The general manager and chief engineer were soon dismissed. Noble hired Harvard professor Les Hogan to manage the overall semiconductor operation. Already on Noble's staff was a highly talented mechanical engineer, Harry DaCosta, who was assigned to Harry. Harry's first task was to push mesa transistors into production as quickly as possible.

Hogan "got" Harry. "I was a strategic thinker," Harry said. "I had achieved that at Western Electric, but there I was just a kid. It makes you hard to fit in an organization. But Les Hogan understood and made the organization adapt around me."[7]

Hogan and Harry shared common work ancestry, since Hogan had also worked for Bell Labs—although his era preceded Harry's. Hogan, who held a chemical engineering degree from Montana State University and a Ph.D. from Lehigh, had worked with Bell Labs while he was in the Navy helping develop an acoustic torpedo.[8] But he joined the Bell researchers formally in 1950. Within three months of his arrival, Hogan had invented the microwave gyrator,

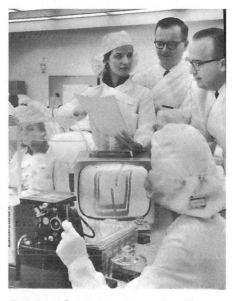

Semiconductor manager Les Hogan, right, and Harry examine mesa yield.
Photo reprinted from 1959 Motorola Annual Report

isolator, and circulator with a little help from future Nobel Prize winner William Shockley, who had an office around the corner and assisted Hogan one day with some of the advanced math required by his endeavor,[9] despite Shockley's own pressing work with his junction transistor. Bell Labs bosses were so impressed by Hogan's quick work, they doubled his salary.

In 1953, Hogan left Bell to be the Gordon McKay Professor at Harvard, where he mentored nine doctoral students. He recalled he got job

Dan Noble
© Motorola Solutions, Inc.,
Legacy Archives Collection.
Reproduced with permission.

offers monthly while at Harvard, but it wasn't until Motorola came calling that he relented. "[I] turned every one of [the job offers] down except Dan Noble...he wouldn't take 'no' for an answer. He just kept after me," Hogan said in a 1995 interview with Rob Walker for Stanford University's Silicon Genesis Project.[10] Hogan's admiration of Noble was evident. "Dan Noble was a very unusual guy.... He started building FM transmitters and receivers while he was a professor at the University of Connecticut and he built the first...FM transmitter in the United States in Connecticut."

From the FM transmitting technology, according to Hogan, Noble went on to invent a two-way, radio communication device for use by Connecticut police departments. The first of its kind in the nation, the technology drew the attention of then Motorola president and founder Paul Galvin, who recruited Noble to leave academia. Noble resisted, much as Hogan did more than a decade later.

As Les Hogan tells it, the Motorola president told Noble, "I'll pay anything. I'll double your salary. I'll triple your salary. I want you. You're gonna be the future of Motorola."

Indeed, Galvin's statement was true for the era. After Noble joined Motorola as director of research in 1940, his company introduced the same year the "Handie-Talkie SCR536" portable two-way radio, which would become the iconic handheld radio of World War II.[11] Motorola's war-time products accounted for virtually all of the walkie-talkies that were built during World War II.[12]

Thus, Noble's reputation and leadership were well established by 1958 when Noble was recruiting Les Hogan to leave Harvard. Hogan acquiesced, arriving in Phoenix mid-June of that year to begin work as Motorola's semiconductor general manager.[13]

"God bless him," Harry said of Hogan. As Harry's frustrations were mounting, Hogan arrived and relieved Harry's worries that perhaps the career change to Motorola had been a mistake. "He was one of the most incredible leaders I've ever been around. He [was] fun to work with... bright."[14]

Within the year, Hogan said in the Walker interview, "I fired just about every engineer that I had there and brought back my friends from

Motorola's Phoenix semiconductor facility, circa 1965
© Motorola Solutions, Inc., Legacy Archives Collection. Reproduced with permission.

Bell Labs. The Bell Labs people were the only ones who knew what a transistor was even then."[15] With Harry's transistor knowledge and Bell Labs pedigree, he was immune from Hogan's firing wave. Harry welcomed the changes.

At the time, Motorola's semiconductor program was small; the Phoenix outfit's thrust had been radio transistors. However, Dan Noble, the number-two man under Motorola president Bob Galvin (who had been handed the reins of the company from his father, founder Paul Galvin), intended on making the Arizona plant a major semiconductor operation.[16] The facilities then consisted of 35,000 square feet and probably no more than 150 people, according to Harry.

Hogan recalled that Motorola sold about $3 million worth of semiconductors in 1958, mostly for their own internal use within the company. "We sold $3 million worth that year at a $3 million loss," Hogan said. "That gives you an idea of what a hilarious thing it was."[17]

In fact, Motorola annual reports during this era indicate the cost of growing the semiconductor division. The company had to invest in expansion and development before any profits could be seen. "Production of Motorola power transistors about doubled in 1957," said the company's 1957 annual report. "Production of germanium switching transistors and silicon power rectifiers was started....We have continued our heavy development expenditures in semi-conductors for which the pay-off is still in the future."[18]

By 1958, Dan Noble's intention to grow the division was evident. The 1958 annual report (the same year of Harry's and Les Hogan's arrivals) commented, "A redirection and intensification of efforts occurred in Motorola's approach to semi-conductors which include transistors. Large development costs continued in 1958, leading to important advances in mesa transistors, rectifiers and zener diodes."[19] The report also said that the company was in the process of adding 86,000 square feet—a new three-story addition—to its Phoenix semiconductor plant. In fact, the 1959 report states that Motorola had added 129,000 square feet to its semiconductor production division.[20] More expansion would follow in subsequent years as it became obvious to industry leaders the future lay in solid-state technology.

Hogan made some key hires that put Motorola "smack on its feet," according to Harry.[21] Hogan brought in, as a sales and marketing team, Dick Rudolph, Joe Van Poppelen, and Tom Hinkelman from General Electric's marketing brain trust in Schenectady, New York, to help Motorola focus. Hogan also hired National Semiconductor's Don Dickson to run zener diodes and Leo Dwork and John Welty to run germanium power transistors. "The marketing effort has been increased," acknowledged the 1958 annual report,[22] but, by 1959, the annual report was touting its shrewd business acumen, saying, "Considerable expansion of the division's marketing organization took place this year to increase the sale of semiconductors for military and industrial application."[23]

The bottom line reaped the benefit of the changes—but slowly at first. "In that first full year of 1959," Hogan said, "we sold $10 million worth of semiconductor [products], and we barely made a profit, about $200,000 in profit. The curve just went [upwards] from there."[24]

When first hired, Harry thought the team might work on filling the company's need for high-frequency components of television sets. But that market was minuscule compared to the potential of the computer market. In an August 1958 *Electronics Industries* article, "New Transistor Design—The 'Mesa'!" written by Harry, two new mesa transistors were spotlighted: a VHF-UHF low-level amplifier transistor and an ultra-high-speed switching transistor marketed as the 2N695.[25] The 2N695 became the Motorola team's focus and, ultimately, would make enormous impact in the burgeoning computer market. Hinkelman and Van Poppelen, Harry said, pushed the computer technology. "They said, 'Forget that [television market]. What's important is the switching [computer] device.' We very quickly moved that device [into production]... because it was exactly my chip design I had already put into production at Bell and Western Electric."[26] Mechanically, Harry and DaCosta adapted parts of the germanium chip structure and the housing for production.

Indeed, soon after Harry's arrival, Motorola began manufacturing the same germanium mesa, high-frequency transistors—at least as far as the basic semiconductor structure was concerned— Harry had designed and produced for Nike Zeus at Bell Labs.[27] However, the Motorola structure was designed for better frequency response and was engineered for higher volume produc-

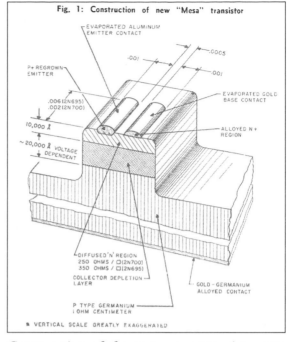

Fig. 1: Construction of new "Mesa" transistor

Construction of the new mesa transistor was highlighted in a 1958 journal article by Harry.
Knowles photo reprinted from *Electronic Industries*, August 1958

tion. Patent infringement was not an issue for Motorola, since Bell Labs and its manufacturing arm, Western Electric, had been under federal constraint to offer open licensing for its transistor technology.[28] A 1949 U.S. antitrust suit against Bell, followed by the possible military classification of junction transistor technology "against the backdrop of the Korean War," as author David Brock explained, led Bell Labs to conclude sharing would be in everyone's best interest.[29] In 1951 and 1952, Bell Labs even held symposiums to share its semiconductor knowledge with other researchers, selling $25,000 patent licenses to other companies to make transistors. Thus, Motorola was one of several companies who joined in this pool of research and production.

Motorola's production methodology resulted in higher yield and reliability. In addition, the process, Harry said, was "amenable to very precise dimensions."[30] Motorola's germanium mesa 2N695 high-frequency transistor, the Motorola version of the 2N559 Bell Labs transistor, included a new etching process in-

2N695 mesa

95

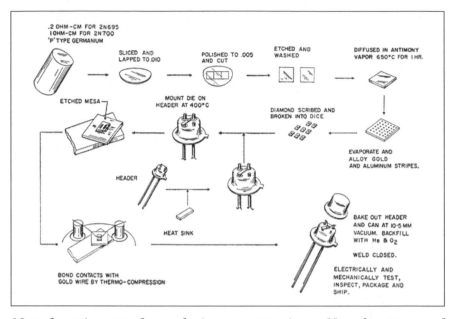

Manufacturing steps for producing mesa transistors. Note the automated etching. Knowles photo reprinted from *Electronic Industries,* August 1958

vented by DaCosta and Harry.[31] The transistor basically consisted of a wafer of germanium with aluminum and gold stripes doped, or loaded, with the chemical element antimony to achieve the correct electrical or frequency characteristics. To automate the etching of the mesa (so named because of the plateau-like appearance) wafer, DaCosta and Harry placed a stainless steel mask with a hole in it above the mesa, blew air through it, while flowing liquid around the outside.[32] The structure formed a chamber that electrolytically etched the mesa. The emitter and base regions were then bonded with two wires via a process which had been developed by an engineer in Harry's earlier Bell Labs Murray Hill development group. The process was improved, however, with Motorola's use of a unique bonding technique adapted for high speed and low cost by Harry and DaCosta.[33] Harry and Hogan invited a group from Bell to visit to share the new processes; that group included Harry's old Bell Labs division boss, Jack Morton.

"It gave us a high-volume way of doing it," Harry said.[34] Since etching and bonding were traditionally time-consuming, the new production process brought costs down to a minimum.[35] "We were beating the socks off of everybody with speed and cost of manufacturing," Harry said. "Hinkelman, Van Poppelen, who was sales manager, and Les Hogan had the idea of coming up with an absolutely revolutionary price on these things of $1.25."[36] At the time, similar devices in the industry, according to Harry, were selling for more than $100 each.

Since Harry had arrived at Motorola, he forced the turnaround of manufacturing processes to be significantly faster and more efficient than at Western Electric.[37] The team of Knowles, his support group, and mechanical engineer Harry DaCosta was a good one. "One of the things Dan Noble did at Motorola was to assign me Harry DaCosta," Harry said.[38] DaCosta "was an incredible person, not just an ingenious engineer...fabulous to work with, creative as hell. We developed methods of chip handling and wire bonding that were far ahead of anybody else, including the folks at [rival] Fairchild Semiconductor."

Harry DaCosta

In fact, whenever Harry met a need on the production line, whether a new piece of equipment or a measuring device—even if it did not exist yet—he and his team would invent it.[39] During his 1958-1962 tenure at Motorola, for example, Harry worked with Carl Zeiss of Germany, a major supplier of optics, to design a special microscope with appropriate depth of field and working range for the Motorola transistor assembly line. In addition, Harry and his group, under Bill Lehner and Clare Rawson, made their own new glass headers and revolutionary, high-volume, high-frequency testing equipment. "At Motorola, I'd describe what we needed, [work with] one of our designers and, within a matter of weeks, do a prototype, then go into manufacturing," Harry said. "We leapt ahead of everyone else. We were the first ones doing high-volume computerized testing. We dominated high-speed transistor manufacturing at Motorola."[40]

From left, Bill Lehner, an engineer, and Al Phillips (future Western Digital founder) in Harry's office

With Motorola's 1958 introduction of its 2N695 mesa transistor and its subsequent high-volume production, the company was in position to attract more business. Motorola sold Autonetics, a division of North American Rockwell, on its mesa transistors soon after, most likely during the 1958-1959 period. Autonetics had received the contract for the guidance system of the Minuteman I, a broad Air Force ballistic missile defense program which received its initial design and funding approval in 1958. In fact, in October of that year, Boeing had earned the original contract for design, assembly, and testing of the Minuteman.[41] Autonetics was one of several associate contractors chosen to work on the huge, multi-year project.

Autonetics had been using micro-alloy diffused transistors, or MADTs, from Philco, according to Harry, to build their prototypes. However, the way the alloy collector junctions were made resulted in, Harry said, an "unreliable device."[42] Because Autonetics had guaranteed the Air Force a seemingly unrealistic less-than-one-percent overall failure rate on the Minuteman, which equated to an incredible 0.0001 percent per 1,000 hours for individual transistors, Harry and Andy Procassini, who was in quality control at Motorola, crunched the numbers on what level of reliability Motorola could promise with their mesa transistor. Harry said Procassini, a brilliant statistician, developed a data analysis program using "step-stress testing of samples in combination with Weibull statistical tools to verify that, in fact, we [had] achieved such lofty goals."[43] With *repeatable* reliability proven and the manufacturing and cost structure in place, "it was not a hard job to sell them on the mesa transistor [and on Motorola]. It worked beautifully."[44]

The 1959 annual report for Motorola bragged of its growing stature:

> Motorola is currently a leader in the manufacture of both power transistors and the ultra-precision Mesa transistor....We believe the Motorola Mesa units are the most advanced transistor devices in the semiconductor art. Their adaptability to miniaturization of complete electronic systems helps answer the need for reduction in size and weight of electronic devices for aircraft, missiles, and rockets.
>
> We also believe the Motorola Mesa is the most precise semiconductor available today, and the smallest, mass-produced transistor manufactured. The active region of Mesa transistors can be covered by an area less than the cross-section area of a human hair, yet they are manufactured by methods so precise that they are turned out on a

With the Missile Age came new technology, including Motorola's
new mesa transistor, which boasted incredible reliability.
© Motorola Solutions, Inc., Legacy Archives Collection. Reproduced with permission.

production line basis to meet rigid standards of reliability. Mesa transistors are produced in meticulously clean laboratories having closely regulated temperature and humidity. Production personnel wear special uniforms to minimize dust contamination.

Extension of the Mesa design to higher powers and higher frequencies will be introduced in the near future. Soon there will be an entire family of the highly-precisioned Mesa transistors, devices that will open whole new areas of transistor application.[45]

Harry on wire bond line

Within the next few years, building on the mesa's success, the Motorola sales team of Van Poppelen, Hogan, Hinkelman, and Harry would head to IBM's Poughkeepsie, New York, facility with the $1.25 per transistor sales price in their heads and the security of knowing Motorola could crank out many thousands of mesa transistors a day.[46] After they gave their pitch on performance, reliability, and manufacturing ability to IBM, IBM purchasing manager Frank Green asked if they wanted to see the production facility for the 7000 series IBM computer.

"We had no idea how many [transistors] IBM was using," Harry recalled. "Frank walked us into a building football fields long. As far as you could see, there were three aisles, and in every cubicle of about 25 feet long, they were putting computer systems together with 30,000 to 40,000 transistors per computer."[47] Green then told the stunned Motorola envoys that the process took about three weeks per cycle. "They were using many millions, *per week*!" Harry said.

The Motorola salesmen recovered from their shock enough to discuss price, proposing to IBM $1.25 per transistor. The response: silence. IBM's Green gave Les Hogan a piece of paper with ".25" —25 *cents*—on it.[48] Hogan immediately said, "We'll do it. We'll figure out how to do it." Motorola had landed the big fish; its semiconductor division embarked on a road of rapid build-up to fill the large IBM order.

"Price determines cost," Harry said.[49] "You determine price first, then you solve the problem of how to bring costs down." At Motorola, costs declined via automation through the many manufacturing advances Harry and his colleagues made and by solving problems in-house.

Thus, Motorola relatively quickly leaped to the top tier among transistor-producing companies. The 2N695 germanium mesa transistor became "*the* standard for a whole generation of computers,"[50] Harry said, as the mesa was used for Autonetics' Minuteman, the IBM 7000 series, and by virtually all major computer makers at the time.

As usual for Harry's work life, the pace at Motorola was hectic. From the moment of his arrival in 1958, he was key to transitioning his small division to a large, true contender at the top of the semiconductor industry. Despite his job's demands, however, he had other important roles to fill in his life at home. Wife Phoebe's unplanned pregnancy came with a bigger surprise—twins. Robert Hugh and Marjorie Barrett were born November 8, 1958, in Scottsdale. The twins joined their three-year-old brother, Harry Holmes, II.

Thus, with barely four years of marriage under their belts, Harry and Phoebe were the parents of three children. Phoebe had some household help, but she commented that the twins were almost easier than when she was caring for little Harry as a new mother.[51] No

Phoebe with twins Marjorie and Robert, 1959

doubt, the difference, in addition to mothering no longer being foreign to her, could be attributed to the absence of the postpartum depression she'd likely suffered after her first child was born. "My happiest times were with the children," she said.

The marriage was still a rocky one. Phoebe said that Harry limited her monthly food and clothing allowance to $300 a month, although he was making a good salary ($23,480 in 1959). However, personal financial records from 1959 and beyond indicate Phoebe had ready access to

her own checking account.[52] Also, Phoebe said she did convince Harry to join a swim club in nearby Paradise Valley, so the children would have a pool. Phoebe's portrait of Harry is one of a jealous, possessive husband, prone to an anger inherited, according to Phoebe, from the violent tendencies she believed Harry's own father exhibited. Harry noted, however, that "Phoebe had not wanted to meet his father and, consequently, had never met him." The young mother did have a network of friends, but she said she was afraid for babysitters to witness her husband's outbursts. Harry found this claim nonsensical.[53]

Harry at an airport in Europe, traveling for work, 1959

"Work was his first priority," Phoebe said, although she remembers him being home for dinner

Harry, II, and the twins, 1959

then heading to bed by 8. "What I did was do everything he wanted and pretend he wasn't there."[54]

Phoebe said that, during what would be four years in Phoenix, little Harry, then the twins, came down with chicken pox. She was sick with pleurisy when she also contracted chicken pox herself. Harry was scheduled for a trip to Italy, so he hired someone to help care for the children. (In 1960, Harry was being recruited by Roberto Olivetti and Signor Floriani of Teletra for a job with the Italian company, SGS. He declined the offer.) "I was so weak and too sick," Phoebe recalled. Apparently, the caregiver was not very caring, because, when Harry returned, Phoebe had him fire the sitter. A maid moved in temporarily to nurse Phoebe back to health.

Health issues elsewhere had a more profound impact on Harry the winter of 1960. In February of that year, Harry's step-mother Thelma called Harry and Hugh from Birmingham to inform the two that their

Harry Holmes Knowles

father, Harry Holmes Knowles, had declined precipitously. Suffering from cerebral arteriosclerosis, Big Harry, a few months shy of 79 years of age, had become increasingly frail, weighing only 105 pounds. Since cerebral arteriosclerosis causes thickening and hardening of the arteries in the brain, it is not surprising that he also had become altered mentally to such an extent that his wife Thelma struggled with his care.[55]

Thelma's son Jim Ramsey, by that time an anesthesiologist in Birmingham, confirmed to step-brother C. Harry that their dad had become dangerous and was threatening Thelma. C. Harry flew home to Birmingham on a Friday and consulted with the doctor and specialist, who recommended that the elder Harry be sent to Bryce Hospital, a mental facility in Tuscaloosa, Alabama, for treatment and observa-

Harry, shown here in Rome, declined an Italian company's offer in 1960.

tion. The younger Harry, who had conferred with Hugh also about the situation, called Auburn buddy and Selma lawyer Joe Pilcher for a legal contact to commence emergency commitment proceedings. "We had to get Dad committed," the younger Harry said. "Joe gave me a lawyer contact, Jim arranged a doctor certificate, and we went before a judge."[56] Within a few hours, Big Harry's fate was sealed. His son Harry later recoiled at how rapidly the process took place "by networking with the right people in Alabama."

On Saturday, March 5, 1960, C. Harry drove his father the one hour to Tuscaloosa, and Big Harry was committed to Bryce.[57] "Dad didn't know what was happening," Harry remembered of the painful time. "We drove in silence, just the two of us. He knew the situation when we drove up. He knew there was nothing he could do. He didn't fight it. There was very little said, but it must have been a terror for him. That's the last time I ever saw Dad." Harry returned to work in Phoenix the next day.[58]

When Bryce Hospital opened in 1861, it was a model facility for treatment of the mentally ill. By the 1960s, however, when Big Harry arrived, standards of care at Bryce had fallen to abysmal levels while the population soared. By 1970, Alabama would rank last among U.S. states in funding for mental health, and a lawsuit would be filed in federal court on behalf of patients. That landmark lawsuit, *Wyatt v. Stickney,* eventually would lead to federal minimum standards for the care of those with mental illness and the shutdown of many of the large warehouse-style hospitals.[59]

In 1960, however, Thelma tried to see her husband every two weeks at first, but he often became agitated during her visits or wouldn't remember when she had last come to see him. Thelma's job precluded work-week visits. Into the summer, the elder Harry repeatedly asked about his release, sometimes violently. Family correspondence files show Thelma agonized over his condition, writing the attending physician in between visits to check on Harry's physical and mental status.

"As long as Harry wasn't violent, I was happy to care for him," she wrote to a family member. "I could not continue to live under the strain that I had been under the past couple of years. I saw this coming and just prayed that the Lord would see fit to take him before he got in this condition....I am very much grieved over him and miss him terribly. We have been married 22 years and were seldom separated."[60]

On the afternoon of August 25, 1961, Harry Holmes Knowles died at Bryce Hospital at the age of 80 of an acute coronary occlusion.[61] C. Harry returned to Birmingham from Phoenix but was too distraught to attend the viewing or the service.[62] The son had lost the parent who taught and nurtured him during his childhood. Indeed, the two had forged a unique, loving bond from their shared difficulties and similar talents.

Big Harry and Thelma in earlier days. C. Harry lost his beloved father August 25, 1961.

Back in Phoenix, Harry's relationship with his own children was complex. He remembers holding the new additions to the family, Marjorie, "the apple of my eye," and Robert, "the quiet one."[63] He maintained that Phoebe didn't nurture the children as

Harry with his children

infants, and that his own sparse paternal instincts were stilted by his wife. "I had to fight through Phoebe to have any relationship with them. She said…that I was domineering, bullying, making her a slave."

Phoebe usually fed the children before Harry arrived home at 6:30, he said, so there were no family meals. After working "long and hard" all week at Motorola, Harry spent the weekends taking the kids out. "I didn't understand the problems Phoebe had with Harry," he said. "He was fine with me. Harry [II] had a filtered father who was distorted by Phoebe. I'd come home [and she] would be screaming, 'This is what he did today,' so I'd admonish him, or rarely, hit him on the bottom with a hairbrush. I fell for that."[64]

Harry readily admitted his inadequacies as a father and continued to seek help in psychotherapy through the years in hope of gaining marital stability. Phoebe acknowledged Harry's search to understand. "He was always sending me to therapists," she said.[65] The remembrances of the couple, decades later, obviously represent a wide divergence of perspectives on exactly what went wrong in the Knowles household and where blame lay. Harry saw Phoebe as precluding a relationship with his own children. He also recognized how the intense nature of his work isolated him, asking in retrospect and in therapy, "Who the hell am I?" However, all blame aside, Harry, at nearly age 80, spoke with poignant clarity and regret: "My biggest disappointment in life is not having done enough with my own kids."[66]

During this Motorola work era, Harry's mother Ruby decided to visit her son and his family in Phoenix. At the time, Ruby owned an Orange Julius beverage franchise in Birmingham, and she was on her way to a work-related conference in the West. But Ruby's opportunity to visit with her son, daughter-in-law, and three grandchildren in any meaningful way was clouded by Ruby's temperament.

Launching an airplane with Harry, II

According to Harry, Ruby came into their home and began issuing orders to the family she had never seen. The visit was brief. "She bossed [us]," Harry said. "Phoebe was even more disturbed than usual. I said, 'Mother, get out. Get out of my house, my life, away from my kids.'" The episode was one more wound in a long history of Harry being disappointed by his emotionally handicapped mother. However, this time, Harry consciously decided he'd had enough and ejected her from his life.

"They never got [the relationship] back together," half-brother Bill Penn said of the incident, "and Mother didn't attempt to mend it."[67] Harry would not see Ruby again except for one time at Bill's home in Birmingham, several months before her May 1989 death.

At Motorola, growth in the semiconductor division had continued at a lightning rate, reflecting the explosion of new technology in the field. Fairchild Semiconductor, birthed in 1957 when eight of Shockley Semiconductor's key scientists left to form their own company in the same town (as Shockley's company) of Palo Alto, California, introduced the first commercial double-diffused silicon transistor in 1958.[68] Fairchild physicist Jean Hoerni followed this feat with the development of the planar manufacturing process in 1959, which protected junctions in silicon transistors with a coating of silicon dioxide.[69]

Meanwhile, in Fall 1958, Jack Kilby of Texas Instruments created an integrated circuit, or IC, which carried multiple electronic components on a single chip;[70] but his device, according to Harry, illustrated the concept more than it proved the theory.[71] (Kilby had interviewed with Harry at Motorola as Kilby was thinking of leaving his former employer, Centralab. Harry

The Knowles family, clockwise from top, Harry, II, Harry, Robert, Phoebe, and Marjorie, gather for a photo at their home in Phoenix.

said he felt Kilby was mostly a tinkerer and would add little to the sophisticated technology and high-volume production being anticipated at Motorola. Consequently, Harry did not offer Kilby a job.) Fairchild physicist Robert Noyce, however, in 1959, conceived of the use of his company's new processes to produce, as Brock's *Understanding Moore's Law* detailed, "a new, planar form of silicon integrated circuit" which could be manufactured.[72] By spring 1960, with Noyce's colleague Jay Last leading development, the first planar IC was fabricated.

The arrival of the integrated circuit was vital in the world of solid-state technology. As discussed in a PBS history of the transistor:

> Transistors had become commonplace in everything from radios to phones to computers, and now manufacturers wanted something even better. Sure, transistors were smaller than vacuum tubes, but for some of the newest electronics, they weren't small enough.
>
> But there was a limit on how small you could make each transistor, since, after it was made, it had to be connected to wires and other electronics. The transistors were already at the limit of what steady hands and tiny tweezers could handle. So, scientists wanted to make a

whole circuit—the transistor, the wires, everything else they needed—
in a single blow. If they could create a miniature circuit in just one
step, all the parts could be made much smaller.[73]

With Kilby at Texas Instruments conceiving that all parts (including
capacitors and resistors, as well as the transistor) of the circuit could be
made of a single crystal and filing for a patent on his model, TI would
be the first to show off its pencil-point-sized solid circuit in March
1959. Because Noyce at Fairchild separately thought of the single chip
in the same time frame and produced his superior silicon planar IC,
however, both scientists are generally credited with having, according
to PBS, "independently conceived" of the integrated circuit.[74] Both men
would receive the National Medal of Science for their work. However,
Noyce would not share Kilby's later Nobel Prize, since Noyce died in
1990, a decade before it was awarded. The Computer History Museum,
however, chronicling Noyce's role, said that "...many believed [Noyce]
would have [shared the Nobel Prize] had he lived."[75] While Kilby would
garner a Nobel Prize for his IC work, it was Noyce's planar IC which the
industry rightly brought to the manufacturing forefront.

Motorola was also working on silicon integrated circuits by the dawn
of the 1960s. In fact, following the buildup of manufacturing for the Autonetics and IBM orders of the germanium 2N695 mesa, Harry moved
his group to focus mainly on silicon IC work for Motorola, directing
production of its first integrated circuits. Noyce and his Fairchild group
had solved the key mechanical problem of how to get small enough wire
contact by using the oxide layer as an electrical insulator, then making
the connections on top of that coating. The advance gave the industry
added research momentum. "The silicon capability of higher temperature operations plus the silicon oxide coatings over which metal inter-
connecting layers could be made, spelled the long-term, future doom
of germanium components," Harry said.[76] It should be noted, however,
that Motorola's germanium mesa transistor remained dominant until
Noyce was able to design silicon components small enough and, hence,
fast enough to compete with the germanium mesa.[77]

"We had phenomenal manufacturing capability—low cost, high
quality, very reliable," said George Scalise, a Purdue mechanical engineer whom Harry hired in the early 1960s from CBS to help with Motorola's IC operation—first within the research and development area,

Motorola trade show

then running the IC assembly and test site.[78] Harry's excitement for the work at Motorola must have been contagious as Scalise was convinced to move from Massachusetts to Phoenix over the course of one whirlwind recruiting weekend. "Harry...had heard about me and wanted me to come out for an interview. Next thing I knew, I was out in Phoenix... in the middle of the desert," Scalise continued in an interview conducted by Rob Walker for Stanford University's Silicon Genesis Project.

"Harry was a brilliant engineer. [He] came out of Bell Labs and did a lot of the original work on the germanium mesa....[On the interview trip,] we went into the factory and just talked and walked and spent until four o'clock in the morning going over everything that was going on there and it was really exciting. I decided this had to be the place to be." Scalise said Motorola took their unique manufacturing capability and applied "that same technology and modified it to build integrated circuits." He also commented on the fact that Fairchild "didn't have anything resembling our cost structure."[79]

Fairchild's approach to production diverged markedly from Harry's Motorola production model at the time. Fairchild moved the assembly portions of their manufacturing to China for cheaper labor costs. Motorola was likewise concerned with meeting the price demands of their clients, but first chose to lower costs with their automation techniques. "My theory was to keep manufacturing domestic," Harry said. "We were concerned about giving communist China all that technology. We thought the way to combat costs was to make equipment faster and easier to use. We were both right."[80]

In a Silicon Genesis Project interview, Les Hogan commented about the off-shore versus domestic production of the era. "We believed in the automation system," Hogan said. "For then, it was the right thing to do. We had to keep it at home to get it done right, then, we took it over there." Hogan said that by the time he would leave Motorola in 1968, Motorola, too, had built a plant in Hong Kong. The combination of automation and lowered labor costs, he said, would make the company $25 million profit on $200 million worth of semiconductor sales that year.[81]

In 1960, however, plant expansion at Motorola was taking place in Phoenix, where 307,000 square feet of production space was due to be added, bringing the semiconductor division's total square footage to more than 530,000 by its scheduled completion in mid-1961.[82] The 1960 Motorola Annual Report boasted that the division's customers were now 75 percent outside clients. In other words, only 25 percent of its semiconductor products were for other Motorola divisions. One of the company's top achievements for the year, according to the annual report, was the "mass production of epitaxially grown...silicon transistors,"[83] making Motorola the first company to market these uniquely crafted devices.[84] The report continued, saying, "This major advance improves quality and promises reduced costs as the result of increased production yields."[85]

Indeed, Motorola was capitalizing on Bell Labs' revolutionary new method of laying down silicon announced at the June 1960 Solid-State Device Research Conference, where Bell Labs scientist Henry Theurer presented a paper on epitaxial transistors. As the Computer History Museum described the process, Theurer added a "thin epitaxial layer of silicon between the base and collector of a transistor....This approach raised the transistor's breakdown voltage while dramatically increasing its switching speed."[86]

Epitaxial layers are formed when a crystal is grown on top of an underlying crystal effecting a matching structure. The Bell Labs process

Harry in Europe

"left silicon growing in one crystal," explained Harry. "Epitaxy, suddenly, broke the logjam of how to get the ideal layered construction of an *N-P-N* or *P-N-P* transistor. It's a very precise and controllable process."[87]

Electronics companies around the country quickly adopted the technique. Within days of Bell Labs' announcement, members of Remo Pellin's materials group at Motorola were, Harry said, "growing the ideal kind of junctions," utilizing the new epitaxial process.[88] Wilf Corrigan, who worked as a Motorola section manager for the epitaxial materials group during this era before serving as a product manager and transistor operations director, remembered Motorola's mastery of epitaxy ahead of its competitors. Armed with a degree in chemical engineering, the young Corrigan and his colleagues were poised for a market edge opportunity.

"We were able to do a lot of the original work on epitaxy," Corrigan said in a 1998 Stanford University Silicon Genesis Project Rob Walker interview.[89] He continued, saying Motorola proceeded to "get it into production...in a very short period of time....Motorola was looking for a difference and so we jumped on epitaxy as the difference. Fairchild was making triple diffused chips...and nobody quite knew how to do this on a production basis, even though Bell Labs and IBM were demonstrating it. We figured out how to do it in high volume before anybody else did."

Corrigan, who would go on to lead Fairchild as its president and CEO before co-founding and running LSI Logic Corporation, reaped a number of patents from his Motorola epitaxial work and called this phase of his illustrious career a high point. (His time at Motorola spanned 1960 to 1968.) "There was this period of time in the early '60s when, for a moment in time, a small group of us...knew that we knew more than anybody else about how to do this," Corrigan said. "Of course, these advantages dissipate. This was 24 hours a day...total involvement....You get so that you believe that you can think like the silicon."

Experiments almost seemed unnecessary, Corrigan said, because they "knew what was going to happen. You could make the adjustments to the temperature and the gas flows just on your intuition. You felt like you knew exactly what the atoms were going to do as they came down on the surface. So, it was a very exciting time... [B]ecause we had the epitaxy process, we were then able to make transistors that were literally a quarter of the size of the competitor transistors... [T]hat's always been the most critical thing—how [to] get that chip size down for the same functionality."[90]

The arrival of epitaxy sparked an epiphany for Harry, who conceived of a one-ampere, high-frequency transistor by using a star structure.[91] The idea, Harry said, was fairly simple when one considered that "because of the current flowing through resistance of the thin base layer, only the outer few microns of the edge of an emitter function."[92]

The original 2N2222 star transistor and Harry's notes, circa 1960

"I said, 'Let's make the whole thing a virtual edge.' With epitaxy, you can get high voltage, and low base-to-collector capacitance, across the base-collector junction."[93] The materials group built the new epitaxial silicon devices in a matter of weeks.[94] "Along with epitaxy, photolithographically forming shapes of any arbitrary geometry allowed tremendous flexibility of emitter base construction," Harry said.

The novel star structure translated directly into Patent No. 3,214,652, the "Transistor Comprising Prong-Shaped Emitter Electrode," filed March 19, 1962, with the sole inventor listed as Carl Harry Knowles under the auspices of Motorola.[95] Prior to the filing, in 1961, Harry had been appointed Motorola's assistant general manager for research and

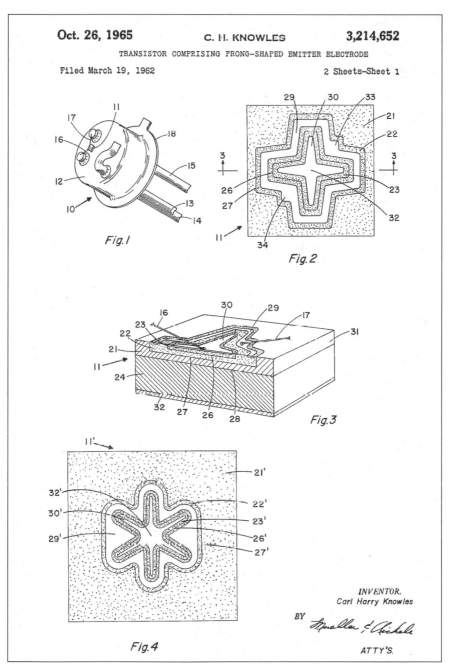

Oct. 26, 1965   C. H. KNOWLES   3,214,652

TRANSISTOR COMPRISING PRONG-SHAPED EMITTER ELECTRODE

Filed March 19, 1962   2 Sheets-Sheet 1

Fig. 1

Fig. 2

Fig. 3

Fig. 4

INVENTOR.
Carl Harry Knowles

BY

ATTY'S.

The first page of Harry's star transistor patent, filed in March 1962 and issued in October 1965. The star design maximized the edge, giving it high frequency and voltage.

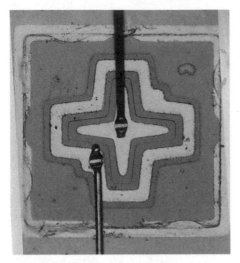

Later model of Motorola's uniquely shaped, epitaxial 2N2222 transistor

development. The new transistor certainly added to Harry's R&D success. The U.S. Patent Office issued the patent October 26, 1965, several years after Motorola christened the star transistor as the "2N2222" and it became a universal transistor with almost limitless applications. The original Knowles patent detailed:

"This invention provides a transistor with an emitter region which has a central, hub-like portion and several finger-like projections extending radially outwards from the central portion....

The fingers...preferably taper so that they are narrower at their outer ends, much like the points of a star." In describing why the invention was an improvement on current transistors, the patent states: "The emitter region has a large ratio of perimeter-to-area which improves the current handling capacity of the transistor. The transistor has a higher frequency response and better low current gain than presently available transistors of the same general power rating...."[96]

"All by itself, the 2222 was a revolution to the whole circuit field," Harry said.[97] With resistance gone, power was saved and switching was more efficient. The 2N2222 design maximized the edge, giving it high frequency and high voltage. Indeed, the Transistor Museum web site curator, Jack Ward, said in 2007, "the 2N2222 has become the most widely used and universally recognized transistor of all time. Billions of units have been manufactured...and there is continuing high volume annual production."[98]

The transistor was highly touted in Motorola's 1961 and 1962 annual reports, which, respectively, claimed that "the star planar incorporates in one transistor all of the latest semiconductor technologies"[99] and that, due to "widespread acceptance...additional production space was required to keep pace with demand."[100] Further, the 1962 report said that Motorola had become the nation's second-largest producer of semiconductor and integrated circuit products.

Motorola's semiconductor division had improved dramatically since its humble beginning in 1955. Even when Harry and manager Les Hogan arrived in 1958, the division's products were basically all for in-house use. By 1962, Motorola was truly top-tier, for which Harry deserved a good share of the credit. He had decided, after putting the germanium mesa transistors into production and launching the company's first silicon integrated circuits, that, perhaps, he had accomplished all he needed for his company. He anticipated a job change.

Thus, it was not Harry who introduced the Motorola 2N2222 product launch to the public. Instead, Jack Haenichen, one of Harry's transistor design engineers whom Harry had hired out of U.C. Berkeley in 1959, announced the 2N2222 at the 1962 Institute of Radio Engineers (which would become IEEE the following year) Convention. Haenichen had been working on silicon planar transistors and N-P-N bipolar transistors when the new epitaxial process emerged.[101] Haenichen, attempting to meet the need for higher breakdown voltage, crafted an annular, or ring-like, planar transistor which was applied to Harry's star geometry.

Harry considered his greatest achievement at Motorola not the super-successful star transistor (for which Harry took a broad view of his role); rather, he was most proud of transforming Motorola into a powerhouse in transistors and integrated circuits. "I was the technical driver," he said.[102] He had perfected key volume production processes, in addition to directing some of the world's first high-speed manufacturing, assembly, and computerized testing techniques.

In late 1961 and early 1962, Harry and Les Hogan toyed with the idea of founding their own company. Changes abounded not only in Harry's personal life, but also in the country, which had inaugurated John F. Kennedy as 35th president in January 1961, following two terms served by Dwight Eisenhower. President Kennedy had asked Americans to consider what they could do for their country and inspired a decade of space-age technology when he announced in May 1961 the lofty goal of sending an American to the moon by the end of the decade. 1962 would bring the Cuban missile crisis as U.S. tensions with the Soviet Union escalated. Under the cloud of threat, however, opportunity shone. Many of society's changes would be hastened by the wondrous advances in solid-state science engineered by Harry and his colleagues throughout the U.S.

As Harry considered his options, in 1962, a headhunter from Westinghouse called and offered Harry the challenge of running his own division. One of Harry's last official acts at Motorola was to sign the patent paperwork on the star transistor. He tendered his resignation to Les Hogan on June 28, 1962.[103] Hogan was not pleased to be losing his technical captain. But Harry was driven to see how good he was. Phoebe had taken the children for an extended visit with her father on Cape Cod that spring and had made it clear Harry was not welcome there.[104] His family situation reinforced Harry's decision; he accepted the job and headed east. After four-and-a-half years in Phoenix, Baltimore would be his new home.

Chapter 6

Westinghouse

(1962-1968)

As Westinghouse molecular electronics manager, Harry consolidated IC efforts.
Deakin Studio

Changing jobs would not have been as tempting had Harry not been upset about his marriage and the Phoebe-imposed separation between him and the children.[1] He had accomplished much professionally at Motorola and was well respected there; it was difficult to leave. Because Les Hogan and Harry were close personally, Hogan's feelings were hurt when Harry left. "I had tremendous respect for Les," Harry said. However, "the challenge of finding out how good I was was there."[2]

In addition, psychotherapy, according to Harry, had brought Harry to a level of self-confidence he had not experienced earlier in his career. For the first time in his life, he could be totally selfish in the sense that he had no family members distracting him. He had dismissed his mother Ruby from his life, an act which, undoubtedly, had shed some deep-seated emotional baggage.

His beloved father had died, and his wife and children were out of his daily worries—at least temporarily.

"I didn't have Phoebe to tie me down," Harry said. "I ran around in my own plane and made myself feel important."[3] Harry had been working on his pilot's license while at Motorola, eventually buying his own plane on arrival at Westinghouse in Baltimore. A 15-year-old, V-tailed Bonanza Model B,

Commuting via his trendy Bonanza airplane

the fairly trendy airplane came in handy; as Harry would spend a good bit of time commuting among three of the four Westinghouse integrated circuit (IC) development groups—in Baltimore, Churchill Borough near Pittsburgh, and Youngwood, Pennsylvania—that would report to Harry.

Westinghouse Electric & Manufacturing Company, which had been founded by George Westinghouse in 1866 in Pittsburgh, Pennsylvania, and helped develop the electricity system in the U.S., was perhaps best known by the public for its home appliances.[4] However, by the time Harry joined Westinghouse, the company's interests were widespread and included solid-state, power-oriented components. Semiconductor-related research at Westinghouse, according to the Computer History Museum, was encouraged via a "partnership with Siemens of Germany in silicon power transistors in Youngwood, the Central Research Laboratory at Churchill Borough, and new product development [as a department of the research lab] at Wilkinsburg, all in Pennsylvania...."[5] Westinghouse was steeped in Department of Defense work and, as a result, also ran the Westinghouse Defense Group in Baltimore to work on integrated circuits for the military and a Defense Group laboratory in Newbury Park, California.[6] Further, a molecular electronics research contract in the late 1950s encouraged a new integrated circuit operation.[7]

Harry became part of Westinghouse's growing IC efforts as its new general manager of the molecular electronics division.[8] Harry's boss, Seymour Herwald, group vice president of electronic components and specialty products, suggested to Harry that he consolidate the IC operations. After using his Bonanza to aerially photograph the Baltimore-D.C. corridor, Harry set up the new IC division his first year, 1962, near the Baltimore-Washington airport.[9] Known as the Elkridge facility, the division was technically located in Elkridge's neighboring town of Linthicum Heights, Maryland, ten miles southwest of Baltimore and not far from the Westinghouse Defense Group. However, Harry preferred the sound of "Elkridge" instead of "Linthicum," so he didn't let geographic technicality stand in the way of a more pleasing moniker.

Harry found that all of the four Westinghouse IC shops were developing the same set of IC devices. "I thought, 'This is absurd,'" Harry recalled. "I was soon known as Hatchet Harry. In order to improve operations and to focus my own technical energies, I had to winnow down, streamline the four teams."

Westinghouse research and development lab at Churchill Borough, near Pittsburgh

Indeed, Harry's charge at Westinghouse was to fire huge numbers of people.[10] "For the first year, I did [little] but run around the country firing people. But we had some brilliant work going on under a guy named Ed Sack…a damn good technician and manager."

Harry moved veteran R&D man Ed Sack from Churchill in Pittsburgh to Baltimore. Sack had worked for Westinghouse since his graduation from Carnegie Mellon with a Ph.D. in 1954.[11] He'd served as manager of the electronics department (working on flat-screen displays) and manager of the solid-state devices department at the Churchill Research Lab prior to becoming engineering manager at Elkridge. Sack rivaled Harry in technology knowledge; they were a good team. "We were in agreement on virtually all organizational and strategic issues," Harry added.[12]

Harry's primary motivation for streamlining was to get products and cash flowing.[13] At the time, Harry thought Westinghouse's Air Force molecular electronics contract was more costly and distracting than profitable. Harry minimalized that contractual obligation by assigning it to the nearby military group of Westinghouse.[14]

Harry remembered his mindset at the time: "There [was] much money to be made [by focusing energy] on getting real transistors, real diodes, real resistors. High speed will get that because speed, speed, speed was everything.…we drive the cost of these things down by mak-

Harry in front of the Elkridge integrated circuits facility he set up near the Baltimore-Washington airport

ing them smaller. We can make money by making them smaller. Performance is up and the cost goes down. I [could] see no end [to that progression]."[15] Harry expounded on the discussion of speed, saying the industry's corporate players needed to move into production as quickly as possible and that reducing component size is what made the individual chip faster.[16]

Harry recruited former Motorola colleague Andy Procassini, the brilliant statistician who had helped sell the mesa transistor with Harry at Motorola, to be his quality control leader and, later, manufacturing director at Westinghouse. (Before Harry's tenure at Motorola ended, however, Procassini would return to Motorola as quality control manager before Procassini joined Fairchild in 1968.) Harry also recruited Joe Hurley from Rheem Semiconductor as marketing manager. Hurley, in turn, hired for materials distribution manager George McCarthy, Jr., who coordinated day-to-day materials flow throughout the IC operations.[17]

In addition, McCarthy provided Harry the end-of-the-month billing reports that helped outline the company's profits and losses.[18] Those reports, according to Harry, often prompted daily and sometimes hourly updates from McCarthy, who readily referred to "his ubiquitous clipboard containing the latest data on each product and project in the factory."[19] The always-tense process of shipping product and analyzing the numbers required all-night work sessions at times. As McCarthy worked with Harry, he saw first-hand his division boss' management style.

"Harry treated me like a close associate," McCarthy said. "One morning, after I'd been up all night working for him, Harry got onto me for getting upset about something; but then Harry apologized. He showed a fairness, especially to the little people in the organization. We had a people-oriented division."[20]

McCarthy recalled that Westinghouse wasn't doing well, so there was great pressure on Harry to get billing numbers up and meet monthly shipment forecasts. As McCarthy struggled with the numbers one month, he realized at 3:30 in the morning that $200,000 more in shipping was needed to meet the quota. "So I sent 50 pounds of junk to Ed Sack—a [highly structured] sort of person and billed him $200,000," McCarthy said. "Harry was hysterical[ly angry about that]." Such was the convoluted nature of the business model at Westinghouse at the time.

McCarthy said some people were scared of Harry because Harry could have a short fuse. "Harry is a tense guy," McCarthy said. "He had great hopes for the semiconductor business—which came to be. He was a go, go, go guy. I understood him, so I wasn't scared of him.

"He was very talented technically, bright. He loved being on the floor. He is funny and emotional and has a big heart. He loves people. Many people at the company loved and respected Harry." Indeed, McCarthy thought highly of Harry's moral compass, too, saying he never saw him drink and Harry was highly upset if he heard of anyone having an affair with a co-worker. Harry also, reportedly, became angry when he learned waiters delayed serving a group of his colleagues at a business lunch because their lunch guest—a visitor from RCA—was black. "Harry heard about it and was livid," McCarthy said. "Here was this Southern boy from Alabama....I loved that about him."

One of the things Harry noticed early on, before he moved Ed Sack from Pittsburgh to Baltimore, was some research on electron microscopy being developed at Westinghouse's Churchill plant.[21] Sack was running the research lab there at the time and remembers using "conventional optical photolithography" to manufacture integrated circuits.[22] Electron microscopy uses electrons for imaging, while conventional

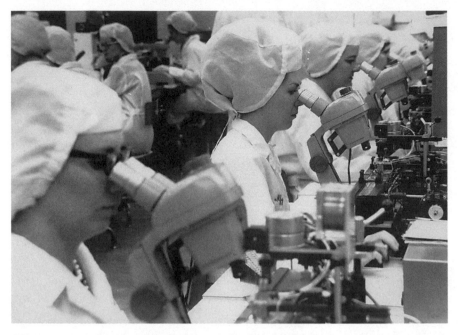

Microscopes were used to help attach wires on the tiny transistor circuit components, as seen in this 1960s photo of Westinghouse's wire bond line.

methods use light. An electron microscope has a higher resolution than an optical, or light-driven, microscope.

With electron microscopy, instead of visible light lithography, Harry saw an opportunity to get better resolution for working with tiny circuitry components. "A constant pressure in electronics," Harry said, "is to design and make them to operate faster, and to make them less costly. Fortunately, both requirements are satisfied with IC manufacturing. Smaller components are faster. In addition, more of them can fit onto a given-sized wafer. Hence, in general, a given circuit function costs less to produce. The limitation on size is constrained by how small the circuit's individual sub-parts can be produced. The higher the resolution of the lithographic process' imaging, the better for both speed and cost."[23]

Dimensions of individual components on an integrated circuit were measured in tens of microns in 1962 when Harry arrived at Westinghouse, and the wafers on which the ICs were made were about one inch in diameter. (The dimensions of individual components would get exponentially smaller, while wafers would get larger, in the future.) Harry was well versed in the manufacturing challenges. He had shepherded Motorola's semiconductor devices to assembly line success via a combination of mechanical manipulation and sheer will. In 1962, according to Harry, Ed Sack proposed the development of lasers to increase resolution, instead of electron microscopy. Harry felt that electron microscopy, rather than lasers, would meet the technological needs for decades to come. Looking back in 2011, Harry declared "laser illumination is still the dominant technology for IC production. Ed Sack was right."[24]

Employee with integrated multi-gate array (large-scale and holding actual size) which allowed for a standard component set for mass production, 1960s

"I had said at best we're going to get [componentry] down to a half-micron, third-micron or so [in size] with optic[al wavelengths], which was short-sighted," Harry said in looking at miniaturization dreams then and now. "What people have done lately is use lasers...[to get] down to [tens of] nanometers in production."[25] (One micron is one thousand nanometers.)

"But the [forecasting] curve...began to then shape what my thinking was on where we had to be," Harry said. "My thinking on it had started with Motorola with a vague idea of 'these are the kinds of things we have to do' [to meet completion and market demand in the future]. I went to Westinghouse with that kind of vision of where we had to take Westinghouse and it was perfectly compatible with the dreamers at Westinghouse—one of which was Ed."

"Harry and I had a good working relationship," Sack said. "Harry brought a significant burst of energy to the Westinghouse molecular electronics program."[26] (Sack would continue to rise through the ranks at Elkridge, becoming manager of technical operations in 1965, assistant general manager in 1966, and general manager in 1967 until he left Westinghouse in 1969 to join General Instrument Corporation. His star

Knowles family home on Gibson Island

Marjorie and Robert at playtime

rose there also, and, in 1984, Sack became the president and CEO of microprocessor manufacturer Zilog Inc.)

Shortly after Harry settled into his responsibilities at Westinghouse, Phoebe and the three children joined him. Previously, Harry had traveled to Cape Cod, where Phoebe was visiting her family, to check on his wife and children. "Phoebe was horribly unhappy," he said.[27] She greeted her husband icily, telling him to sleep on the sofa. Angry at the cold reception, Harry turned around and went back to Baltimore. However, eventually—probably in time for near-seven-year-old Harry, II, to start the school year—Phoebe moved south. She and Harry and their children, Harry, II, and twins Robert and Marjorie (who were closing in on four years of age) all moved to a home on Gibson Island, a private, gated, yachting community thirty miles southeast of Baltimore. Harry filled the home with Westinghouse appliances and the Knowles marriage moved unsteadily forward.

At Westinghouse, business pressures continued as Harry pushed the technical envelope as best he could in the slow-to-change environs of his company. Visionaries, such as Harry and Ed Sack, weren't necessarily nurtured. Rather, they were burdened with accounting minutiae. "I didn't manipulate the forecasts," Harry said. "I wouldn't play their game. I learned bad business principles at Westinghouse."[28] Still, despite the roadblocks, Harry would build his division to a level at which West-inghouse was selling $10 to $12 million a year (at a thin profit), making the company third in IC sales in the country behind Fairchild and Motorola. Texas Instruments was also in the top tier.

Fairchild Semiconductors in Palo Alto, California, formed in 1957 when eight of Shockley Semiconductor's scientists departed and started a company with $1.5 million in venture capital from Fairchild Camera and Instrument Corporation, had an impressive list of technical achievements under their belt.[29] Such landmarks included Jean Hoerni's planar manufacturing process in 1959 and Bob Noyce's and Jay Last's planar form of integrated circuit shortly after (as discussed in Chapter 5). "The microchip age had been launched," summarized Chemical Heritage Foundation senior research fellow David Brock.[30] "Between 1961 and 1965 the market for the integrated circuits greatly expanded. In 1961 Fairchild Semiconductor earned $500,000 on integrated circuit sales. In 1966 Fairchild and other integrated circuit producers on the San Francisco peninsula garnered $60 million from sales of microchips, representing half of the U.S. market."

Still, consumers had to be educated about the new devices as they struggled to wrap their minds around the ever-changing solid-state market offerings. In addition, semiconductor industry scientists and leaders also had to keep up with rapid innovation while making efforts worth their while from a business standpoint. For consumers to be interested in products, prices had to be low enough, which meant costs of manufacturing complex circuitry had to continue to descend. That was possible through better manufacturing technology. Miniaturization was key.

"Silicon transistors were—from their beginning to the present day—fabricated in a batch process," Brock said. "Using photolithographic, mechanical and chemical processing steps, manufacturers created multiple transistors on a single wafer of silicon. The ultimate measure of such a manufacturing process was its yield....Given a satisfactory yield, a smaller transistor meant that more of them could be made on a single wafer, making each one cheaper to produce."[31]

The industry's discussion of miniaturization had been going on since the 1950s and continued to be a central theme at the 1960 Solid-State Circuit Conference, but it was not until 1964 that the momentum of the discussion reached pivotal status. "By 1964," Brock continued, "the new market for silicon integrated circuits was still largely limited to the military sector, but during the four years since 1960, many leaders in the semiconductor community had become convinced that integrated circuits were the future of electronics."[32]

As the semiconductor industry transformed itself during this era, so too the country experienced sweeping transformation. Civil rights leader Martin Luther King, Jr., spoke eloquently of having a dream to 200,000 people gathered for the August 1963 civil rights march on Washington, D.C. The same year, other dreams were crushed for the whole country when President Kennedy was assassinated in Dallas on November 22. Harry, exploiting his Bonanza, flew his Methodist minister and family over the Kennedy funeral procession to the Capitol on November 24. Vice President Lyndon B. Johnson succeeded Kennedy; with Johnson's election in 1965, he would serve as president until 1969.

However, in the first part of the decade, in preparation for the Institute of Electrical and Electronics Engineers' 1964 annual, international conference in New York City, convention leaders recruited industry papers for presentation. The principal organizer was Harry's old colleague Les Hogan, Motorola vice president and semiconductor manager. Hogan contacted Harry in 1963 and asked him if he'd like to participate in the IEEE conference and talk about the future of electronics. Since Hogan had been upset with Harry upon his leaving Motorola, Harry saw the invitation from Hogan as a chance for reconciliation.[33] Still, giving papers was never one of Harry's preferred tasks.

"My first reaction," Harry said, "was 'Les, thanks [but] I'm not the guy you want. There are better people around and I don't have the time. I'm busy trying to get a Westinghouse division profitable in a Westinghouse environment.'"[34]

However, the magnetic Hogan convinced Harry the paper would be fun. "Once you commit to it," Harry said, "then you [realize you're] going to have a few hundred friends out there. I better do something impressive. I'm not a paper writer. I like production and dealing on a production floor."

Harry's audience was more than a thousand, as it turned out. His talk followed other industry leaders such as Hogan from Motorola and Robert Noyce, co-founder of Fairchild. Harry's premise regarding the future of the electronics industry was that component cost and customer expectations would continue to drive the technology toward increased circuit speed and lower costs.[35] "The complexity problem facing both designers and users of integrated circuits," Harry said, "is that cost increases as each component becomes more complex, as the number of components on a block increases."[36] Harry thought the solution would lie in improving manufacturing technology. "In each case, as the technology improves, the cost decreases...yield improves, and cost drops."

Harry's presentation, which included graphs of the cost per function of an integrated circuit versus the complexity of the circuit,[37] looked at the speed of integrated circuitry from 1958 to 1964 and beyond, noting that integrated circuit logic speed had doubled every year for seven years.[38] "The speed increases because of the decrease in the size of transistors that can be placed on a circuit, and cost declines as well," Harry proclaimed.[39]

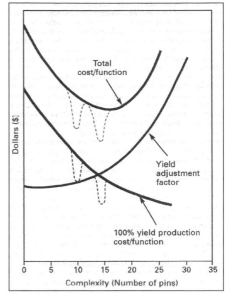

Harry's 1964 presentation of cost per IC function vs. circuit complexity

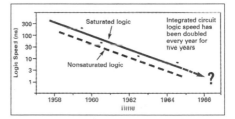

Harry noted that IC logic speed had doubled every year for seven years.

Figures reprinted from *IEEE Spectrum*, June 1964 (as shown in *Understanding Moore's Law* by Davd Brock)

"Knowles thus offered a graphic view of the relationships between yield, complexity, technology, and cost for integrated circuits," *Understanding Moore's Law* author David Brock, who called Knowles' talk "forceful, speculative, and wide-ranging," explained.[40] "Knowles' presentation of 1964...attempted to present the vision of the integrated circuits future through two distinct arguments: one of cost, the other of performance. He argued that at any given time in the progress of manufacturing technology, there was a particular level of integrated circuit complexity associated with a minimum cost per function. Moreover, he implied that this economically optimum complexity point would move over time to higher levels. Concerning the matter of performance, he said that logic speed had doubled every year for seven years, and that as 'transistors can be made smaller...the speed of circuits will be increased.'"[41]

"One of the things that I talked about," Harry reflected in 2007 in an interview by Brock, "was what's clearly going to happen in the next few years is that you will have the capability on a single chip of surpassing the world's largest computer. I felt this was going to happen within ten to fifteen years."[42]

Harry's line of thinking reflected the industry's opportunities for growth also espoused by other visionaries in the field—one of those being Gordon Moore, director of research and development at Fairchild.

Ironically, Harry could well have been a colleague of Moore's at Fairchild, along with Noyce, Last, Hoerni and the others, had Harry, in the late 1950s, accepted William Shockley's invitation to leave Bell Labs and join Shockley Semiconductors. (Moore, Noyce, and six others had left Shockley in 1957 to form Fairchild Semiconductor.) It was an irony not unnoticed by Harry in later years and a chance blocked by Phoebe's dislike of Shockley.[43]

The dissemination of Harry's 1964 IEEE presentation, however, melded the minds of Harry and Gordon Moore in history. A year later, in 1965, Moore published his own view of the future of the semiconduc-

While his 1964 predictions were considered wildly optimistic at the time, Harry would prove to be the more accurate.

tor industry in *Electronics* magazine. The magazine editor had written to Moore in January asking him to forecast for its 65,000 readers what would happen in the industry in the next 10 years as part of the publication's 30th anniversary issue.[44] Less than a month later, Moore's manuscript, "The Future of Integrated Electronics," was sent to the magazine, which published the article under the title "Cramming More Components Onto Integrated Circuits."[45] Moore's paper and his refinements in subsequent years grew to such stature that it became a guiding model for semiconductor industry forecasting and research efforts. In fact, by

1970, computer scientist and California Institute of Technology professor Carver Mead had dubbed the model, "Moore's Law."[46]

Moore, in a 2005 speech celebrating the 40th anniversary of "Moore's Law," remembered the formative thoughts that preceded his now-famous 1965 article, reflecting on his response to the 1964 IEEE New York conference (at which Harry had presented his own predictions).[47] Moore said that "the IEEE convened a panel of executives from leading semiconductor companies: Texas Instruments, Motorola, Fairchild, General Electric, Zenith, and Westinghouse. Several of the panelists made predictions...." He spoke of Texas Instruments' Patrick Haggerty predicting that, in ten years, "the industry would produce 750 million logic gates a year." Moore marveled and found the idea perceptive. Les Hogan at Motorola predicted the "cost of a fully processed wafer" would be $10.

"Harry Knowles from Westinghouse, who was considered the wild man of the group," Moore continued in 2005, "said 'We're going to get 250,000 logic gates on a single wafer.' At the time, my colleagues and I at Fairchild were struggling to produce just a handful. We thought Knowles' prediction was ridiculous.[48]

"As it turned out," Moore said, "the person who was the 'most wrong' was Haggerty, the panelist I considered the most perceptive. His prediction of the number of logic gates that would be used turned out to be a ridiculously large underestimation. On the other hand, the industry actually achieved what Knowles foresaw, while I had labeled his suggestion as the ridiculous one. Even Hogan's forecast of $10 for a processed wafer was close to the mark....The suggestions of Haggerty, Knowles, and Hogan reflected the general views of the semiconductor industry around the time I was working on my 1965 projection [for *Electronics* magazine]."

Harry Knowles' 1964 presentation and Moore's 1965 paper carried similar themes. Knowles said logic speed had doubled every year for seven years. Moore said the "complexity of integrated circuits—as measured by the number of components per integrated circuit—had doubled every year between 1958 and 1965, with attending increases in performance."[49] Moore also said the trend would continue for the next decade. While Knowles presented two separate arguments, one of cost and one of performance, according to Brock, Moore "made an *integrated* argument, *connecting* cost with performance."[50]

Brock argued that Knowles' graph of cost per function versus the complexity of the circuit was "static, that is, it [represented] a single moment in time during the development of manufacturing technology." Knowles' "metric for cost...is simple: U.S. dollars. His measure for integrated circuit complexity is less direct, gauged by the number of pins on the packaging of an integrated circuit, rather than a feature of the integrated circuit itself.

"Moore adopted a clearer, more direct metric for integrated circuit complexity than Knowles' package-pins: transistor count," Brock continued in *Understanding Moore's Law*. "Moore's 1965 observation was that at any given moment in the evolution of integrated circuit manufacturing technology, there was an optimal complexity point, as measured by the number of components on an integrated circuit, leading to a minimum manufacturing cost per component. Over time, with the development of technology, Moore argued, this optimal point would shift to both greater complexity and lower minimum manufacturing cost."

The similarities of Knowles' and Moore's papers, according to Brock, "show the true context of Moore's 1965 publication of Moore's law: the attempt to communicate to broad technical audiences that integrated circuits were the future of electronics as a whole by using arguments about cost and performance.... While the commonalities between Knowles' and Moore's arguments are important...the differences between them are highly significant. Moore's idiom was far more successful than Knowles'. Moore crafted his argument into a clear and accessible presentation, grounded in the available data (however limited), with a direct, intuitive metric for integrated circuit complexity....[Moore] focused on the economic advantage that integrated circuits would gain over time, and the inherent economic dynamic that would support the continued development of semiconductor manufacturing technology."[51]

Quickly, integrated circuits grew in complexity and speed.

Moore, who, along with Noyce, left Fairchild in 1968 to form the highly successful Intel Corporation, adjusted his model in 1975, saying complexity of circuits by the end of the decade would come nearer to doubling every two years instead of every year.[52] "This prediction became a self-fulfilling prophecy that emerged as one of the driving principles of the semiconductor industry," expounded a Computer History Museum semiconductor timeline. "Technologists were challenged with delivering annual breakthroughs that ensured compliance with 'Moore's Law'....On reviewing the status of the industry again in 1995 (at which time an Intel Pentium microprocessor held nearly five million transistors), Moore concluded that 'The current prediction is that this is not going to stop soon.' Devices exceeding one billion transistors exist today."[53]

While Moore and Brock both acknowledged Harry Knowles' bold vision and although Harry actually published the basic principles of Moore's Law in 1964, Harry remained humble about the role he played in forwarding the theory that became the semiconductor industry's most famed growth model. Rather, he heaped the praise on Moore. "One of the most powerful economic discoveries of the 20th century was Moore's Law," Harry said.[54] "The quantification of everything technical depends on Moore's Law. Billions of dollars depend on it.

"Moore's Law stated explicitly where we're going to be five, ten years from now...[providing] an absolute guidepost," Harry expounded. "You save...development costs...and it has eliminated so much wasted energy and it has brought us along technically.[55] Moore's Law says 'that's where you need to design systems at a given point in the future; and, furthermore, the price of the electronics is going to be here.'"[56]

Unlike Harry and Moore, Harry's company, Westinghouse, was not known for its institutional vision. In fact, in 1964, when Harry was preparing his IEEE presentation, the administrators at Westinghouse, according to Harry, were primarily concerned that Harry might be generating price declines with his sweeping comments of industry change.[57] By the time of the first presentation of Moore's Law, Harry had been battling uphill for several years at the bureaucracy-heavy Westinghouse. A perusal of Knowles Westinghouse correspondence for 1965 reveals Harry as a manager mired in endless details of customer service, production delays, personnel and work-flow concerns, and constant pressure for reports and forecasts aimed at profitability but often yielding only more paperwork.

Harry argued for focusing product lines, attracting new business, and honing his company's integrated circuit science. He documented his worries about his division in numerous memos to Westinghouse

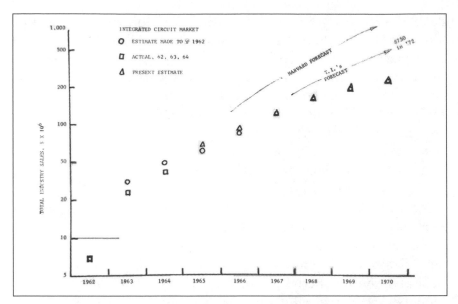

Harry's IC market predictions made in 1962 to his bosses, shown above with circles, were amazingly close to actual.

executives, including his boss, Seymour Herwald. In an April 8, 1965, five-page memo, Harry warned that the division had reached "a critical point in its existence. In summary, we have overcome production and engineering problems; we are currently tied to one diminishing important customer; we are not selling to others."[58] With IBM shrinking its order and a lack of significantly large new business negotiations, Harry thought Westinghouse was trending in the wrong direction.

While Westinghouse shared in a portion of the plentiful IC business provided by Autonetics' Minuteman contract, as did industry leaders Texas Instruments, Fairchild, and Motorola, Harry pointed out that the $7 million of 1965 Autonetics commitments to Westinghouse would most likely total only $5 million for the year. (The Air Force's Minuteman II ballistic missile system, which had successfully launched a test missile in September 1964, helped refine mass integrated circuit production in the U.S.) Likewise, about $9.5 million in total projected Westinghouse shipments for 1965, according to Harry, would be closer to $6.75 million. Compared to competitors Fairchild and Texas Instruments that were bringing in about $1 million a month, Westinghouse was off pace—especially when considering Harry's projection of only $7 million in probable shipments for 1966.

Although Harry thought Westinghouse had good engineering and facilities, he said the sales teams were spread too thin and he feared for the future. "The Molecular Electronics Division," Harry said in his memo, "today faces its biggest hurdle: Either we start selling or we start trying to profitably get out of business as slowly as possible. I choose the former."[59]

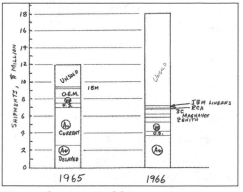

Harry documented his worries concerning the decline of shipments for Westinghouse in 1965 and 1966.

Despite Harry's push for improvement, the next year, in Harry's eyes, only brought more of the same bureaucratic roadblocks. Harry's loves were innovation and production floor adaptability; his employer emphasized accounting and was hardly known for flexibility or risk-taking. Minimizing an Air Force contract his first year at the company, Harry, in a sense, attacked the sacred military cash cow almost immediately. Still, Harry pushed through successful IC work—in spite of the challenges—because he intuitively sensed the pulse of the industry and its future.

By April 1966, however, Harry had run afoul of his bosses one too many times and was relieved of his general manager duties. "We weren't making enough money; we were only breaking even. Perhaps more important, Westinghouse valued adherence to the annual business plan rather than to growth and innovation—more appropriate measures to the semiconductor industry," Harry said. "I'd always been a technical guru. They weren't happy with the business side but liked the technical performance."[60]

Harry's happy days at Westinghouse were limited.

According to Harry, his demotion came shortly after he refused to award a job (to add onto the Elkridge facility) to a traditionally favored contractor without a competitive bid. Thus, Harry was moved into other duties, coordinating Westinghouse's patent licensees, and was named manager of solid-state strategic planning. Not the first exposure to the company's politics, Harry commented in retrospect, "It was a dumb decision to go to this sleepy organization."[61]

"I saw Westinghouse and I were not meant for each other," Harry said. "It was only a matter of time before we parted ways."[62] Westinghouse's obvious message was that Harry needed to find other employment. Still, it would take time to get his life in order, and he needed to earn a living. Ideas about another professional direction—outside of semiconductors—began to germinate. Related to his exploration of options, he requested literature from various companies about gas lasers and measuring tools known as interferometers. His research would solidify into a strategy in the near future.

By this point, Harry already had spent four years of his life based in Baltimore. During those years, his children grew to ages 10 and 7. Son Robert recalled that while his father worked at Westinghouse, Harry's home time was mainly confined to Saturday and Sunday.[63] Work consumed most of his week.

The oldest child, young Harry, got into trouble in the Gibson Island schools. His mother Phoebe said he was referred to a psychiatrist, who diagnosed the problem as the youngster being too smart for his grade at the time.[64] Still, discipline was a problem, despite father Harry's stern hand, and the family moved to a rental in Baltimore suburb Towson to enroll young Harry in military school. They maintained the Gibson Island residence, however, spending summers there. For distraction from Westinghouse and home worries, Harry had bought a sailboat in 1963 and commenced to teach himself how to sail. He recalled later that sailing was "almost all vector analysis" and learning the complex rules of yacht racing.[65] He won the Chesapeake Bay Men's Sailing Championship in July 1965,[66] an unsurprising triumph when one considered the intensity Harry tapped for any competition. However, that intensity had a downside; the children were terrified to sail with him because of their father's short temper.[67]

Working on his sailboat, **Alouette**

The tension between Phoebe and Harry had remained. Harry felt disconnected from his children not only because of a shortage of time with them but because, he said, his wife had a shield around them.[68] "She said I was the evil-doer," he said.

The Knowles family spent most of the summer of 1966 at the Gibson Island house. Harry had been in therapy and was in the throes of a three-week session of corporate-sponsored sensitivity training. Amidst all the self-reflection, "I decided this woman and I were not compatible," Harry said of Phoebe. After years of marriage angst and with his Westinghouse days obviously winding down, Harry told his wife in August she needed therapy and that either she could go to counseling with or without him, or the marriage was over. Phoebe, who was equally unhappy in the marriage, did not respond positively to the ultimatum.

By September, Harry and Phoebe separated, with Phoebe taking the children back to Towson for the beginning of the school year and Harry staying behind at Gibson Island. "The only way I could get any sense was to leave the marriage," Harry said. "With no guilt. I didn't miss the kids; it was too late for them. They were already set in their dislike for me. There was nothing I could do."[69]

Robert remembered his mother telling him and his siblings, when they went back to Towson, "Dad's not coming." In retrospect, he said, he thought what they felt was relief after so many years of family stress.[70]

Phoebe and Harry entered into a legal separation on March 28, 1967;[71] Harry filed for divorce June 13, 1967, after 13 years of marriage.[72] Their children, Harry, II, and twins Robert and Marjorie, turned 12 and 9, respectively, that year. "I felt an enormous relief after the divorce," Phoebe said in 2007.[73] Although her mother was deceased and she was alienated from her father, she did have the support of her aunt.

"What I learned from my marriage is that you should go and see where someone comes from," Phoebe said. Harry, however, noted that Phoebe had "consistently refused" to visit his family in Alabama during their marriage.[74] Still, Phoebe was able to look at marriage philosophically in later years, saying, "I believe there is such a thing as real love and you shouldn't settle for less. Harry and I always fought. But I didn't waste time hating Harry [after the divorce]. Underneath this shell of Harry Knowles, there is someone nice."[75]

During the separation, Harry traveled extensively for Westinghouse, coordinating patent licenses with Siemens in Germany, Phillips in the Netherlands, and Mitsubishi in Japan. During one of his trips to Germany, in October 1966, he met German native Ursula Fuss. He later discovered she was the daughter of an ex-Nazi storm trooper. Harry brought Ursula back to Gibson Island. After the divorce from Phoebe became final, in a misguided act of chivalry, Harry married Ursula. Another marriage was the last thing Harry needed. "Weeks into the marriage," Harry said, "I said, 'This isn't going to work. Go home.' And she did."[76] Harry divorced Ursula as quickly as he could.

Harry in Japan

Harry's tenure at Westinghouse languished on as he tried to make sense of his personal life while plotting an exit from his employer. By 1967, Elkridge, according to the Computer History Museum, "housed about 1,200 employees in a 170,000-square-foot facility and had sales of $15 million."[77] Harry, in his demoted role, spent as much time away from his windowless Elkridge office as possible. With no love lost, he left Westinghouse permanently spring 1968. Westinghouse folded the molecular electronics division into the nearby defense operations the same year.[78] Harry's time there had provided technical success, lessons in corporate culture and finance, and a chance to play a role in the historic unfolding of Moore's Law. Personal life lessons also abounded. The obviously hasty mistake of marrying Ursula aside, Harry's divorce from Phoebe was a relief to them both after so many years of pain.

German native Ursula Fuss, Harry's second wife

"At the end of all that," Harry said. "I really studied who I was and what I wanted to do."[79] He decided to get out of the big-money, huge corporate world of semiconductors. Harry Knowles wanted to get back to basic hands-on work he loved. His re-invention of himself would mark the beginning of an incredible American success story.

Chapter 7

Metrologic Early Years

(1968-1976)

Harry at the beach with his children, from left, Robert, Harry, II, and Marjorie, 1968

Divorced, jobless, and unsure of his future, Harry peered into his work soul that spring of 1968 and found...himself again. He truly enjoyed taking an idea to invention and transforming invention into production. He left the mind-numbing grind of corporate politics behind with his departure from Westinghouse. Harry was free to live anywhere and do anything.

"It was the end of my marriage, my kids didn't want to have anything to do with me, and my Westinghouse job had ended," Harry said. "It was a completely fresh start."[1]

Fleetingly, Harry was tempted to call Fairchild Semiconductor physicist and co-founder Robert Noyce about working for the California silicon giant. (In July 1968, Noyce would leave Fairchild to form Intel Corporation with colleague Gordon Moore.) However, Harry preferred working with small groups; he had grown weary of the semiconductor industry's increasingly prevalent large business model, so he decided to strike out on his own. Harry wanted to turn an idea into his own company. "I had no money. It was sheer insanity," Harry said.

Harry's idea was to use the wavelength of light as a tool for making fine industrial measurements.[2] The thought had first occurred to him while in graduate school at Vanderbilt; at the time, he had discussed his

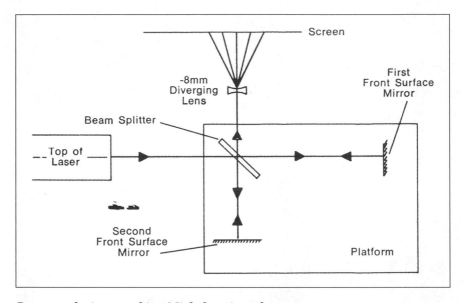

Beam paths in a working Michelson interferometer
©National Science Teachers Association, as appeared in "Classroom Laser Experiments" by C. Harry Knowles in *The Science Teacher*, Volume 38, Number 9, December 1971

theories with his half-brother and acoustic pioneer Hugh Knowles, who was nearly 24 years Harry's senior. "My original thought came from a Vandy graduate physics experiment," Harry said, "using the Michelson interferometer...to measure relatively short distances [with] monochromatic light."[3]

While at Motorola and visiting his old employer, Bell Labs, Harry had seen a special kind of light—a laser. In fact, Art Schawlow, the man who later became known as the co-inventor of the laser (for his work with Charles Townes),[4] had been one of Harry's instructors in a "Physics of Waves" course at Bell's Kelly College training program. Harry recalled that Schawlow had said of his creation: "The laser is a solution searching for problems to be solved." Harry said that "for the many problems to be solved over the following decades, laser light was so revolutionary that significant time would pass before lasers would assume huge economic significance."[5]

A laser, a term which began as the acronym, LASER, for Light Amplification by the Stimulated Emission of Radiation, is a focused beam of light caused by the emission of excess energy. While ordinary light occurs via changes in energy also, it does not require outside action.

With a laser, however, one stimulates an atom or molecule to release extra energy in the form of light. Lasers amplify this light, causing a high-intensity beam.[6] "Laser light has four unique characteristics, any one of which would make lasers extremely important," Harry explained. "One, it can be more powerful than previous types of light, which means it can be focused to high densities. Two, laser light has spatial coherence, or the light is strongly correlated over long distances. Three, it is coherent over long periods of time; and, four, it is monochromatic, that is, it has high color purity. Over the years, lasers, using combinations of these characteristics, would become pervasive in all our daily lives, as semiconductors have."[7]

Now, in 1968, Harry returned to the theory that had been simmering on the back burners of his mind for the years since his lab experiment at Vanderbilt and that he had begun to explore again as his Westinghouse prospects waned. He drew a model of an ultra-sensitive laser interferometer, an apparatus with which Harry hoped to make fine measurements.[8] Harry thought that by using integrated circuitry and laser light in an interferometer, he could "count the fringes of light, thereby, making measurements to an accuracy of about 100 angstroms, or one millionth of a meter."[9]

The problem, according to Harry, was two-fold: how to get lasers and the fringe-counting electronics at the cost and performance that he felt the markets demanded. "Highly monochromatic, that is, single-wavelength lasers already in the market, such as those by Spectra-Physics, were incredibly expensive—about $10,000 for the laser alone," Harry said. "I knew, based on my own 1964 forecasting concepts [that became known as Moore's Law], that the size and cost of the necessary electronics would be coming down dramatically. Thus, I could foresee lasers being produced for only a few dollars each at the quantities and high accuracy needed for machine tool applications."[10]

First, however, Harry needed to set up shop. He moved to New Jersey, where he had spent his Bell Labs days, focusing in on South Jersey, a hotbed of needed resources such as industrial and scientific equipment; glass blowers; and optical suppliers.[11] Harry rented 1,000 square feet of space above the DyDee Laundry service in Westmont, New Jersey, a small town southeast of Philadelphia. "I had to build a laser, so I figured I needed to get near small groups of folks who had the design and production expertise," Harry reasoned. "New Jersey was the logical place

Why a Laser? *by C. Harry Knowles*

With excerpts from Metrologic Instruments, Inc., 1984 Laser Handbook & Catalog

When I began Metrologic in 1968, I sought to use the wavelength of light as a tool for making fine industrial measurements, but company focus soon gravitated toward the production of helium-neon lasers for use in educational kits and, as technology developed, bar code scanners. However, in the beginning, I had a choice to make: what kind of light would I use?

I was familiar with a revolutionary kind of light known as the laser, co-invented by Charles Townes and an instructor from my Bell Labs days, Art Schawlow. The laser became the preferred light for Metrologic applications. Lasers would prove not only essential to the development of many products at Metrologic, but served as the basis for our long series of educational laser classroom instructions and exercises, beginning in 1971. Lasers of virtual limitless types have been developed for taking advantage of one or more of the characteristics described below.

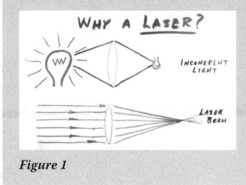

Figure 1

Light from a laser differs from ordinary light in four important respects, any one of which makes a laser extremely valuable:

1. Spatial coherence: The beam from a laser can be concentrated easily into a narrow beam, a valuable asset in laser scanning. (Figure 1)

to be and was close to potential investors, sources, and markets in the Northeast corridor around New York City.

"I started building lasers all by myself, just to see if they would work. I thought, 'I don't know much about lasers, but I can learn anything.'"[12] Harry defied prevailing practice for startup companies and their founders. Entrepreneurs regularly based their new companies on technology developed at previous employers. Not Harry. His knowledge of lasers was virtually non-existent; he was building a company, seemingly, out of thin air. "This was not only unheard of, it was plain stupid," Harry commented.[13] "But such was the way I wanted to challenge myself. I was better off not understanding how complex it all was."[14] Since Harry had

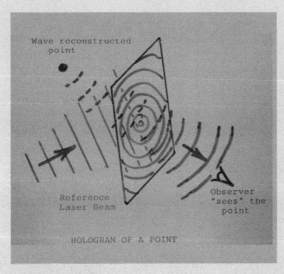

Wave reconstructed point

Reference Laser Beam

Observer "sees" the point

HOLOGRAM OF A POINT

Figure 2

2. Coherent in time: Ordinary light is incoherent with crests and troughs being emitted at random from different parts of the light source. However, laser light can be coherent with crests and troughs in phase regardless of the time generated within the laser, hence, valuable in holography and fine measurements. (Figure 2)

3. Monochromatic: The laser light is monochromatic, i.e., it is mostly of one color, or one wavelength. The typical output of Metrologic's helium-neon lasers has a wavelength of 633 nanometers.

4. High intensity: Laser light can be intense, that is, its energy can be highly concentrated. Although light from a powerful ruby laser or a carbon dioxide laser can be made to burn through concrete or steel, the light from the typical classroom helium-neon laser is relatively safe. Even if focused on the hand, it cannot be felt.

not built lasers before, he had to teach himself, relying on Drexel University Library in Philadelphia and issues of *Scientific American*. "I was a tinkerer," Harry said, "and had my own feelings on how things worked. There was also a superb series of articles coming out of Bell Labs on optics and lasers."

On May 1, 1968, Harry founded his own company, Metrologic Instruments, Inc., the name being based on his original concept—to "measure using logic." Metrologic had one employee, Harry; its target customers were precision machinery companies. "Part of that market did show up later on," Harry said. "I had an arrogant naiveté. Entrepreneurship does involve a lot of arrogance."

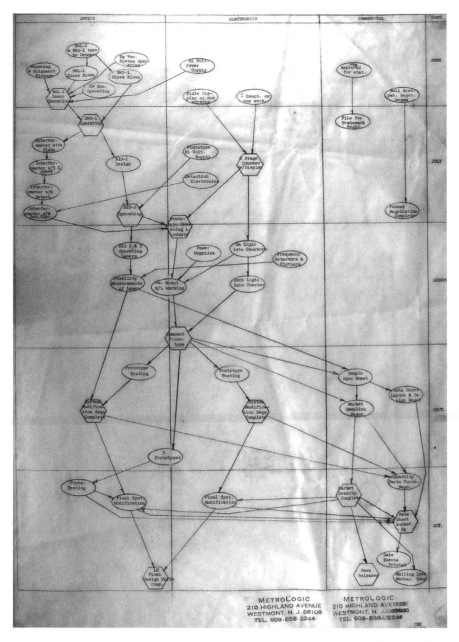

This Metrologic PERT (Program Evaluation Review Technique) chart as drawn by Harry in June 1968, plotted optics, electronics, and commercial activities over time. Note that Harry planned an agressive series of accomplishments for his fledgling company during the five-month period of June through October.

142

From 1968 to 1969, Harry tinkered and learned and created. Harry was alone for about a year before he started adding people to his fledgling company. "Everything was on a shoestring," Harry remembered. He blew his own initial glass models, a skill he had learned during

his Vanderbilt days. He pulled parts from a technical surplus warehouse, Evey Engineering in Vineland, New Jersey, about an hour's drive from Westmont. Gaylord Evey, the owner, often sold used equipment to Harry for a few cents on the dollar and suggested that Harry could pay when he was able.[15]

Robert, Harry, II, and Marjorie blowing glass, one of their father's essential skills

Still, money was tight and the future uncertain. The nation itself was going through its own uncertain times, as 1968 had seen the protests against the Vietnam War rage on as American casualties continued to mount. The country witnessed the assassinations of civil rights leader Martin Luther King, Jr., in April 1968 and Democratic presidential candidate Robert F. Kennedy in June the same year. With anti-war sentiment at its height, President Lyndon B. Johnson did not even seek his party's nomination at the Democratic National Convention in August 1968. In the end, Republican Richard M. Nixon defeated Hubert Humphrey in the race for president.[16]

Fall 1968 also saw personal tragedy strike the Knowles family. Harry's sister-in-law, Josephine, wife of brother Hugh, was diagnosed with liver cancer.[17] Jo had been a constant, guiding female in Harry's life. She even had advised Harry not to marry Phoebe the night before the wedding; but when he did, and later experienced marital troubles, Jo was his encouraging correspondent. Harry had turned to Jo's smart, mothering generosity throughout his early adult life. Hugh, meanwhile, depended on Jo not only as his wife and the mother of their children but as the vice president of his acoustical electronics company, which Harry said was the largest manufacturer of hearing aid transducers in the world at the time.

A few weeks before Jo died of her illness on April 12, 1969, Harry visited her at her home in Elgin, a Chicago suburb. Jo, knowing that she had only a few weeks to live, set aside a Sunday for Harry, whom she had known since he was a boy in Birmingham, Alabama. By the age of nine, Harry found a friend and confidante in Jo, who held Stanford University degrees in psychology and never hesitated to listen to Harry and respond with advice. Referring to that Sunday visit, Harry said, "I have never spent a day that was more meaningful in my life. Jo represented to me about as close to a mother as I ever wanted to have—a combination of love, intellect, and guiding spirit. I was able to express openly gratitude, love, indebtedness...it was one of the most marvelous days.

"She meant so much to me," Harry said.[18] "You tend to be reluctant to tell how much you love someone. But I could tell Jo how deeply I loved her. Hugh, Jo, and I just drove around, but it was magnificent." Jo's funeral service a few weeks later was brief, followed by a celebration of her life. Harry found it a fitting tribute.

Since Harry's salve for his emotional wounds was always work, he returned to the task of grooming Metrologic into a more professional and solvent operation. On May 19, 1969, Metrologic Instruments, Inc. incorporated officially. Remembering that he had several friends who had wanted to bankroll him to build transistors, Harry approached them to ask for funding for building lasers.[19] By August 1969, a month after Neil Armstrong's walk on the moon, Harry had the first laser "ready to go," he said. "I went to my friend Arthur Lipper [the renowned investment banker and financier] to ask for money, but he told me that then was a bad time. The financial markets had declined about then."

Despite the lack of investors, Harry found other ways to hone his business plan. In late 1969, Metrologic entered into a distribution relationship with mail-order catalog kingpin Edmund Scientific. Through Edmund, Harry was able to test the market potential for his lasers and to focus on developing production capabilities.[20]

Harry had a prototype of his new helium-neon laser "that was greatly simplified from that required by industrial interferometry," Harry said.[21] He also had an urgent need for money; he looked to his forte—production—and sales orders to raise capital.[22] Since he had no money for advertising, he relied on his public relations savvy. He wrote to the editors of

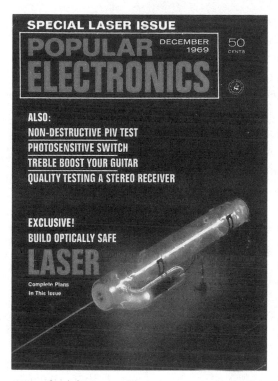

SPECIAL LASER ISSUE

POPULAR DECEMBER 1969 50 CENTS

ELECTRONICS

ALSO:
NON-DESTRUCTIVE PIV TEST
PHOTOSENSITIVE SWITCH
TREBLE BOOST YOUR GUITAR
QUALITY TESTING A STEREO RECEIVER

EXCLUSIVE!
BUILD OPTICALLY SAFE
LASER
Complete Plans
In This Issue

Metrologic's laser kit appearance on this December 1969 cover sparked cash flow.

the four major science magazines of the time—*Popular Science, Popular Mechanics, Mechanics Illustrated,* and *Popular Electronics*—touting his laser as "the world's first laser hobby kit." The only response was immediate, from *Popular Electronics* technical editor Les Solomon. Intrigued, Solomon called Harry and requested that he come to New York to show him his laser kit. Harry spent that weekend, with electronics help from friend and Vanderbilt professor Wendell Anderson, handmaking all the kit materials to prepare for the meeting. Solomon must have been impressed because he asked Harry what else he had and featured the kit on the cover of the December 1969 issue, which hit mailboxes about Thanksgiving time.

"That kit, via direct mail, became," Harry said, "the top do-it-yourself—how to build your own laser for $79.95—science project of Christmas season 1969-70. Les said, in mid-1970, that it was the most popular such kit the magazine had ever run. Orders started pouring in. At that time, we had made only a few lasers that were sold through Edmund Scientific. I had no idea that we would get a flood of orders. By mid-January, 2500 people had pre-paid $80 each. I deposited the cash. The FTC [Federal Trade Commission] said later you can't do this. You can't hold customers' money for more than 30 days. We held the pre-paid cash for up to three months while we caught production up with orders."

Metrologic's cash flow had begun and Harry ramped up production in the company's new location, a 1500-square-foot house next to an industrial park in Bellmawr, New Jersey. Leaving his small space in Westmont behind when he ran out of electrical power capability, Harry had bought the 800-square-foot house of recently widowed Mrs. Glad-kowski in April 1969 and converted and expanded it into a factory. (He preferred, then, as in later times, to own rather than rent.) Harry's workers, growing from three in June[23] to about 20 that year,[24] worked urgently to meet the *Popular Electronics*-sparked, Christmas season orders. In fact, Harry's key assistant at the time, operations vice president Desmond Spittlehouse, who had worked for Harry at Westinghouse as process engineering manager, actually lived in the factory at night. Another former Westinghouse employee, George Redinger, joined the team and, ultimately, would run a section of production at Metrologic for 30-plus years. The employees made, assembled, and processed

Herb Gottlieb

tubes, electronics and mechanical housings. Blown glass tubes cost about $12 and mirror sets cost Metrologic about $15 each. "At 1500 lasers per month, we were profitable," Harry said.

Harry then targeted his lasers for high schools, taking out ads in *Physics Teacher*, the American Association of Physics Teachers' magazine.[25] At a National Science Teachers Association school ex-

hibit in Atlantic City in May 1970, he met Herb Gottlieb, the "quintessential" high school physics teacher from Bayside, New York. Together, they designed laser experiments that became a fixture on the *Physics Teacher* magazine's back cover for several years. They incorporated these experiments into a popular teacher's booklet, *101 Ways to Use Helium-Neon Lasers in the Classroom*. By the end of 1970, Metrologic was selling instructional laser kits to high school and college science teachers in profitable quantities. One of the kits even used laser light for measuring, although not at the industrial-quality level in Harry's original business plan. "Interferometric measurement with laser light is quite simple," Harry said. "We showed high school kids how to do it with one of our kits."[26]

In 1970, "we were the world's largest producer, with respect to quantities, of lasers," Harry said. "They were cheap and they worked. We began to chase the big boys like American Optic and Bausch & Lomb

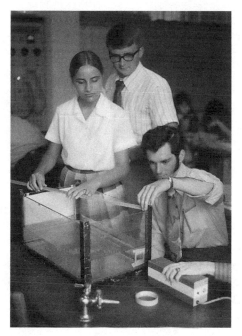

Using Metrologic's box-like laser in a high school experiment to measure refraction in water, 1971

out of [the laser] business. They wanted to buy from us."[27] Whereas, in 1969, Metrologic billed only $39,000 in sales; by 1970, the young company had climbed to $395,000 in total sales billed. By 1971, Harry prodded the sales billings to $670,000.[28]

Harry's biggest challenge in the early days was cash flow. "Many Thursday nights," he said, "I didn't know how I was going to make payroll on Friday." Thus, Harry became creative about turning possible laser applications into Metrologic revenue. This driving motivation is what prompted the book about how to use lasers in the classroom; the book informed at the same time it created demand in the educa-

tion world for Metrologic products. In addition to the high-volume-demand hobby and science instructional laser kits, the company built lasers for medical aiming equipment and even laser acupuncture (despite Harry's feeling that acupuncture was "bogus science").[29]

Since cost-cutting was essential for survival, Metrologic did as many tasks as possible in-house. The most expensive parts of a helium-neon laser were the two specialized mirrors, so Harry decided to make his own.[30] He bought a World War II-era Frankfort Arsenal polishing machine from Evey Engineering and developed the grinding and polishing of mirrors to combat those optics costs. From there, Harry took savings another step and recruited help to set up a lab at Metrologic for the critical optical coatings of the mirrors at each end. After having a vacuum coater built from nearby Denton Vacuum Company, Harry tackled the problem that the coating design, called "dielectric coating," was carefully guarded proprietary information. With some initial help from a fresh doctoral graduate, John Meckley, at the University of Pennsylvania, Harry designed a program of his own. While slow at first, taking 15 hours to run one simulation on a TI-59 handheld programmable calculator, the program was improved immensely when re-worked for a better computer platform (in BASIC computer language on a TRS-80). Analyses now took about five minutes to run. Metrologic would use the home-grown program, as Harry updated it for use by George Redinger and others for designing coatings, for many years.

"We could design our own coatings for more optimum laser output and characteristics," Harry said. "One of the great advantages over our competitors that we had at Metrologic was our optics and coating lab, and what it did for our costs and turn-around time on new products. We designed our new products around known and controlled processes, not depending on outside vendors."

Harry remembered this time as a frontier open for exploration. Metrologic played a role in expanding the world's thinking on how lasers could be used.[31] "When I started Metrologic, lasers, as my teacher Art Schawlow later said, were a solution for which there were no problems. Lasers were revolutionary, but they were destined to become pervasive throughout society."

One project which Harry said was typical of the early Metrologic days was a job to develop a portable methane detector for a north-of-Dallas contractor, J.W. "Bill" Christie, whose client was the town of Irving, Texas.[32] In Irving, aging gas pipelines were leaking gas, and the

Metrologic's portable methane detector: an interior view minus the casing, left, and assembled

town needed to find the leaks before any tragic mishaps occurred. At the time (1972-1973), according to Harry, there was no such thing as a sensitive, portable methane detector; so Harry designed one. His team, led by staff member Chic Naylor, built it.[33] Harry said that it was well known that helium-neon lasers could be made to emit a 3.39-micron infrared beam which was strongly absorbed by methane gas.[34] Thus, when the potential client from Texas offered a $30,000 contract for a detector, Metrologic was ready for the challenge.

Within a few months, Metrologic delivered the "most fantastically sensitive and portable gadget," Harry said. "It had a five-part-per-million sensitivity and looked like a very small garden sprayer. We proved it worked and fulfilled the contract, but the client would not pay. We were damned near broke and dropped the project."

Harry said he sued Christie in federal court in Dallas. Although Christie's field supervisor, according to Harry, testified in federal court that the unit worked, Metrologic still lost the lawsuit.[35] He had not patented the device because he had no money to prepare and file the necessary documentation. "We had great energy and confidence and stupidity," Harry said. "Technically, we were brilliant, but business-wise, stupid."[36]

In an attempt to add some organization to his management tasks, Harry had decided in 1971 to hire a personal assistant who also could serve as office manager.[37] Assisting him in the hire was Philadelphia native Janet Kurtas Starzynski, who worked for a headhunter agency. When Harry explained to Janet what type employee he needed for the new position, Janet, according to Harry, said at first, "Only one person is that good, and I'm not looking for a job." However, by mid-1972, Metrologic had a new employee—Janet Kurtas Starzynski—and the

Janet

persuasive Harry had a new personal assistant. Soon after, Harry asked Janet to dinner, marking the beginning of a dating relationship.

Janet had two children, Diane and Donnah, from a previous marriage.[38] Add in Harry's three children, and dating could never be simple. Harry had various spans of time with his children since his divorce from Phoebe in 1967. In fact, within a year or two of the divorce, Harry, II, lived with his father in Philadelphia when the child became too rebellious for Phoebe;[39] but, because of the younger Harry's unstable behavior, he did not stay for long.[40] He chose to return to his mother in Baltimore.

While Harry, II, was gone from Baltimore, much quieter brother Robert found his homelife more peaceful.[41] With all three children and Phoebe back together, however, the family searched in vain for a sense of equilibrium as Harry, II, continued to act out and sister Marjorie settled into a pattern of refusing to attend school.[42] Working mom Phoebe struggled to maintain order.

By 1971, Robert, who had become sick with mononucleosis, needed refuge and moved to his father Harry's home on South

Robert sailing, 1970s

21st Street in Philadelphia.[43] Due to his illness, Robert had to repeat seventh grade that fall; but, away from his chaotic Baltimore life, he made a full recovery. Of the three children, Robert saw his father the most after the divorce. Harry wanted to see his children every few weeks, but Harry, II, and Marjorie did not want to go. With the extra time with his father, Robert, no doubt, had become more adept than the others at navigating

Marjorie, circa 1973

his father's personality.

Robert was still living with Harry summer 1972 when Janet and Harry began dating. In August, however, Robert had gone to Baltimore to spend a few weeks with his mother.[44] Labor Day weekend Harry and Janet and her two children climbed into his Camaro to head to Gibson Island to go sailing. Harry planned one stop at Phoebe's Kenilworth Avenue apartment in Baltimore to pick up Robert, Harry, and Marjorie. When Harry arrived, he discovered that Phoebe was missing and the three teenagers had been left on their own for about three weeks. Phoebe, distraught from dealing with Harry, II, and Marjorie, had become severely depressed and checked herself into a mental hospital.

"That summer, the kids were driving her crazy," recalled Robert.[45] "I was there just three weeks, and it was the Wild West. [Brother] Harry was drinking, and he and Marge went joyriding in Mom's car. Mom asked to be committed. After one month, she was out and back to work. She was just exhausted." Robert, while he recognized his mother's struggles, saw Phoebe as a valiant fighter, a divorced mother try-

Harry during calmer sailing days

ing to make ends meet and to salvage some sanity along the way. "I think Mom was a real hero for those years," he said.

Still, father Harry needed to solve the immediate problem of his abandoned children. He gathered clothes and piled them into the ever-shrinking Camaro, now loaded with seven people bound for a sailing holiday in his 22-foot, Albergh-designed Ensign.[46] The excursion was destined for disaster. The in-for-repair sailboat motor was not ready for pickup, so Harry sailed from Gibson Island without it. He also discovered he had no working radio. The two families sailed for about five hours before docking in Worton Creek bay on the eastern shore of Maryland. They cooked and slept on the sailboat, with Harry, II, in a small dinghy off the back, the twins in the cuddy, and the rest on the floor.

During the night, the rain and winds began. "A hurricane was passing over," Harry said. More likely, however, was that Harry's boat was being pelted with the effects of Tropical Storm Carrie, which had spent the last several days traveling up the East Coast.[47] By morning, the other boats at dock with Harry had all left. The slightly beaten holiday crew set sail for their originating port, Gibson Island.

From there, the gang headed for Janet's house in Camden, New Jersey. Her small dwelling was soon filled with wet towels and clothing and rambunctious children. "I was amazed at Janet's stability through this," Harry said.[48] "I came downstairs and found Janet washing dishes. I said, 'You know, I think we ought to get married.' Janet said, 'You think I've passed some kind of test? Take your kids and get out!'"

Harry was unsure what to do after such a passionate rejection. "I didn't have anywhere to put the kids. I didn't show up at work for a couple of days." Harry rented a house on Zelley Street in Moorestown, a New Jersey town of about 12,000 residents located 15 miles east of Philadelphia. After moving all three children into the house, he returned to work to find that Janet had had a change of heart. According to Harry, she asked him, "Is the offer still good?"[49]

Harry and Janet were married November 2, 1972, at Harry's church, Philadelphia's First Unitarian Church. On the way to the church—with Harry, Janet, and the children once again squeezed into the Camaro—Harry realized he needed to make one stop. While Janet circled the block, Harry dashed into Wanamaker's department store in downtown Philadelphia and bought Janet's wedding ring.[50] After the wedding, Harry and Janet moved their blended family into another Moorestown home—on Chestnut Street—hoping their melting pot of children could get along.[51]

When Janet and Harry married, Harry, II, was 17; twins Robert and Marjorie were 14; and Janet's children, Diane and Donnah, were 12 and 8, respectively. The children were enrolled in the Friends School in Moorestown. "It was a good thing Dad did for us, moving us to Moorestown," Robert said. "The Friends School saved me, turned me around academically. They cared."[52]

Still, the combined brood failed to establish a healthy family dynamic. Harry was a stern taskmaster and father; and Janet, it seems, concentrated on her own children. Peacemaker Robert coped, but Harry, II, and Marjorie descended further into their rebellion—Harry, II, openly, resulting in being arrested for driving under the influence and, ultimately, being sentenced to Gaudenzia House in Philadelphia for rehabilitation. "Harry [II] was a suburban kid," Robert said in recalling the episode and the rehab center. "He was taught drugs there." Marjorie, meanwhile, quietly experimented with alcohol, unknown to her father.

Harry at Disney World, 1972

The East Linden Street family home was built on about 20 acres in Moorestown.

Within the following year or two, the Knowles family built a home (425 East Linden Street) on 20-plus acres of land in Moorestown.[53] Eventually, Marjorie's behavior worsened and became apparent, resulting in her father buying her a bus ticket back to Baltimore to live with her mother. However, Marjorie knew something her father did not—that her mother was having serious alcohol problems of her own during this time. Thus, Marjorie didn't go to her mother's home and, instead, spent interim time living with other families. Ultimately, Marjorie did return to live with her mother for her senior year of high school. The Knowles daughter had changed her approach to school and was determined to attend college. In 1977, she graduated from high school number 13 of 800 students and, subsequently, attended the University of Maryland.[54]

Harry, II, went on to get his GED and earn a scholarship to the University of Pennsylvania, followed by attendance at Drexel University. Robert would eventually earn a degree in business at the University of Maryland and a CPA certification.[55] Life would not take the three Knowles children on easy paths—especially Harry, II, who would be plagued by substance and alcohol abuse for many years, and Marjorie, who battled many roadblocks to her educational and career pursuits before also graduating from the University of Maryland. However, the three were armed with fine minds and courage, attributes shared with their parents.

The travails of his children, while a distraction, were not an obsession for the elder Harry Knowles. Harry had established a potential-filled company and there was work to do. His energy was firmly focused on Metrologic. In 1972—the year Harry and Janet married—Harry expanded the company's Bellmawr headquarters building to 6,000 square feet,[56] providing needed space to the industry's top-volume manufacturer of helium-neon lasers. He also had expanded the number of employees, which rose to about 40 that fall.[57] Sales billed in 1972, according

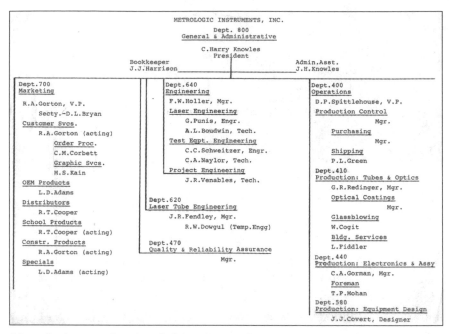

Metrologic organizational chart, November 1972

to internal documents, totaled $864,000,[58] with lasers accounting for 75 percent of Metrologic's sales. The company's prime market was education—even outside the U.S. as foreign sales reached about 25 percent of Metrologic's total.

Harry was unaware at the time, but lasers were about to turn a major corner in application with the country's movement toward universal coding on consumer products—a system which would culminate in the now-familiar modern bar code. This code development was being driven by the Grocery Manufacturers of America and the National Association of Food Chains. The groups had reached a consensus in September 1969 that a coding system for their products was needed to streamline the checkout and inventory processes.[59] By summer 1970, the newly formed Grocery Industry Ad Hoc Committee had met and a numeric format had been defined.[60] The committee was chaired by Heinz Company president R. Burt Gookin and included the leaders of heavy hitters Kroger, General Foods, Bristol-Myers, General Mills, and others.[61] Companies such as National Cash Register (NCR), RCA, and IBM were asked to submit proposals for a product code and symbol.[62]

A standardized code language would have to be created for products and be scanned automatically. Various coding experiments had occurred in previous decades, beginning with a 1932 attempt to use punched cards and readers for purchases.[63] In 1948, however, Bernard Silver and Norman Joseph Woodland, then of Drexel Institute of Technology in Philadelphia, began work on a bar code. In the end, their system offered two options, a bulls-eye symbol and a "straight-line pattern quite similar to present-day linear bar codes ...made up of a pattern of four white lines on a dark background."[64] Applying for a patent in 1949 and receiving one in 1952, Woodland and Silver sold their patent to Philco in 1952. In turn, Philco later sold the patent to RCA.

In 1967, RCA tested a scanning system using the bull's-eye code in a Cincinnati Kroger grocery store, but there were systemic problems: the scanner struggled with reading the inconsistently printed ink of the bull's-eye code[65] and products did not come pre-coded. Kroger employees labeled items themselves. The patent expired in 1969 before a national consensus on standards could be established. Also in 1967, the Association of American Railroads began use of a code on its railroad cars; the Sylvania optical system failed to work and was discontinued in 1975.[66]

With many portions of America's national goods and delivery system already looking for solutions, the timing was perfect for the uniform grocery product code Ad Hoc Committee's call in 1970 for proposals. One of the bidding companies, IBM, assigned veteran engineer George J. Laurer to head the development of what would become a 12-digit Universal Product Code, or UPC, and symbol.[67] Laurer and his colleagues began their research with Woodland and Silver's earlier design but struggled to meet the one-and-a-half-square-inch space requirement of the bid.[68] As IBM's work continued, the Ad Hoc Committee created, in March 1971, a Symbol Selection Subcommittee, which would ensure the winning bid included all the parameters needed for a machine-readable symbol.[69] Representatives from First National Stores, Heinz, Del Monte, Procter & Gamble, Winn-Dixie, and General Foods were among those serving the selection group.

In January 1972, the Uniform Grocery Product Code Council's Board of Governors held its first meeting in Chicago.[70] The meeting marked the formal beginning of an era of standardization for grocers and their suppliers. "1972 was the birth of the utility of the bar code," Harry said in 1999. "People had played with bar codes before, putting them on railroad cars, but getting retailers to put the UPC on products was the key."[71] By fall 1974, the Uniform Grocery Product Code Council would become the Uniform Product Code Council to reflect its extended scope beyond the grocery industry. (The name shortened again in 1984 to UCC and, in 2005, to GS1-US to represent the supply chain's global standards body.)[72]

On December 1, 1972, IBM made its presentation to the selection committee.[73] Laurer had solved the key problems, having developed a new linear code. Woodland, who was on staff at IBM at the time, even helped prepare the proposal. The bar code symbol consisted of vertical black and white lines of varying widths and density; these lines conveyed product information via a scanner and reader. Since the symbol used vertical lines, print resolution and ink smears were not as major a concern as with bull's-eye code designs. Scanners bounced light off the IBM bar code's dark lines and white spaces in between, sending gathered data to a computer to interpret the information for the user, such as a cashier. The most effective scanner light available was laser light, and Harry Knowles happened to be the top-volume producer of the laser industry's workhorse—the helium-neon laser.

Laser scanning of codes was occurring already in isolated pockets. In fact, David Collins, who had developed the abandoned railway car tracking system first tested in 1961, later left Sylvania and worked for Compunetics, which installed two of his laser scanning systems in the late 1960s in a General Motors plant and a General Trading Company distribution center.[74] "The bar codes held only two digits of data, but that was enough," said auto-ID distributor National Barcode's Tom Reynolds in writing on the history of bar code scanners. He continued: "Switching to a black and white bar code, the real innovation of [Collins'] system was the use of a laser beam as a light source. The laser light was smaller, cooler and could be moved back and forth rapidly over the code, giving rise to the terms 'bar code scanner' (because the laser would pass over the code many times per second) and 'laser line' (the optical illusion of the laser scanning over the bar code)." Also aiding the advance of bar code scanning technology were the drops in computer size and cost for lasers and transistors.

Thus, IBM and its competitors vying to be awarded the bid were building on an ever-growing knowledge base. "Most of the other companies," recalled Laurer on his web site, "had optical codes and scanning equipment in the market place already. IBM did not. [My task was to] design the best code and symbol suitable for the grocery industry. After considerable effort I conceived an approach and detailed the symbol. [Others] worked with me to theoretically calculate the readability and to write IBM's formal proposal to the industry."[75]

The IBM bar code was, as Reynolds described, "split into halves of six digits each."[76] The first digit indicated the class of bar code, such as general merchandise or a variable weight item. The next five numbers told the product manufacturer, and digits seven through 11 represented the product's unique number. The 12th digit was a check character for verifying the code. IBM, as with all the contenders, was asked to demonstrate its equipment for evaluation by Battelle Memorial, a non-profit scientific institute in Columbus, Ohio.

12-digit UPC

The laser scanning demonstration went well and the code proved reliable. On April 3, 1973, the Ad Hoc Committee adopted IBM's Universal Product Code as the industry standard, favoring IBM's sleek, linear design.[77] On June 26, 1974, a 10-piece package of Wrigley's Juicy Fruit chewing gum became the first grocery item scanned using the Universal Product Code (UPC) at a Troy, Ohio, Marsh Supermarket. Dayton-based National Cash Register (NCR) designed the then $10,000 checkout counter which included a $4,000 scanner from PSC, Inc.[78] "Laurer's design for that bar code was exquisite," Harry said "IBM's idea of a helium-neon laser scanner and UPC would be standard."[79]

Harry wasn't part of the early grocery consortium movement and said he "didn't understand the impact of it immediately." While the road to the IBM UPC was being paved—during the 1971-to-1974 timeframe—Metrologic was busy with its existing laser product lines. (Sales billed in 1974 totaled $1.2 million.)[80] Harry, in his strategic laser manufacturer position, however, would quickly become pivotal in the newly primed scanner market.

Larger companies such as IBM, NCR, RCA and Spectra-Physics possessed the experience and inside track to provide the grocery market with large in-bed, or inside-the-counter, scanners. "I didn't want to compete with these guys," Harry said.[81] However, Metrologic began servicing smaller scanner producers such as Univac with lasers, laser optics, and associated electronics for their scanners.[82] "I found I knew more than their engineers about the optics and signal electronics," Harry said, "and the conversion of those reflected signals into digital signals."[83]

A local customer, Vern Lundquist, representing a group of his friends in the printing support world, asked Harry if he could produce a whole scanner. He said, "Sure."[84] A brilliant young digital engineer was then hired—Rich Gapin, who designed the computer components, while Harry finessed the mechanics, optics and linear electronics. Starting in August 1974, Metrologic had its first working scanner by Thanksgiving, three months later.

By January 1975, only five months after the project start, Metrologic was testing a new production scanner prototype on a high-speed, web-fed milk carton printing line at the Weyerhauser printing plant in nearby Pennsauken, New Jersey. The world's first high-speed, on-press UPC scanner, called the "Monitor 101,"[85] acted as a verifier of bar codes on printed materials.[86] As the materials fed through the high-speed web printing presses, Metrologic's Monitor 101, which was mounted above the presses, provided quality control by verifying that the correct UPCs were being printed within specifications.[87] Verifiers became rampant in the industry because of consumers' concerns that they would be overcharged (since price tags were

Monitor 101 could check density, resolution, and accuracy at 1200-feet-per-second speed.

now being replaced by bar codes). "Our response to these concerns was total quality control—thou shall not misread a label," Harry commented in a 2004 article on the 30th anniversary of the UPC.[88]

Individual grocers and suppliers did not embrace the new technology overnight or without complaint. Compliance was voluntary, not compulsory. Mandated, however, via historic 1973 federal legislation, were new nutritional labeling requirements on all food containers.[89] Implementation of the new law, plus the influence of respected grocery industry leaders who served on the originating UPC committee, hastened acceptance and unprecedented—albeit, at times, grudging—cooperation.

A PricewaterhouseCoopers report commissioned to mark the 25th anniversary of the UPC said of that first Ad Hoc Committee that its members embodied "...all areas of the supply chain so that all interests were represented. The members of the Committee leveraged their experience, knowledge, and reputations in advocating the adoption of the UPC to all levels of the supply chain to ensure critical mass would be achieved. In short, their leadership provided the critical difference between success and failure."[90]

Success was definitely on Harry's mind. By spring 1975, it became obvious to Harry that, while his Monitor 101 performed well technically, Surescan, the group of local printer sales representatives with whom he had an agreement to market the product, did not know how to sell the technology and had garnered orders for only about 12 units.[91] Harry decided that a smaller, "off-press" verifier with laser technology, to simulate the supermarket scanners, would sell far better than the on-press Monitor.[92] Thus, with Surescan's knowledge, Metrologic developed the "Verifier 315." The design team included Rich Gapin on the digital aspects, Chic Naylor on mechanics, and engineer Jim Tucci, backed by Harry, on the linear electronics.[93] "We used much of the digital system of Monitor 101, but with a handheld, tethered head," Harry said. With

Rich Gapin

Chic Naylor

this design, according to Harry, Metrologic became the first company to develop the handheld laser scanner.[94]

Harry was ready to show off a prototype of the handheld at the November 1975 national packaging show's host hotel in New York City.[95] In one room of the New York Hilton, he said, Surescan demonstrated the Monitor 101, while next door in the suite Harry demonstrated the prototype Verifier 315 and a separate handheld "X-scanner" which could read bar codes omnidirectionally "by simply passing the 'X' over a [UPC-printed] package." The Verifier 315 prototype included a primitive trigger (as did its design drawing), Harry said, but the resulting commercial product would not have one because it actually was not needed.

At this time, handheld scanners were an anomaly. Bar coding was being driven by grocery stores that used large, costly, in-bed scanners. "'What are you going to use it for?' people asked," Harry said.[96] "When we invented this to find our own niche, I thought, 'Well, someone's going to want handheld [scanners].'" His thoughts proved prophetic;

handheld scanners were destined to eventually outnumber the larger scanners ten to one. In 1975, however, the handheld was a minor curiosity at the industry show.

Still, Harry's handheld invention caught the eye of others in the industry. Jerry Swartz and Sheldon Harrison, co-founders of Long Island-based UPC Film Masters, Inc., a subsidiary of Stony Brook Applied Research which later became Symbol Technologies, were attracted, Harry said, by press-released information on the handheld scanners and called Harry to request a meeting. They visited Metrologic in early December 1975, with a keen interest in the Verifier 315 scanner.[97] Swartz, a Stony Brook engineering professor and physicist, had formed his company in 1973 out of his garage and began his climb in the UPC industry producing master film for printing quality bar codes.[98] As Harry recalled, with Swartz' attention now firmly on laser scanners, Swartz told Harry, in reference to the Verifier 315, he thought he could sell "a ton of them."[99] Swartz proposed that Metrologic do the engineering and production and UPC Film Masters do the financing and marketing.[100]

Harry drew up a formal agreement of their joint venture, with Swartz asking for exclusive sales rights and a waiver from Surescan on any potential claims.[101] In 1976, Swartz' UPC Film Masters ordered 48 Verifier 315s[102] and sold them to large packagers. During the course of the next several months, Swartz visited Bellmawr several times, as Harry recalled. Harry, in his open manner, treated his new business partner royally with hosted tours of the Metrologic plant and environs. He said he even showed Swartz, "who was considering a move, New Jersey farmland in scouting tours for potential new homes." The relationship between the two entrepreneurs was professional but it was also personal.

"We jointly approached J.C. Penney," Harry said, "and I came very close to getting a contract for a number of scanners when I developed a deep sense of distrust with Jerry, [who] wanted half the money. I backed away from [the contract] in about mid-1976."[103]

Harry dissolved the relationship with the ambitious Swartz and his company soon after. "Jerry...with his group of engineers, used our V315 to refine their own lower-cost...microprocessor-based verifier," Harry said. Swartz, now armed with an inside knowledge of Metrologic and its technology, would never gain Harry's trust again. Even so, Harry could not have imagined then what trouble would erupt from Swartz and Symbol in Metrologic's future.

Chapter 8

Metrologic Storms

(1975-1993)

With the dissolution of the short-time Metrologic-UPC Film Masters (later Symbol Technologies) partnering efforts, Harry was eager to put that soured experience behind him. The Bellmawr facility buzzed with lab and production activities. Harry had gathered engineers and designers with a work ethic similar to his own. Associate engineer George Kolis, who joined Metrologic in 1975 and would work there until his retirement 35 years later, recalled the early days at Bellmawr—the "house near the dump."[1]

The facility, a one-story, converted bungalow, had a full basement, with labs and work stations now sprawled in every spare space after its 1972 expansion to 6,000 square feet. Colleague and hardware engineer Bob Blake, Kolis remembered vividly, came to his cellar work table one morning to find a dead rat facing him. The commotion that followed brought Harry down to investigate. "What's going on?" Harry asked. "Harry picked up the rat by the tail," Kolis said, "and threw it out. Then he told us: 'Get back to work.'"

Kolis was one of Harry's go-to guys, part of a loyal team including George Redinger in production and David Wilz, who would be paired

From left, software engineer George Kolis, hardware engineer Bob Blake, and optics manager George Redinger were key members of Harry's Metrologic team for many years.

with Kolis on several projects. Kolis would construct the digital designs, and later would engineer each of Metrologic's increasingly complex Application Specific Integrated Circuits (ASICs). Industry standards at the time, according to Harry, typically dictated that each ASIC took at least two, often three or more, attempts to get the circuitry correct. The deliberate Kolis completed his ASICs mistake-free the first time every time.[2] Meanwhile, Wilz was a key designer of software. Harry first heard of Wilz from another employee who relayed that Wilz was the brightest student in the computer programming classes at Camden County Community College. Harry sought Wilz out during lunch at a local diner where the student was working as a bus boy. Harry introduced himself and hired the potential-filled Wilz, who would advance greatly at Metrologic, later leading the company's extensive software engineering groups.[3]

Harry was a great believer in individual talent, as his hires reflected. Although Kolis lacked a college degree, Harry was no elitist; he knew Kolis could do the work. In fact, for Metrologic's early scanners, the Monitor 101 and Verifier 315, Kolis built the circuits (designed by Rich Gapin), while colleague Chic Naylor handled the mechanics. According to Kolis, Harry often would ask the seemingly impossible under pressure-filled time constraints. However, Harry's faith paid off more often than not. "Harry drove from the top," Kolis said, "but he didn't get in our way. He let us work."[4]

Richard Hamilton

Richard Hamilton, who worked with Metrologic in the company's early years as an insurance broker and later as a risk manager, talked about Harry's management style and relationship with his employees.[5] "Harry Knowles is the brightest person I've ever known. In meetings, he could come at you with both barrels. He's tough, driven. If you didn't know Harry, that could get to you. But the other side of it is, Harry and Janet helped a lot of their employees who were in need. They did it quietly but they helped. Harry is loving and [tough] at the same time."

Later versions of the Monitor 101 and Verifier 315 would contain an advanced digital processor. "I challenged Rich Gapin," Harry said, "to make the high-speed decoding digital hardware to be software pro-

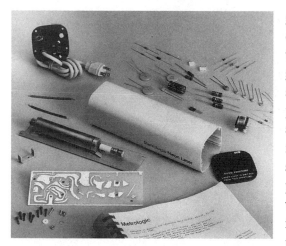

The helium-neon laser, shown here disassembled, also could be ordered as a build-your-own-laser educational kit. Metrologic laser lines and applications grew with each year.

grammable. Rich Gapin's design was remarkable in that, even though the programming language was somewhat primitive, it was programmable and yet ran at high TTL-type speeds, many times faster than the slow single-chip microprocessors at the time. I was looking ahead to making scanners for supermarkets and to scanning bar codes different from UPC codes. The Metrologic TTL [transistor-to-transistor-logic] computers were much faster, however, they cost much more. Our technology was way ahead of its time but, commercially, barely successful."[6]

Metrologic sales billings were running at about $1.4 million in both 1975 and 1976, but profits proved minimal or elusive in the company's early years when growing infrastructure held priority.[7] In 1976, a second expansion occurred at Bellmawr, bringing the Metrologic facility to 18,000 square feet.[8] By that time, the engineering department occupied the new second floor over a portion of the factory. The space was needed for scanner development but also for the bedrock of Metrologic's business at this juncture: its existing and ever-improving laser tube lines. The offerings listed in the 1976 Metrologic catalog are extensive (with dozens of lines) and include lasers for use in education (whether kits for teachers or students), research, communication, construction, holography, alignment, optics, subsystems of other manufacturers, and speed-of-light measurement.[9]

The catalog boasted that "1975 was a good year for Metrologic. We boosted our sales and tripled the size of our plant....In a time of inflation, we've kept our prices the lowest in the industry. Many of the prices in this catalog are even lower than last year—like the return of a $99.50 laser [the ML-600]. Our growing sales base helps us pass those savings on to you."[10] In addition, Metrologic expanded its laser tube lines to

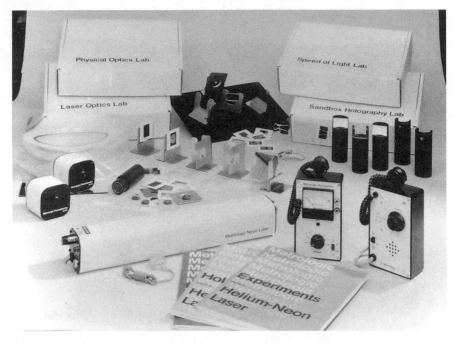

Metrologic laser educational kits included laser optics, top center; speed of light lab, left center; physical optics, center; sandbox holography, right center; laser power meters or photometers, right front; and, in front, the helium-neon laser, the backbone of Metrologic's laser lines.

range from a new, short one-milliwatt tube to a then-powerful 12-milliwatt tube and redesigned its products to comply with BRH (Bureau of Radiological Health) and OSHA (Occupational Safety & Health Administration) federal regulations. "But not all is changed," claimed the catalog. "Our laser warranty remains the same: two full years—the longest warranty in the laser industry."

Already, Metrologic, as its catalog reflected, had built a reputation for low cost and lengthy warranties. "We sold in spite of relatively low reliability because of our low cost," Harry said.[11] The sales network included national and overseas distributors. The New Jersey company's growing customer base ran the gamut from manufacturers and scientists in need of laser units to educators and students in pursuit of knowledge to the relatively new markets stemming from bar code scanner demand. The 1976 Metrologic catalog detailed the intricate steps of making a laser, as well as highlighted the company's Monitor 101 laser scanner—thus projecting the company's familiar role of educator while looking forward to its future in the bar code scanning industry. Although Metrologic manufactured parts (lasers, laser optics, and scanning subsystems) for companies making the large, in-counter bar code scanners found in supermarkets, Metrologic, the catalog said, also produced "complete laser scanners, bar code readers, UPC verifiers, and decoding computers."[12] The relative novelty of the Metrologic scanner product lines is reflected in the fact that prospective customers were instructed to request additional information for details on scanners.

Expanding scanner product lines soon followed. The company produced the industry's first laser carton counter in 1977. While an interesting technical achievement, Harry said that the product was not commercially viable.[13] However, Metrologic designed a rather successful scanner specifically for Computer Library Services Inc., or CLSI, of Newton, Massachusetts. Capitalizing on new software that CLSI had developed for libraries, Metro-

SS-200 magazine scanner for return-room automation, top, and MS-106 industrial bar code scanner

logic made the industry's first single-chip, microcontroller-based laser bar code scanner and library scanner (the "MS 105") in 1978. That same year, Harry and his team designed a scanner for magazine return (the "SS-200," later also identified as the "MS-102"), along with a high-speed industrial bar code scanner (the "MS-106").[14] Central to the manufac-

turing of these scanners was the use of a much lower-cost single-chip micro-processor computer that Metrologic paired with high-speed buffering memory to store data ahead of the processor's own computations. "Thus, Metrologic scanners could now operate at high speeds, but compete in low-cost applications," Harry explained.[15]

Metrologic competitor Symbol's magazine scanner, the Laserscan 550

As Metrologic reached the end of the decade, its inventive effect on the scanner industry became increasingly apparent. Competition in the marketplace was more intense, as relative newcomers Metrologic and Symbol Technologies wrestled for

165

pieces of the scanner market. Metrologic's approach was to tackle the industry via competing for non-supermarket clients and to welcome support-role or sub-system contracts. Powerhouses such as NCR, IBM, and Spectra-Physics still ruled the in-bed, grocery scanner market, which had been growing slowly but inevitably since that first UPC grocery story item, a pack of Wrigley's Juicy Fruit gum, was scanned in 1974. However, unlike the clientele of the powerhouses, Metrologic's loyal following depended on the New Jersey company for the industry's linchpin components—lasers—and Metrologic's ability to build those lasers inexpensively.

This ability is reflected in Metrologic's 1979-1980 catalog, which boasts the latest innovations in its wide-ranging laser tube lines. Clients could now buy longer-lasting lasers with hard-seal mirrors (no leaky epoxy sealing agent) and steel-ceramic tubing.[16] Prior to this period, only glass tubing was

In 1979, customers could choose this Metrologic laser, designed for long shelf life with hard-seal mirrors and steel-ceramic construction.

employed by Metrologic. "The development of hard-seal tubes," Harry said, "was another step in our efforts toward increased reliability."[17] While the epoxy-sealed, glass laser tubes were still available and reasonably reliable, the newer steel and hard-seal construction performed better when the product was in storage or non-use for extended periods of time. (Later, reliability was improved further when Metrologic developed an all-glass-seal tube.)

In 1979-1980, limited warranties were one year long (instead of the generous two-year span advertised in the 1976 catalog), but laser purchases came with a 15-point inspection report reflecting new quality control procedures.[18] As the sole contractor to the U.S. government for lasers that were used for tank gunnery training, Metrologic also offered additional screening and testing for those clients requiring maximum product assurance. Known as the High-Reliability Testing Program, the extra screening included a 40-point inspection, exposure to temperature extremes, and cyclical and continuous week-long test runs.

The 48-page catalog is dominated by a 32-page educational laser handbook section detailing technical definitions and drawings, laser specifications and characteristics, and the client's available laser options and features. Seven pages of the section are set aside to describe and illustrate how a laser works, ending with a short explanation and drawing of how a laser scanner works.[19] The many educational pages were billed as a reference section—meant to be kept by teachers and other users to expand their knowledge of the science behind the laser.

With more than a decade of growing Metrologic accomplished, Harry had every reason to approach the 1980s with confidence. The 1970s in the U.S. had brought the Watergate scandal, the resulting 1974 resignation of President Richard Nixon, and the end of the Vietnam War. The nation's bicentennial had ushered in the presidency of Jimmy Carter, whose term included 16 percent inflation, 22 percent interest rates,[20] an energy crisis caused by rising oil prices, and the Iranian hostage crisis. That crisis, which began November 4, 1979, when Islamic students seized the U.S. embassy in Iran and took 90 people hostage, would not end until 444 days had passed and Carter had lost his reelection bid to Ronald Reagan.[21]

Considering the national challenges of the 1970s, Harry's management at the helm of Metrologic was indeed successful. In 1979, sales billed totaled $1.7 million, but sales booked reached $2.5 million.[22]

Harry's entrepreneurship was characterized by focused and incredibly long hours that were equal parts inspiration—resulting in amazing inventions—and terror— the gut-wrenching, unrelenting struggle of balancing the costs of weekly payroll, facilities, and investment in new product development with the undulating influx of revenue. As vice president of administration, wife Janet helped Harry with these tasks by assisting with the company's accounts receivable and payable, payroll, procurement, and personnel.[23]

"What inspired inventiveness," Harry explained, "were the week-to-week pressures we were living under. Humankind

Janet, 1970s

167

Harry, 1980s
Moorestown Studio

does respond to stark terror. If you don't have it, you get lazy. I wasn't a genius. I was just stupid enough to get into a situation that forced the invention."[24]

By 1980, Harry and Janet, with his and her children all grown, enjoyed a freedom to shape their time as they wished. Harry, who, more often than not, had placed work as his highest priority, was no longer haunted by the guilt and strain of his first marriage. With Janet, Harry's third marriage rallied around Metrologic; the company was a powerful unifying mechanism. As a result of Janet's devotion to Harry and his work, the couple's off-the-clock time proved enjoyable. With a teammate at his side, Harry was not only productive—he was happy.

To begin the decade, Harry developed a convertible, handheld, portable laser scanner with a stand, the "MS-131." Introduced in 1981, it was Metrologic's first miniature, low-cost laser scanner for retail use. "In the early '80s," Harry said, "the handheld took off."[25] Bar code scanners no longer resided only in grocery stores in the form of expensive, in-counter systems. "Prior to this time, the scanner market was nearly 100 percent large supermarket scanners," Harry said. "It seems obvious, looking back, that handheld scanners would flourish and eventually dominate the market. But we had no way of knowing that then because the scanner market developed slowly at first."[26] The new handheld scanners made the technology available to retail outlets

The MS-131, Metrologic's first miniature, low-cost scanner, was convertible and could be operated as a handheld or mounted on a stand.

across the country because they were cheaper and smaller. In addition, the advantages of automating inventory were becoming apparent in the marketplace. Formerly reluctant retailers wanted in, and Harry was eager to provide product lines to accomplish that goal.

The development of Metrologic's handheld, portable laser scanner with built-in decode followed in 1982. Known as the "MS-190," the model reflected the technological advances Metrologic made with each new product line. Scanning a bar code includes several steps, first of which is activation of the system, or sensing the presence of an object in the scan field. This activation can be initiated with a trigger or without a trigger. Next, a moving mirror scans a tightly focused laser beam across the scan field, detecting light of variable intensity reflected off the scanned object—which produces a signal. A bar code symbol is detected on the basis of that signal. Finally, the bar code is decoded by producing the data corresponding to the specific bar code symbol.[27] Thus, by having a built-in decode, the MS-190 provided the desired product information within the scanning unit itself as opposed to reliance on a separate computer system to interpret the bar code.

Also that year, Metrologic produced the "MS-165," a high-speed scanner for reverse vending machines for bottle and can returns and another example of the company's expanding scanner product lines. Harry, never a hands-off company president, felt continuously drawn to his labs and production floor. Harry was in the height of his strengths there. After all, he was the lead inventor or co-inventor of virtually all of their vast laser offerings. "I thought, 'I am good at engineering and production. I'm not nearly as good at sales and marketing,'" Harry said.[28]

He decided to bring in someone else as president to handle the business side of Metrologic, freeing Harry to concentrate on invention and production. In April 1982, Harry hired Michael L. Sanyour, former president of Subaru America and former vice president of Volkswagen, as president of Metrologic, effectively giving him part of the company. Sanyour was granted an annual salary of $75,000 and was offered the option to purchase 348 shares of Metrologic's common stock for $100,000. (Harry owned 696 shares of stock.)[29] "Janet said, 'This is a terrible mistake,'" Harry recalled. "He had been of short tenure at his previous jobs. I brought him in as president. I went back into the lab."[30]

Michael Sanyour, 1984
Photo by Ralph I. Shockey

Less than a year after joining Metrologic, Sanyour was having enough accounting conflicts with Janet Knowles that he fired her—in February 1983.[31] Obviously, family tension followed. But Harry had committed to Sanyour as president, and Harry gave Sanyour time to prove himself. "As president," Harry said, "he fired Janet, and I let him."[32] Sanyour had taken over the banking relationships; and Janet's oversight of purchasing and logistics for the company halted, at least temporarily. In May 1984, Sanyour "asked Janet to come back to run purchasing," Harry said, "so she did." Harry, meanwhile, buried himself in his work, throwing the weight of his attention on the promotion of the MS-190 scanner. Harry had succeeded in garnering a contract with NCR for NCR to "incorporate [the MS-190] in 'point of sale' devices it sold."[33]

The NCR relationship hit a snag, however, in the form of a third party—Symbol Technologies, formerly UPC Film Masters. Harry had severed a business partnership with Symbol founder Jerry Swartz in the 1976-1977 time frame, but Harry's now arch-rival was his chief competitor. What made the rivalry particularly personal was that, in Harry's view, Swartz had gleaned inside information from Metrologic in those early days, then had gone back and developed his own product based on what he had learned from the trusting Harry.[34] The small UPC Film Masters startup—founded by Swartz in 1973 in New York—had morphed into Symbol, a rising star in the laser scanner industry. In fact, Symbol became a publicly traded company in June 1979 with "an initial offering of 456,500 shares on the NASDAQ exchange." (In 1988, Symbol changed to the New York Stock Exchange.)[35] Within four years, Symbol would bring in Mars Electronics' Raymond Martino as president and COO, with Swartz continuing as chairman and lead researcher. During this time, Symbol's revenues were modest—about $5 million per year—but that would jump by 1985 to $13.9 million annually, with number of employees topping 150.

"Symbol decided very early on they were going after big venture money," Harry said. "They went public early and diluted their own control. I wasn't comfortable doing that prematurely."[36]

In November 1982, however, Symbol executives were busy protecting what they saw as Symbol property. With Metrologic having won an NCR contract for Metrologic MS-190 scanners, Symbol notified NCR—Metrologic's largest customer—that "the handheld laser scanners NCR was purchasing from Metrologic infringed one or more claims in a patent application Symbol had on file with the Patent and Trademark Office."[37] Symbol went as far as to show NCR an internal company letter from Symbol's patent counsel, Alan Israel, to Symbol chairman Jerry Swartz. Israel told Swartz that in his opinion, "anyone attempting to design a practical hand-held trigger-operated laser

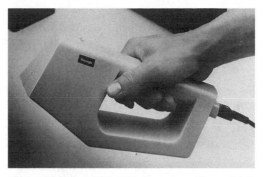

The triggered MS-190 Scanhandler, which offered scanning and decoding in one scanner, drew the attention of rival Symbol.

scanning head will be hard-pressed to avoid infringing this very broad claim." On February 29, 1980, Symbol had filed for a patent with the U.S. Patent and Trademark Office for a handheld laser scanner it had developed. NCR immediately asked Metrologic for clarification.

A later court ruling detailed the reaction of Metrologic: "After consulting its patent counsel, Metrologic concluded that Symbol would be unable to obtain a valid, enforceable patent with such broad claims covering handheld, trigger-operated laser scanners and that Metrologic's [MS-]190 scanner would not infringe Symbol's patents, once issued. Nevertheless, Metrologic and Symbol met on several occasions to discuss Metrologic's handheld laser scanners, the claims of the pending application, and the possibility of various business arrangements between Symbol and Metrologic. The discussions, however, did not result in any agreement...."[38]

Considering the history between Harry and Symbol's Swartz, it is not surprising that Metrologic and Symbol failed to strike any chords of harmony. Metrologic's NCR contract continued. Harry and his attorneys did not feel one could patent a scanner trigger on a portable device; to Harry, it was obvious and too sweeping a stroke to be an enforceable exclusive right of Symbol. Still, on June 7, 1983, the Patent and Trademark Office (PTO) issued U.S. Patent Number 4,387,297, known as the "297 patent," for Symbol's new gun-shaped, trigger-operated, handheld laser scanner. The patent-granting had not been seamless, however. In fact, during the "prosecution of the '297 patent...the examiner originally rejected the claimed invention as obvious in light of the disclosure in the '798 patent,"[39] a previous Symbol patent for a verifier known as the Laserchek. But after Symbol asked the PTO examiner to explain the rejection, Symbol amended its patent application to "include the handle, trigger and sighting means [later referred to as the 'aim and shoot feature']....The examiner allowed the claims in view of the amendment." The amended claim distinguished the new scanner enough from Symbol's '798 patent, or Laserchek product, so the patent was granted.[40]

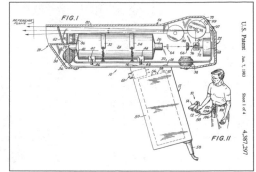

From the USPTO's Symbol '297 patent, a side sectional view of the gun-shaped, trigger-operated, handheld scanner

Symbol had asked Metrologic and fellow laser scanner competitor Spectra-Physics to provide documentation relevant to the validity of Symbol's patent claim during the PTO process. By acknowledging previously conceived competitor products via inclusion of "prior art" of those products, Symbol could build a stronger case for patenting with the PTO. Spectra-Physics declined to submit anything, thus refusing to aid Symbol; but Harry was more trusting. Metrologic sent Symbol materials of prior art including advertising for the Verifier 315.[41] Symbol tendered the Verifier 315 references to the PTO with its amended '297 patent application; the PTO determined that the issue of Metrologic having developed the Verifier 315 previously "raised no new question of patentability." The PTO completed the reexamination of Symbol's '297 patent December 16, 1983. By early 1984, Symbol had begun advertising the product of the '297 patent—their new LS 7000 laser scanner.

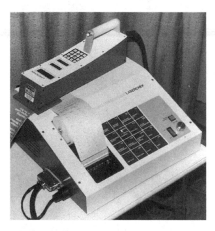

Laserchek portable bar code verifier, for which Symbol filed with the USPTO in May 1978 and was issued the '798 patent in February 1981. Note the similarity with Metrologic's Verifier 315 on page 186.

In January 1984, Symbol sued California-based Spectra-Physics for infringement of Symbol's '297 patent. Symbol "notified Metrologic, who was manufacturing and marketing the [MS-]190 handheld laser scanners, that Symbol would determine its future actions based on the outcome of the liability phase of the Spectra-Physics suit."[42] Ultimately—in January 1986—the Symbol-Spectra-Physics case would be settled. Metrologic and Harry interpreted Symbol's inaction toward Metrologic since 1982 as a signal that no litigation was pending, but Harry would find later that Symbol appeared to have set its sights on Metrologic already as a lawsuit target. New Jersey's Metrologic, meanwhile, had continued its NCR contract and was busy with development of further laser scanner product lines.

In 1983, Metrologic Instruments completed the final expansion of its Bellmawr facility, adding 9,000 square feet to bring total plant size to 27,000 square feet.[43] Harry still deferred the business side of the operation to Metrologic president Mike Sanyour, while chairman Harry spent his workday in the trenches of the lab or on the production floor. "My genius was solving problems on the floor," Harry said.[44] With sales at $4.6 and $5.2 million,

From left, architect Herman Hassinger and his assistant (unidentified) designed the final Bellmawr expansion, which was completed in 1983. Also shown here at the expansion groundbreaking are Mike Sanyour with shovel, the Bellmawr mayor, and Harry, far right.

respectively, in 1983 and 1984,[45] Metrologic projected $8 to $10 million in sales for 1985.[46] Unknown to Harry, however, money was going out faster than it was coming in as bank debt increased to nearly $3 million in 1985 and total liabilities crept toward $4 million. With the costs of fulfilling the NCR contract, ramped-up inventory, payroll demands, expansion of facilities, and complex costs of long-range product development—merely a few of the web of financial obligations inherent to a large company such as Metrologic—Sanyour's task was a challenging one. The Harvard MBA graduate Sanyour needed to balance revenues and expenditures, but sales of the MS-190 had plummeted after NCR returned 900 of its 2,000 ordered units to Metrologic for repair.[47] The 1985 projection would not be met; revenues that year would total $4.9 million, with $1.5 million in losses.[48] Ultimately, Sanyour, along with Metrologic, would suffer the consequences of the revenue shortfall.

Finally, on Friday, July 26, 1985, Bob Duvall, representing First Pennsylvania Bank, Metrologic's main creditor, came to his friend Harry and asked him, "Harry, do you know what shape Metrologic is in?" Harry answered, "No, but Mike says everything is fine." Harry remembered how Bob summarized the situation: "Bob said, 'We're calling the loan. You're going to have to go into bankruptcy. We're going to pay to get through bankruptcy, but you have to take over. Come back with a plan for positive cash flow.'"[49]

Here was another mountain for the never-say-die Harry. The 57-year-old had founded Metrologic; he served as its chairman, but he also was the inventive soul of the company. His employees depended on him. He was not about to let them down.

Harry and Janet had made plans for that weekend. They were to reunite with several of Harry's college friends from his Auburn days. They gathered in Orange Beach, Alabama, at the beach house of Joe and Anne Pilcher. Such friendship was too important to Harry to cancel the trip. He and Janet flew in Harry's Bonanza (since Harry had maintained his pilot's license) to the beach and had a "marvelous weekend." Come Sunday, however, they flew back to Philadelphia with a plan.

Harry met with Metrologic's attorney, Arthur Abramowitz of Davis, Reberkenny & Abramowitz, and Sanyour. As part of the Chapter 11 bankruptcy filing and reorganization, Sanyour would leave Metrologic and be compensated for the return of the purchased company stock (to Harry as sole shareholder) and money that Sanyour personally had loaned Metrologic. In a 1986 *Philadelphia Business Journal* article, Sanyour acknowledged a difference of opinion between him and Harry, saying, "There was a bend in the road that was called Chapter 11 that I really didn't feel was the appropriate way to go."[50] (Before the year was out, Sanyour was hired as president of the Mount Laurel, New Jersey, firm of Avante-Garde Computing, Inc. He would go on to become mayor of Moorestown, New Jersey, and a principal with Philadelphia investment firm CMS Companies.)

But Harry wasn't willing to take on more credit and needed immediate resolution to pay his employees. Together, Janet and Harry worked out a systematic approach to Metrologic's problems. "Janet pulled off a miracle during that two weeks

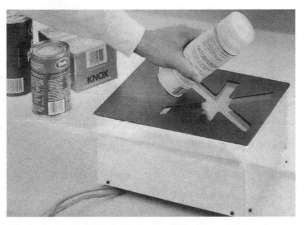

Metrologic's MS-260 included this original version from 1985 and another (shown on page 195) marketed as the world's first mini-slot, in-counter laser scanner for retail use. Products often evolved into different looks and lines as technology and presentation advanced.

[following the beach weekend]," Harry said.[51] "She organized accounts payable, inventory with detailed values, and accounts receivable by herself, by using a TRS-80 computer program I had developed years earlier. No one was around to help. I crafted our strategy, developing a cash flow plan and a profit and loss projection. I decided what products to keep and drop and whom we could do business with. NCR was phased out; we got out of industrial [accounts]. We focused on retail mini-slot and handheld scanners. The marketing efforts were to be more focused, and around standard products." On August 13, 1985, Metrologic declared bankruptcy and submitted its plan of reorganization.

One of the products being kept was a new one, the "MS-260," the world's first mini-slot (with "mini-slot" being Metrologic's trademarked descriptor), in-counter laser scanner for retail use. Debuting in 1985, the mini-slot was pegged as a revolution for the scanner industry by Metrologic, because the MS-260 brought the advantage of in-counter scanning—previously reserved only for grocery stores—to the smaller retail outlets in a miniature, cheaper form. Within two months of declaring bankruptcy, Metrologic already was experiencing positive cash flow.

During the bankruptcy proceedings, Metrologic reduced its workforce from about 125 to 95 employees.[52] Despite uncertainty, only two

Front center, Harry and Janet (on Harry's left) are joined outside the Bellmawr headquarters by their loyal employees, post-1983 expansion.

key professionals quit. "All other employees stuck with us," Harry said. "Nearly 100 percent of vendors stuck with us. We paid the vendors back through tight communications, favorable pricing, and preferential treatment, and built a relationship in South Jersey for bringing the business back from bankruptcy. It was a matter of turning the crank, reassuring customers. I had no choice but to go forward."[53]

Associate Engineer George Kolis recalled this period in Metrologic's history as an example of the faith employees had in the word of Harry Knowles. "We were a big family," Kolis said. "When we went through bankruptcy, people just showed up for work. We didn't know if we'd get paid. But Harry told us not to worry about it. We were a team."[54]

Within six months, Metrologic was out of bankruptcy. "I can't say enough positive about how Janet handled [the situation]. It was a high-stress period," Harry said. On February 11, 1986, Metrologic's plan of reorganization was confirmed by the bankruptcy court.[55] Harry was president and sole owner of Metrologic again.

"As I came out of bankruptcy," Harry said, "I decided 'you're not going to be Mr. Nice Guy.' Meetings are going to be brutally efficient and short. It was a complete autocracy. It was a conscious decision in

1985. We became very efficient. You don't do that job [of pulling out of bankruptcy] by being a nice, sweet, patient person. You have to go after the goal energetically."[56]

That Metrologic pulled out of bankruptcy so quickly was remarkable; to do so with its work force remaining staunchly loyal is unique indeed. The feat directly correlated to the fact that Harry *was* Metrologic and Metrologic was Harry. Metrologic corporate culture was a direct reflection of Harry's personality and management style. Finances could be turned around because Harry had complete autonomy to react immediately. His style was the opposite of bureaucratic; when he saw the need to drop less profitable accounts, he did so swiftly. When in need of additional revenue sources, his reaction was to go to the lab and invent new products. If product development slowed, he would adjust schematics with the engineers on the fly. Production floor changes happened instantly. Positive results followed. They were not always well-documented, neatly packaged results. But they were results nonetheless.

Metrologic's rebound came at a time when the national economy was enjoying solid progress as unemployment slowly made its way down from a 1982 high of 9.7 percent to 7 percent in 1986 on its way to a decade low of 5.3 percent in 1989.[57] With the recession over, President Reagan had been reelected to a second term in 1984.[58] The laser scanner industry experienced continuous expansion and validation from such groups as the National Mass Retailing Institute, which, in 1986, endorsed the UPC (Universal Product Code) for use in point-of-sale transactions in retail outlets other than supermarkets, for which the UPC had been specifically designed. In addition, Wal-Mart, K-Mart, and Federated Department Stores told their suppliers that they must use bar codes on their products.[59] The mandates were further evolvement of major UPC endorsements in the 1980s, including the U.S. Department of Defense priming industrial applications of the bar code via its adoption in 1981 of a bar code system known as "LOGMARS" which used the UPC on all products sold to the military. The U.S. Postal Service had joined the bandwagon in 1982, adopting the "POSTNET" bar code to sort mail by zip code automatically.[60]

With Metrologic reorganized and re-positioned, Harry was poised to take advantage of the bar code's penetration into virtually every world marketplace. The time had come to go global. In 1986, Metrologic opened its first overseas office in the Munich suburb of Garching,

Metrologic's first European employee, Manfred Arnoldi, right, with Harry and Janet

Germany, as a result of having met potential distributors the year before at the Scantech industrial fair in Hannover, Germany. From Metrologic's one-square-meter "booth" in Hannover, Harry met Manfred Arnoldi, who became Metrologic's first European employee.[61] By the end of 1986, Metrologic had $6.9 million in sales and a net income of $700,000.[62] The Germany office milestone marked the beginning of what would become a vast worldwide empire. The added European dimension, with the six-hour time difference, also meant that Harry's work hours were even more unusual. Janet tolerated Harry getting up early—in the middle of the night—faxing and e-mailing to get Germany's day started. "2 to 3 a.m. is a very productive time of day," Harry said. "You get quite creative."[63] The nightly habit became entrenched and would continue and expand in importance throughout Harry's career.

For rival Symbol Technologies, 1986 meant another patent infringement lawsuit on the heels of resolving its suit against Spectra-Physics. On November 14, 1986, Symbol sued Opticon, Inc., a Japanese company which had released its own triggered, handheld laser scanner, the "MSH-840," a few months earlier in August. Symbol claimed Opticon's scanner was patterned after Symbol's LS 7000 and violated Symbol's '297 patent.[64] The extended process of litigation, however, would delay the suit's effect on Metrologic. While Harry was aware of the aggressiveness with which Symbol was pursuing patenting and found Swartz' approach to the laser scanner industry arrogant, Harry felt Metrologic had no choice but to continue development of its handheld line.[65] Besides, he had little time to worry about Swartz.

As 1987 saw Symbol move into a new corporate headquarters, the year brought a promising new product online at Metrologic—the "MS-290," the "world's first handheld laser scanner with modern, ergonomic design." As with many of Metrologic's products through the years,

Knowles had personally conceived of this "90" series of scanners, heading the 290 development team and soliciting clients.[66] Metrologic had achieved significant success in the short two years since bankruptcy; U.S. clients included K-Mart, Pep Boys, Rite-Aid, Chief Auto, Fred Myers supermarkets, and Zayre.[67]

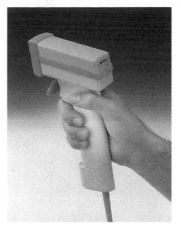

The ergonomic MS/MH-290 triggered handheld proved popular but attracted a lawsuit from Symbol.

Metrologic's success did not go unnoticed by Symbol, which viewed Metrologic's MS-290, triggered, handheld scanner as a market threat and, of course, in their view, a violation of existing Symbol patents.[68] On January 26, 1988, Symbol sued Metrologic and Harry Knowles for infringement of Symbol's '297 patent, in addition to a related scanner product patent (called the "186 patent"). Patenting moved to the forefront of Harry's worries. Even Metrologic's introduction of another product—an omni-directional laser scanner for supermarkets (the "MS-360") —in 1988 and Harry being selected that May as a finalist for the Delaware Valley Entrepreneur of the Year Awards, did little to allay the Symbol lawsuit storm clouds.

Early MS-360, November 1988

"I ignored [Symbol's] patent," Harry said. "I thought a button, or trigger, was an obvious component, and that obviousness precluded a patent. That was a bad mistake."[69]

Metrologic had filed for patents on its products through the years, but, historically, Harry had been inconsistent in protecting intellectual property and naïve about new developments in U.S. patent law. Actually, the structure of the patenting legal system had changed in 1982, when the Court of Appeals for the Federal Circuit (CAFC) was created with exclusive jurisdiction over appeals of patent board decisions and over all district court decision appeals relating to patents.[70] The creation of the

CAFC was a direct result of the inconsistency of various regional circuits regarding patent law. As one history of U.S. patent law explained it, "During the 1970s, there was a growing feeling that certain [U.S. District] circuit [court]s were anti-patent and others pro-patent, so that forum shopping was rife."

Prior to 1982, according to Harry, about 80 percent of patent lawsuits resulted in a win for the challenging plaintiff. "After 1982, that [balance] switched to 80 percent chance of the patent-holder winning. Symbol attorneys were brilliant and understood the significance. When I came out of Bell Labs, I had a loose idea of patents. At Westinghouse, I even helped manage patent licenses. But I didn't adequately understand until the late 1980s," Harry said.[71]

Harry gravitated to the creating and not the bureaucracy of patent prosecution. Amidst the sea of lawyers involved in the Symbol lawsuit, however, Harry discovered how lacking Metrologic patenting had been in the past. According to the PTO's patent listings, Metrologic filed only four patents from 1974 to 1976 for its inventions.[72] Patent filings picked up again in November 1985, when the Philadelphia law firm Caesar, Rivise, Bernstein, Cohen & Pokotilow, Ltd. began advising Harry and prosecuting (in the world of patent law, prosecuting is equivalent to filing and obtaining) patents for Metrologic. The Caesar firm would file about ten patents for Metrologic from 1985 until September 1990; but, since the firm's advice, according to Harry, added to Harry's misjudgment of the Symbol patent threat, Metrologic and the Caesar law office were destined for a parting of ways.

"In business, only the very best patent prosecutor is good enough," Harry said. Along with the Philadelphia law firm's advice, "...my own naivete in patents and lack of publishing and, generally, being overly self-confident and negligent at times got me into the Symbol situation."[73]

While Symbol filed suit against Metrologic and Harry Knowles in January 1988, at the same time, Symbol was still in the midst of its patent lawsuit against Japanese scanner company Opticon. Although the Symbol-Opticon case had commenced November 1986, the patent legal system was a laborious one and 1988 still found the case in pre-trial mode. Helping the defense in the Opticon suit, though risky, was an unavoidable key for Metrologic's legal strategy, as two of the alleged patent infringements for which Symbol was suing Opticon were the same patents (Symbol's '297 and '186 patents) named in the Symbol-Metrologic

Harry campaigning for town council

Gifts to Harry for Rotary Club service, 1984
Photo by Ralph I. Shockey

suit. In addition, Harry almost certainly would be subpoenaed, so he considered his Opticon participation a necessity. The outcome of the Opticon suit would strongly indicate the fate of the Metrologic suit.

Harry, two years out of bankruptcy and a hero to his employees for saving their jobs, had turned Metrologic around financially in quick order. He even had opened the overseas office in Germany and toyed with taking the company public (although he, for the time-being, backed away from that idea in 1988). He was well known in the New Jersey community, both as an employer and civic leader, having been elected to the Moorestown Township Council and as president of the local Rotary Club in the early 1980s. Yet, despite his brilliance as a leader, Harry once again faced incredible challenges—this time to defend his company's lifeblood products.

The year 1988 was difficult in other ways, too. Harry's half-brother, acoustical pioneer Hugh S. Knowles, died at age 83 on April 21, 1988, 19 years after Hugh's wife Jo had died.[74] Hugh and Jo had been a guiding and supportive presence since Harry's childhood in Birmingham, Alabama, even providing Harry a short-term loan during the early days of Metrologic to purchase property in Moorestown, New Jersey, for the family. Hugh, who had led Harry to his passion for photography and cameras, had encouraged Harry to study transistors at Bell Labs, a move that secured Harry's entree into the world of invention. Hugh, Harry said, was "*the* major inventor in the world of hearing transducers, with an impenetrable patent position."[75] Indeed, through Hugh's company,

Hugh Knowles, 1970s

Knowles Electronics in suburban Chicago, Hugh distributed his hearing aid transducers—the highly miniaturized microphones and speakers—worldwide and became a model of entrepreneurial success for Harry. Although Harry had not been in frequent contact with Hugh in recent years, Hugh, no doubt, was proud of Harry's success at Metrologic. Harry, in turn, would miss the half-brother with whom he so obviously shared the inventive psyche of their father.

The Metrologic family, however, was the family which dominated Harry's thoughts as Symbol's litigation against Opticon and Metrologic proceeded. With the turning of the calendar, as George H.W. Bush took office as president, Opticon and Symbol hurtled toward a 1989 trial date. On April 17, 1989, the bench (non-jury) trial of *Symbol Technologies v. Opticon* began in the New York Southern District Court of Judge Kimba M. Wood. Specifically, Symbol claimed that Opticon's MSH-840, MSH-850, and MSH-860 handheld, triggered laser bar code scanners directly infringed upon three of Symbol's handheld scanners protected under the '297 patent (Symbol's LS 7000 scanner), the '186 patent, and the '470 patent. The '186 patent was a variation of the LS 7000; Symbol's '470 patent was an improvement on the '297 patent.[76]

Symbol was especially stringent in guarding these patents because the LS 7000 and its spin-off products had brought in about $150 million in revenues to Symbol through 200,000 units sold. Opticon argued that Symbol's patents were invalid because, first, Symbol had withheld pertinent information from the PTO or misled the patent office and, second, the patents were obvious and, therefore, unpatentable. Opticon had an uphill battle concerning the first issue since the PTO already had reexamined the patents in question and affirmed validity.

Symbol's LS 7000
Photo courtesy Lab
Extreme, Inc.

To examine the issue of obviousness, the court followed a protocol previously established by the Supreme Court, which dictated that the "scope and content of...prior art" be determined.[77] Prior art could be such things as a mechanical drawing, prototype, or a product which existed before the patent in question was created. Such prior art could prove Symbol's handheld, triggered LS 7000 laser scanner was not a new invention but obvious because its essence had existed previously in another product.

Key to Opticon's defense was C. Harry Knowles, whose Monitor 101, X-scanner, and Verifier 315 of the mid-1970s, as well as a Metrologic scanner proposed to Playtex in 1977 (known as the "Playtex device"), all could be construed as prior art—if Opticon could prove it in court. Symbol had already subpoenaed Harry to testify. In the *Symbol v. Metrologic* court ruling filed in 1991, the court commented on Harry's Opticon trial testimony: "Although Metrologic and Knowles were not parties in the Opticon suit, Knowles testified for two days on direct examination on behalf of Opticon and for seven days on cross examination by Symbol. Knowles also voluntarily submitted voluminous Metrologic records to Opticon to assist in their defense."[78]

Nine days of testimony in Federal Court would be grueling for anyone, but Harry suffered further burden. As Harry testified during the April 17 through June 20, 1989, trial, on May 11, 1989, Harry's biological mother, Ruby, died in Birmingham at the age of 87.[79] Harry attended the funeral, along with his half-brother Bill Penn who had helped care for their mother in her final years. What conflicting emotions must have been felt by Harry, who, after struggling a good portion of his life to understand Ruby's lack of maternal love, ultimately had discharged her from his life when he lived in Phoenix during his time at Motorola. She had visited Harry in Phoenix, but the stay had ended in an unpleasant disagreement and Harry asking Ruby to leave.

Harry had seen his mother only once since then, during a Christmas holiday in Alabama at the home of brother Bill and his family. Ruby was at Bill's house on Christmas day, when Harry came. "They did okay," Bill Penn recalled. "I thought this was the beginning of a reconciliation. But, at 3:00, Mother said, 'I have to meet my friend for cocktails.' She left her son she hadn't seen in 20 years. You never knew what Mother [was going to do.] She was a hard, difficult woman. I would tell Mother about Harry's success, but it didn't register. She'd dismissed him."[80]

Still, Bill had an understanding of his mother's shortfalls, including

Harry in later years visiting Jefferson State Junior College, to which his mother gifted her estate

her inability to love in a normal way. She had remarried in 1962 to a successful Birmingham piping engineer, inventor, and plant owner, Harry Y. Carson, who owned hundreds of acres in Pinson Valley in Alabama. Seventy-five acres were given to Jefferson State Community College, which later dedicated two Carson-funded campus buildings to its benefactors—the Ruby K. Carson Science Education Center and, adjoining, the H.Y. Carson building.

Bill, who retired in California from the Air Force and had run a non-profit company there, had returned to Birmingham when H.Y. Carson became ill to assume the roles of vice president and general manager of Carson's company. Although Carson had two daughters of his own, Bill felt he was treated equally by his step-father. Bill honored his legacy by working diligently and looking after Ruby; following Carson's death, Bill sold the business. The income went to his mother and helped her live well through her later years. Bill and his wife, Catherine, would check on Ruby every day at her house; she had a relationship with Bill she never had with Harry.

Bill remembered Ruby's final days, saying he had taken her out for her birthday on May 6, 1989, and his mother had become ill. She had a history of heart trouble and was admitted to the hospital. On May 11, as Bill sat in the waiting room, he said he "heard the code blue sound." Ruby died that day. Her obituary, in addition to noting her gifts to the college, mentioned her membership on the Birmingham Beautification Board, her Citizen of the Year Award from the Eastern Area Chamber of Commerce, and her service as a captain in the Women's Army Auxiliary Corps during World War II.[81] Ruby willed her estate completely to Jefferson State; she left nothing to either of her sons.[82] Nevertheless, the gentle Bill was at peace with the situation, always making allowances for his mother, whom he considered broken emotionally. He also understood his brother Harry's perspective; he had observed first-hand the effect Ruby's harshness had on his little brother.

Ruby and her sons, Bill, left, and Harry, 1980s

Harry had little time to dwell on his mother's death during the *Symbol v. Opticon* trial that spring 1989. His nine days of testimony included being grilled on countless details concerning Metrologic's Monitor 101, the on-press verifier debuting in 1975; Verifier 315, the handheld laser scanner which caught Symbol's eye in 1975; and Harry's X-scanner, a handheld scanner which, in prototype form, had a trigger. Prototypes of all three of these devices had been demonstrated, Harry said, at a November 1975 New York packaging trade show hotel. Metrologic sales representative company Surescan showed the Monitor 101, while Harry demonstrated the Verifier 315 and X-scanner.

What became a crucial point of the Symbol-Opticon lawsuit was the fact that Symbol's patented products under discussion each had a trigger. Its '297 patent invention was described by the court as a "portable, light-weight laser scanning head that operates without physical contact with the bar code. In gun-like fashion, the user sights the bar code, unobstructed by the device, then depresses a trigger to initiate decoding. Each time the trigger is depressed, the handheld device sweeps a scanning laser beam laterally across the bar code by use of mirrors. The examiner considered this 'aim and shoot' feature to be a novel distinguishing characteristic of the claimed invention over the prior art."[83]

The Monitor 101 as prior art was rejected by the court. Mounted on a high-speed printing press, it was neither handheld nor activated by a trigger. Metrologic's Verifier 315 had been considered by the PTO when examining

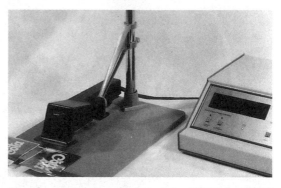

Verifier 315, as marketed in 1976 by UPC Film Masters and made by Metrologic

Symbol's '297 patent and, although Harry had provided advertising for the Verifier 315 to the patent office, the PTO still determined Metrologic's product posed no hindrance to granting the '297 patent to Symbol. Amazingly, the 1976 advertising flyer referred to "Verifier 315 of UPC Film Masters, Inc."[84] (which later changed its name to Symbol Technologies), reflecting the fact that Symbol had marketed the Verifier 315 as its own laser scanner during its short sales representative relationship with Metrologic. The court discussion said the Verifier 315 had "none of the aim and shoot features of plaintiff's patents nor did it have a trigger or a sighting guide. In addition, because of the device's hooded construction, the user's view of the bar code during operation was obstructed by the device itself."[85]

However, Harry said the prototype had a trigger, although it needed none in its commercial manifestation.[86] Such an example would show Metrologic as having preconceived the trigger instead of Symbol. But truth proved elusive during the original *Symbol v. Opticon* trial. Only on later appeal would Harry's drawings gain any significant legal recognition.

At the trial, Harry even demonstrated a Verifier 315 purchased originally by Westvaco Corporation and given to George Reed upon his retirement from Westvaco. During trial, the device became known as the "Reed Verifier." "We borrowed the Verifier 315 and actually demonstrated it before [Judge] Kimba Wood," Harry said. "Bob Blake did an incredible job of making the thing work again over a two-day period getting it ready for the trial after I borrowed it from [George]."[87] Since Harry and Blake had sparse documentation and the Verifier 315 had been out of production for years, there were no directly interchangeable spare parts for the borrowed Reed Verifier, according to Harry.[88] Reed, continued Harry, "also acknowledged that he had a copy of the old preliminary data sheet that he had received at the [New York packaging] show showing the trigger. But the Verifier 315 had no trigger, so was ignored by Judge Wood."[89]

As Harry demonstrated the Reed Verifier, he also testified as to the modifications Blake had made, such as replacement of the old laser tube, a lens, and two faulty digital chips. No changes had been made to the verifier's housing, Harry testified. However, the court felt Harry contradicted himself when he later said that the tubular housing had been replaced. "It became apparent at trial," the court ruling said, "that the Reed Verifier had been modified by Mr. Knowles in a number of additional respects....the Court does not find credible Mr. Knowles' testimony that the Reed Verifier as configured at trial and as shown to the Court existed as prior art...."[90]

Harry ran into similar problems with his testimony concerning the X-scanner, which, Harry said, "operated in a similar manner to plaintiff's invention at issue: 'You pull the trigger, it reads the bar code and it also tells the system to now transmit that code out the RS 232, the communications port.'"[91] Metrologic employee Charles "Chic" Naylor "testified at his deposition that he built three versions of the X-scanner during the mid-1970s. Mr. Naylor testified he did not follow blueprints or other drawings in building the device but was guided solely by Mr. Knowles' verbal instruction."

The lack of documentation on the X-scanner was not surprising considering Harry's legendary approach to quick design modifications. In addition, Metrologic could not locate an X-scanner at the time of the trial; although a picture of one Naylor believed was taken in the early 1970s was submitted. Because Opticon's attorney failed to call Naylor to the witness stand at trial, the court refused to acknowledge the photo's validity. Further damaging the court's

X-scanner, 1970s

187

views on the X-scanner was the fact that when Harry claimed he had shown, in 1975, the X-scanner to George Reed and Symbol's own Jerry Swartz and Shelley Harrison, all three denied ever seeing one.

The court was not convinced Harry's recall was accurate. Considering the time lapse and details involved, a flawless testimony would have been nearly impossible. However, the constraints of the Opticon-centric setting added to the pressure of the situation. "I had no chance to review technical or legal details," Harry explained, "since this was Opticon's trial and their priorities prevailed in our testimony. The financial implications and personal pressure of sitting all those days before a federal judge were enormous. I was naïve to the extreme in trusting truth and my own recollections."[92] In fact, the court ruling declared that "defendants have not shown by clear and convincing evidence that an operable X-scanner ever existed. The Court further finds that the tentative specifications and sketch of the X-scanner introduced into the trial record are not prior art as prior printed publications."[93]

However, in Opticon's 1991 appeal, the Federal Circuit would disagree with District Judge Kimba Wood on this matter, saying that the district court should not have excluded the X-scanner sketches and tentative specifications "on the theory that 'prior art'...must be enabling."[94] The excluded sketches clearly showed the X-scanner had a trigger and could be operated in portable or permanent mode. Still, the Federal Circuit Court did not see the district court's error as preventing that court from "alternatively reaching its factual conclusions regarding those materials." The district court concluded the X-scanner had to be dragged across a bar code to read the code rather than "aimed and shot" as in the '297 patent. That the court reached this conclusion based on the expert testimony of Symbol's own Jerry Swartz did not convince the Federal Court that the district court "committed reversible error in crediting Symbol's evidence."

"In the trial," Harry said, "Jerry's disputing of my testimony made me out as a liar. I felt that Jerry, speaking from his power of commercial success, treated the truth with such open disregard, it was incredible to me.[95]

"We were very open with Jerry [Swartz] and Shelley [Harrison] on their several visits to Bellmawr between December 1975 and mid-'76.... Of course, [at trial,] Jerry totally denied all that openness. It seems that [Judge] Wood felt that anyone who did that was either stupid or lying...

so she did not believe me. I wanted to put Gapin, Blake, Chic, etc. on the stand to rebut that. However, it was not our trial, and I had been on the stand for [nine] days total and Judge Wood was tired of the matter—so felt Opticon's attorney."[96]

As with the other three Metrologic products—the Monitor 101, Verifier 315, and X-scanner—the district court failed to see the wooden model of a small, portable laser scanner Metrologic proposed to the Playtex Corporation in 1977 as prior art.[97] The court said Opticon had not proved a working prototype of the scanner existed and rejected a photo of a wooden mockup, sketch, and proposal as prior art. Ultimately, District Judge Wood rejected all of Opticon's defenses in her May 3, 1990, opinion in the *Symbol v. Opticon* case, stating that Opticon's MSH-840, MSH-850, and MSH-860 scanners directly infringed upon Symbol's '297, '186, and '470 patents. Then, on June 14, 1991, the U.S. Court of Appeals for the Federal Circuit upheld the district court's ruling against Opticon.[98]

The lapse in time between Harry's ordeal testifying at the Opticon trial in spring of 1989 and the 1990 district court decision can be attributed to the vast amount of post-trial activities. In fact, the attorneys for Symbol and Opticon had not fully submitted their post-trial legal memos and alleged findings of fact until October 3, 1989. By the time 1990 arrived, Harry's lawyers were operating at full speed representing Metrologic and Harry in the *Symbol v. Metrologic and C. Harry Knowles* lawsuit, which had begun January 1988. Representing Harry was the New York law firm of Hopgood, Calimafde, Kalil, Blaustein, & Judlowe; in addition, Max Goldman served as local attorney for the defendants.

In May 1990, in light of Judge Wood's ruling in favor of Symbol, Harry and Steve Judlowe and his Hopgood legal team met to discuss concerns that Metrologic might be barred from its triggered handheld scanner market. A decision was made to aggressively grow Metrologic's patent portfolio, which had only about a dozen patents total at that time. One of Hopgood's attorneys present, Thomas J. Perkowski, a Long Island native who had an electrical computer engineering degree from Clarkson University and a law degree from Franklin Pierce Law Center, was chosen to assume the role of Metrologic's patent prosecutor. Perkowski, who had worked with Hopgood for two years, would replace Metrologic's previous patent law firm completely before the year was out. From the onset, Perkowski's mission was to surround Metrologic's

Patent prosecutor Tom Perkowski

intellectual property with as much protection as possible.[99] He lost no time, filing his first patent on behalf of Metrologic in September of that year.

As feared, with the May 1990 district court ruling against Opticon and the ongoing lawsuit against Metrologic, the courts placed an injunction against Metrologic on triggered, handheld scanners. The court was ordering Metrologic to abandon its handheld line, including its successful MS-290. "By 1990, our technology had led us into virtual domination of the handheld scanner market," Harry remembered. "We had taken all the major orders for handhelds from K-Mart, Montgomery Ward, Gap. When the court decision came in May, we couldn't supply our retailers. We became pariah [not only to retailers but] to our distributors [who sold to small retailers nationwide]. We were almost run out of business. There's nothing like stark terror to motivate you. We had to re-invent the handheld scanner."[100]

In 1990, Metrologic sales amounted to $16.7 million (down from $18.7 million in 1989), but the projected sales total on pending handheld scanner orders was much more.[101] The court injunction, Harry said, destroyed about two-thirds of Metrologic's business—more than $20 million of $35 million expected in 1990—but Harry was not one to surrender. After all, he had survived overwhelming challenges in his company's history before. He also had more than 200 employees faithfully depending on him. In fact, Harry moved that staff and all of Metrologic's U.S. operations into a 58,000-square-foot building in Blackwood, New Jersey, that year.[102]

Harry did not disappoint his Metrologic family. Within a couple of months of the court ruling, Harry personally designed another new product and a revolutionary way around the injunction—a triggerless, automatically activated handheld scanner. Product development was fast-tracked for the new, first-of-its-kind scanner, which debuted in 1991 as the "MS-900" series. Although sales in 1991 reflected further

Aerial view of Metrologic HQ, 90 Coles Road, Blackwood

post-court injunction effects and fell to $12.3 million, the MS-900 scanner line would prove highly profitable for the scrappy Metrologic in the near future. Harry proudly declared, "We revolutionized the marketplace by going triggerless."[103] Also designed in 1990 and introduced was another industry first, Metrologic's small, hands-free projection scanner, the "MS-700."

"Harry was a fighter," patent prosecutor Perkowski said. "He was scared at times, but he was a fighter. I got 50 patents on the 900-series scanner. It became the company cash cow."[104]

Early MS-900 series scanners, recalled Perkowski, were of a "boxy, German-type design."[105] (By 2000, the product line would evolve into Metrologic's sleek and successful "Voyager" scanners, or 9500 series.)

The MS-700, meanwhile, provided the point-of-sale (POS) market an omni-directional projection scanner which not only competed with, but, according to Tom Perkowski, beat out a similar omni-directional Symbol scanner product, the LS-9208. Product specifications from Symbol and Metrologic detailed that Symbol's LS-9208 scanned

Early prototype of the Metrologic MS-900, which revolutionized scanners once again by going triggerless

Hands-free projection scanner, MS-700

at 1,500 scan lines per second,[106] while Metrologic's MS-700 boasted a scanning speed of 2,000 scan lines per second.[107] The MS-700 bore omni-directional capabilities, Perkowski explained, because it was engineered with four mirrors on a polygon which spun within the scanner box. The laser hitting each mirror provided many passes or directions for product codes to be read.

"Metrologic was making serious inroads into retail POS," Perkowski said. "Before Symbol, National Cash Register out of Ohio owned POS. [Symbol's] Swartz thought they'd be the next chosen ones. They had Ph.D.s; they were smart. But Harry Knowles was hard-core engineering and manufacturing. He had tremendous confidence and was trusted. Metrologic put out [lower-priced] products and cut into the profit margins of other companies."[108]

Thus, it was with great sense of purpose that Perkowski filed as many patents as possible. He knew Harry's latest products would enrage competitors while ensuring survival for Metrologic. In fact, the 900 scanner series was successful enough, according to a 1991 Harry Knowles Metrologic memo to employees, to prompt Symbol to quickly file another patent lawsuit against Metrologic.[109] "I had a sense of righteousness," Perkowski said. "I would die before I let [anyone] take down Metrologic."[110]

The scanner industry as a whole was experiencing fundamental changes, as the 1990s solidified auto-ID's transition from the use of helium-neon lasers to more reliable semiconductor lasers. Metrologic's bedrock staple product—the helium-neon laser—had become antiquated. However, Harry foresaw the changes and established a supply relationship with NEC, one of the companies making semiconductor lasers, or visible laser diodes (VLDs), at the time. NEC's major competitor, Toshiba, according to Harry, supplied Symbol.[111]

Shortly into Metrologic's association with NEC, NEC decided to get out of the laser diode business and gave Metrologic only six weeks' notice of such. Metrologic needed a new supplier and fast. The Symbol-aligned Toshiba was out of the question. Harry turned to an old contact in Japan: Akio Morita, founder of Sony. In the early 1960s, when Harry worked for Mo-

Harry touring Sony, 1960s

torola, he had toured the rapidly expanding Sony while in Japan during a worldwide trip. Harry spent several days there at Sony sharing with their scientists how to make germanium mesa transistors. Harry said that, at the time, Sony "was nowhere with transistors" (although he predicted in 1961 that a large share of the television and radio market would go to Japan by 1964 due to Japan's lower-priced transistors).

Thus, when Harry faxed a letter Fall 1990 to Sony Chairman Morita (during a Japanese national holiday, no less) asking if they could form a relationship to have Sony supply Metrologic's laser diodes, Morita responded immediately, saying Sony would build a manufacturing line for Metrologic. "In today's corporate culture," Harry reflected in 2011, "there is no way that sharing could be repeated. Because I shared my knowledge years earlier and lifted Sony, later, Morita saved us." Harry turned Metrologic's potential supply disaster into great profit by qua-

Early laser pointer

drupling his laser diode order with Sony and diverting a portion of the diodes from scanners to some of the industry's earliest laser pointers for Metrologic's education market. Harry pointed out: "Scanners are more expensive to make than pointers."[112]

As Harry threw his energies into solving supply issues and his promis-

Shortly before the **Symbol v. Metrologic** *opinion was issued, Harry lost "Mom," his step-mother Thelma, who died July 22, 1991, at the age of 89.*

ing new scanner lines, his legal team was busy with the earlier Symbol lawsuit. The lawsuit, *Symbol Technologies, Inc. v. Metrologic Instruments, Inc. and C. Harry Knowles,* would not be going to trial as both sides moved for summary judgment by New Jersey District Judge Stanley Brotman. The writing was already on the wall for the defendants after the Symbol-Opticon outcome. On August 8, 1991, Judge Brotman issued his opinion, saying that Metrologic and Harry infringed upon Symbol's '297 and '186 patents with Metrologic's MS-290, MS-490, and MS-590 scanners.[113]

As expected, in the lawsuit, Metrologic had argued that Symbol's silence from 1982 to 1988 meant that no Symbol lawsuit was on the horizon. Symbol rebutted, saying that it filed a suit against Metrologic promptly after the MS-290 scanner was launched by Metrologic in 1987. Further, Symbol claimed it was only logical that the suit wait until after the Spectra-Physics suit was resolved and Metrologic was out of bankruptcy. The court felt that communications disputed Metrologic's view. Metrologic also maintained that in a conversation between Harry and Symbol's president in 1987, Symbol indicated it was not interested in suing Metrologic. Symbol president Raymond Martino denied that claim.

One interesting episode to come to light within the context of the lawsuit occurred June 6, 1984, when Symbol chairman Jerry Swartz wrote a memo to the file documenting patent advice given Swartz. That advice said, "Metrologic/NCR is the ideal combination to sue in New Jersey." The defense team argued that the Swartz memo proved the "silence was calculated and in bad faith," since Metrologic would naturally incur debt and investment costs developing scanners while Symbol was silent. The court disagreed, and Symbol argued that Metrologic was well aware of the risks.[114]

In the court summary, Metrologic conceded that if Symbol's patents were valid, Metrologic infringed the '297 and '186 patents. The

Several of Metrologic's scanner offerings. Center: triggerless MS-900 series scanner, pictured with a ScanPal data collector on the left and a decoder on the right. Clockwise, starting at far left are: MS-800 series scanner, MS-362, MS-700, and MS-260 mini-slot.

court declared Harry in direct infringement also and personally liable as Metrologic president, sole owner, and board member, in addition to being the "designer, manufacturer, and seller of the Series 90 scanners." The court rejected Harry's argument that he had no intent to infringe and was relying on counsel and held Harry liable for inducing infringement.

Despite the 1991 ruling, the Symbol lawsuit would languish in the courts for two more years as rivals Symbol and Metrologic repeatedly attempted to settle. Meanwhile, 1992 saw the introduction of three new Metrologic products: the "MS-860" mini-slot in-counter scanner; the TECH series scanner, a low-cost industrial scanner for harsh environments;

MS-860 mini-slot, in-counter scanner

195

and a price-competitive handheld scanner, the "MS-951." The following year Metrologic brought out the industry's first triggerless, wearable laser scanner.

Finally, in 1993, a Camden, New Jersey, magistrate pushed a settlement onto the warring lawsuit parties. Symbol and Swartz agreed to a $7 million settlement from Metrologic and Harry. "Swartz thought we were dead," Harry said. "But the $7 million

Janet and Harry pose with a plaque commemorating the 25th anniversary of Metrologic, 1993.

was mostly in the form of royalties, so it was not in our books as debt.... [The] $7 million settlement, paid over time, was far cheaper than an appeal would have been.[115] There was personal animosity between Jerry Swartz and [me]. Symbol was arrogant in the marketplace. But Metrologic's products and its customer service would not fail us. Ultimately, we were profitable."[116]

With new products at every turn, Harry had resurrected his beloved company yet again and protected his now—in 1993—230 employees at their expanded 63,000-square-foot Coles Road headquarters in Blackwood.[117] As he completed 25 years at the helm of Metrologic, he naturally reflected on the triumphs and the fires that had proved his team's mettle. With Harry's personality, however, one could be sure he did not reflect for long. His success was built on a constant drive forward; he already had Metrologic's next destination mapped on the horizon.

Chapter 9

Metrologic Modern

(1993-2001)

Metrologic HQ at Blackwood

An outsider examining Metrologic in 1993 on the heels of the potentially disastrous Symbol lawsuit settlement would have found a surprisingly active company. Apparently, whatever roadblocks arose, Metrologic and Harry could never be declared down for the count. Metrologic was settled into its new Blackwood, New Jersey, factory home where a hectic production floor pace resulted in a welcome stream of products, including the already successful MS-900 and 700 scanner lines.

The MS-900 series of handheld, triggerless scanners, development of which was prompted by a court injunction in 1990 against Metrologic's triggered handhelds following Symbol's patent-infringement litigation, held wide market appeal. "These scanners," stated an annual report to the Securities and Exchange Commission, "generally are used in retailing, libraries, industrial warehousing, production lines and commercial applications because of their low cost, size and versatility. Using infrared motion sensor detectors, the MS-900 series turns on automatically and can be manually presented to a bar code or fixed mounted and used as a stationary scanner."[1]

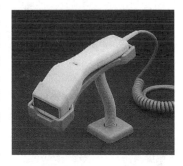

MS-951 triggerless scanner

Alternatively, the MS-700 omni-directional scanners were higher-end, fixed-position, projection scanners for high-volume retail customers, as well as magazine processing centers and "other applications where greater scanning throughput is required." Harry conceived the MS-700 during a trip to Japan, solving what he dubbed the "sushi problem."[2]

Clear packaging of sushi products carried top-side bar coding, but the delicate products could not be flipped over to be scanned at checkout. The MS-700 read bar codes in multiple directions—including top and side—at high speeds. Another product for high-volume customers, the MS-800 series of mini-slot, in-counter scanners, developed in 1991, catered to users (such as supermarkets) with limited work space and continued to be offered by Metrologic. Thus, the Metrologic catalog combined established linchpin products with a steady supply of newer offerings.

Metrologic's market success translated to an increase in sales in 1993, rising to $23.6 million by the year's end, up from $17 million in 1992.[3] However, with patent litigation settlement and other legal expenses topping $5 million, as well as the sales-related costs and administrative and research expenses, 1993 ended with an estimated net loss of $1.6 million. Yet, the bottom line did not stall the Metrologic CEO. With the Symbol litigation crisis resolved, Harry returned to a goal he had first eyed in 1987: taking Metrologic public.

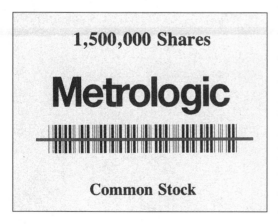

Going public addressed the crucial problem for Metrologic of how to finance anticipated growth that clearly would outstrip current cash flow. The solution was getting an influx of capital through the sale of common stock, in this case, traded on the NASDAQ Stock Market under the symbol "MTLG." While the effective date of Metrologic's initial public offering (IPO) was September 29, 1994, the sale of 1.75 million shares in October 1994, at a price of $9.50 per share, netted Metrologic a modest but welcome $14.5 million after offering costs.[4] With a portion of the proceeds, the Metrologic leadership quickly paid off two loan notes totaling $3.6 million as the company was steered toward sounder financial status.

"The company got $15 million for a small part of the stock," Harry said. "I still owned most of the company."[5] Metrologic remained very much *Harry*. Fresh on Harry's mind was how quickly the Symbol court case in 1990 had nullified two-thirds of his business before he and his team re-invented the entire handheld scanner market by going triggerless. Reflecting in 1999 on why he took the company public, he granted that he could have sold the company instead of staying to transform it. However, a new owner would have cut jobs. Harry and his employees were family. "The company stuck together. There was so much love," Harry said. "The reason for going public in 1994 was to take care of our people."[6]

Before the Symbol settlement and before Metrologic went public, Harry indicated such a concern for his employees in a June 1993 letter to half-brother Bill Penn.[7] "What a relief it would be to get some financial strength, finally, and to be able to reward our valuable employees in permanent ways, not to mention getting some nest egg of our own," Harry said in a mention of continuing IPO consideration. "But first, we have to get the lawsuit settled in order to get a reasonable value," Harry continued in the letter. "The next few weeks are going to be very critical and delicate. I hope I have the strength, patience, discipline, and wisdom to get through them in a reasonably optimum way."

Key to maneuvering the complexities of taking Metrologic public, according to Harry, was William L. Rulon-Miller, then co-head of the investment banking department at Janney Montgomery Scott, a Philadelphia financial services firm Rulon-Miller had joined in 1979. Rulon-Miller held a degree from Princeton and an MBA from the Wharton School of the University of Pennsylvania. He would later (in 1998) be added to the Metrologic Board of Directors partly due to his diligence in 1994. In a Metrologic press release, Harry said of Rulon-Miller, "I ha[d] been impressed with Bill for many years, and in particular, his management of our initial public offering."[8] Harry also said that Rulon-Miller served "selflessly and most intelligently" on behalf of Metrologic.[9]

"I met Harry before the bankruptcy," Rulon-Miller recalled.[10] "We were not in a formal relationship then. There are lots of good ideas out there, but only a handful of guys turn good ideas into a company. Harry was one of those. I was impressed by the way he came out of bankruptcy. Most of the time, an entrepreneur throws up his hands. Then came the

Bill Rulon-Miller

whole thing with Symbol with re-engineering of product....Here was a goal guy who could roll with any punch. If you can look at a problem, come up with a solution, and execute the solution, you are probably an even better prospect for going public. Harry was focused, energetic, tough. This was a man with tremendous tenacity who would make it work."

Rulon-Miller said the forecast of the ubiquitous nature of scanners indicated the market would grow in all sectors—commercial, retail, and industrial. "I expected the company was going somewhere," Rulon-Miller said. "It looked good. Metrologic got close to going public before. There is a time when the public is receptive and when it is not. But now, the Symbol lawsuit was settled and the market was looking good. I didn't have my money in it, but I liked Harry. In some ways, I had a disinterested perspective. I could watch Harry navigate to the other side. He decided he wanted to build a bigger company, to reach for the brass ring."

However, as Rulon-Miller emphasized, Harry's motivation was not rooted in greed. "The best entrepreneurs," Rulon-Miller said, "respect people and have a desire to improve and generically make the world a better place. Harry wanted his employees to succeed. He, like the best entrepreneurs, cared and took care of them."[11]

The process of going public takes six to nine months, according to Rulon-Miller. "You get an outside board of directors, clean up the bylaws, and get lawyers to align the company with SEC [Securities and Exchange Commission] regulations," he said. "We drafted a registration statement and got underwriters and accountants in place. Prior to the IPO is the time to get the house in order toward functioning administratively to meet SEC expectations. When doing an IPO, you want to be confident the next six months will be good. Initially, Metrologic was well received; it ended up at $9.50 per share on the IPO—which was fine. But it wasn't a straight line. There were times when the stock wasn't doing well; it went up and down. Harry was still the largest shareholder and still CEO of the company. However, instead of answering only to himself, he now had [shareholders] to answer to."

In addition to the CEO, other Metrologic personnel helped transition the company toward its new publicly traded status and ensure rising sales. CPA Thomas E. Mills, IV, formerly Ferranti International's senior vice president of U.S. operations and KPMG Peat Marwick's audit manager, was named the company's chief financial officer in May 1994 as the company increasingly formalized its accounting procedures. As a public company, Metrologic had outgrown the Mom-and-Pop approach of Janet handling the books. Accountability demanded a strong CPA and much stricter standards. Mills would recall in a 2004 *New Jersey Business* magazine interview how excited he was for the CFO challenge of taking Metrologic public: "When I came on board, there was only one full-time accountant and a couple of clerks. The company had diminished its working capital line and its general ledger did not agree with the financial statements being published by a [local] accounting firm…[or] with Ernst & Young financial statements…for Metrologic's [IPO] form….I took the job for the challenge of taking the company public."[12]

Tom Mills

Dale Fischer

Also in 1994, Dale M. Fischer, who served as international marketing and sales manager from 1990 to 1993, became vice president of international sales; William G. Smeader, who worked as director of manufacturing from 1988 to 1993, expanded that same role as vice president of manufacturing; while Benny A. Noens was named vice president of European sales and managing director of Metrologic Instruments GmbH, the German subsidiary.[13] Of Noens, who had been serving as the European sales manager from 1991 to 1993, Harry said, "Benny in Europe did an incredible job in sales. He built distribution [as in the U.S.,] on the same basis of customer service."[14]

Bill Smeader

Joining the Metrologic family in 1994 was a Knowles family member, Birmingham native

Benny Noens

Ginger Ramsey, right, with Janet

Ginger Ramsey, daughter of Jim Ramsey, Harry's step-brother. Armed with a 1989 MBA from the University of Alabama and in search of alternate career paths after several years of managing restaurants, Ginger expressed interest in Metrologic to her uncle, who responded by inviting her to New Jersey to work. Harry was generous but fair; his niece had to earn her opportunities. "I had to get to know the product," Ginger said. "I was started at the bottom, so employees saw that. For at least three months, I worked in customer service and tech support [answering] phone calls. I was thrown in the middle of it and had to figure it out."[15]

Ginger lived with Harry and his wife, Janet, for about six months during her 1994-1996 tenure at Metrologic. Janet, who still worked as vice president of administration at Metrologic, became Ginger's pal, and the Knowles duo both mentored their young niece. "They were such a loving couple; they tried to live life to the fullest," Ginger recalled. "Janet always came first with Harry, even when he was in a bad mood. They were that affectionate. There was no time of walking on eggshells or tension." Thursday was sushi night, she said, and Saturdays were shopping days at COSTCO.

Because Metrologic started as a small company, Ginger said, it had a "familial feel." Harry and Janet treated everyone equally. "They were very personal with the folks on the [manufacturing] floor," Ginger continued. "They were always practical and even-keeled. It was never about being rich. They cared about the people."

Ginger said that Harry never stopped strategizing and was always thinking of what would grow the company in the next ten years. "We were in an upswing, a building time. Sales were growing internationally; product development was on fire," Ginger said. "I credit Harry and his vision. He's a scientific genius. It was his baby. Harry was hands-on to a degree that's understandable when you've built it from the get-go." Such a management style occasionally vexed his executive staff, Ginger

Metrologic was about family as shown in this photo of Harry and Janet with Cathy Almeida playing Santa on the manufacturing floor.

said, but the overriding characteristics of the relationship were "mutual respect and understanding with his team for the company to be the best it could be."

The traits that Harry could not tolerate, according to Ginger, were insecurity and dishonesty. "He had a little bit of a temper, and if you were timid or insecure, he would eat you alive. If you were dishonest, he could see it a mile away."[16]

In time, Ginger shared some marketing ideas with her mentors. Harry already had the thought of developing marketing into its own department, apart from the sales division it operated within at the time. Ginger helped him by developing a customer database of end users and a marketing newsletter. Before she left in 1996, she became a marketing manager and was helping with trade shows and reporting to the head of North American sales. Nevertheless, Ginger's first love was music; and she eventually followed that interest to Los Angeles, where, in 2000, she became Ginger Ramsey Grippe and vice president of marketing and product manager for record producer and Interscope Chairman Jimmy Iovine, whom *Billboard* magazine later would herald as one of the most powerful forces in the U.S. music industry.[17]

In 1994, however, Ginger watched her uncle Harry strive to meet the demands inherent in a public company. "When you're public," Ginger said, "there's a whole new set of pressures to stockholders to replicate and increase growth percentage. Domestically, we were still trying to increase our market share against Symbol. Harry had big expectations."

Those expectations were realized; sales rose to $35.9 million in 1994, up more than $12 million from the previous year. While the costs associated with those sales were significant at $20.6 million, Metrologic's net income by year-end was back in the black at $5.8 million.[18] In 1994, Metrologic also debuted its first one-way radio frequency, networked scanner, the "MS-6130." The year also marked the second time in two years that Metrologic received the Governor's Cup for Entrepreneurial Excellence, an award which echoed Metrologic's status as one of New Jersey's fastest-growing companies.[19]

The MS-6130 provided cordless portability with wireless data communication.

By 1995, with about 25 company patents, and sales reaching more than $41.5 million, Metrologic's laser scanners were being sold in more than 80 countries worldwide through a vast network of distributors and resellers.[20] While all products were developed and manufactured in Blackwood, New Jersey, at the time, Metrologic had five U.S. sales offices, another in Brazil, and the Munich-area facility, which housed large inventory for subassembly and distribution and served as the sales and service operation for Europe.[21]

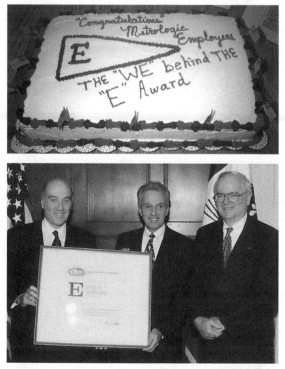

From left, U.S. Secretary of Commerce William M. Daley, Dale Fischer, and Harry with Metrologic's 1995 E Award in Washington, D.C.

Metrologic also was recognized with two Presidential "E" Awards for excellence in exporting—one in 1992 awarded by President George H.W. Bush and another by President Bill Clinton in 1995. The "E Star" Award was the highest award the U.S. could give exporters and recognized, according to a 1995 Metrologic press statement, "outstanding contributions to the increase of U.S. trade abroad" and "competitive achievements in world markets." Metrologic vice president of international sales Dale Fischer com-

Harry and Janet at the New Jersey Inventors of the Year awards dinner

mented at the time on the impact of selling to more than 80 countries, saying, "...our foreign business continues to add significant sales and financial strength to our company."[22]

In fact, industry observers recognized Metrologic's astute position in the scanner marketplace during this era. Examining the company's history in a 1997 *Business News New Jersey* article, Diana G. Lasseter wrote, "While a fraction of the size of the giants, Metrologic has made its mark in other ways. It was one of the earliest developers of laser bar code scanners....According to Molly Walker, eastern regional sales manager with *Automatic ID News* in Edison [New Jersey], a trade publication for automated data capture systems users, Metrologic was one of the first companies to recognize the potential for bar code scanners overseas."[23]

With Metrologic's global reach and increased visibility as a public company, it was not surprising that 1995 also brought individual accolades to Harry via selection as one of New Jersey's Inventors of the Year. The prestigious award was given by the New Jersey Inventors Hall of Fame in recognition of Harry's pioneering role in laser technology and bar code scanning and his inventions' wide-reaching applications across supermarket and retail stores, banking, health services, transportation, and manufacturing.[24]

To meet market needs, Metrologic's 63,000-square-foot Blackwood facility was expanded in 1995 to about 115,000 square feet. By the end of 1996, the New Jersey plant served as the workplace for most of the company's 378 full-time employees, 194 of whom were manufacturing staff.[25] Not any of the employees were under

Harry with Gloucester Township Mayor Sandy Love at December 1994 groundbreaking of Metrologic expansion

205

a collective bargaining agreement; in other words, no union had established inroads. Harry felt the relationship between management and staff was a good one.

"Metrologic was built on the model of treating employees the way employees want to be treated and should be treated," Harry said. "I learned a lot about unions working for Bell, Motorola, and Westinghouse. The latter was a good lesson on how *not* to handle *not* having a union. Motorola was a good lesson in how to not have a union. We had several forays [at Metrologic] by Teamsters, and the employees literally threw the ballots back at the organizers."[26]

Harry found that a certain management code cemented trust. "The key is open communication on all matters," he said, "and an open door into the CEO's office for all people at all times. And not being greedy at the top. My salary was *always* very reasonable, justifiable...and published at all times."

Tom Perkowski, Metrologic's patent prosecution attorney since 1990, observed how Harry interacted with his employees during what would be Perkowski's 18-year relationship with Metrologic. In crafting the company's patents, Perkowski especially spent a good deal of time with the engineers and Harry as they discussed their latest inventions. "Harry hired capable people and taught them what they needed to know," Perkowski said. "It was always a physics or science class with him and the engineers. The whole company ran that way. He invested in discovery."[27]

Harry invested in his people, too, according to Perkowski, who was struck by the roughly 240 two-by-three-foot poster-size Metrologic employee photos Harry took, as an extension of his lifetime hobby, and hung all over the building. At every turn, the photos reminded every-

Harry, left, gathering with some of his engineers and a member of his marketing team for a patent presentation photo. Continuing from left: Chic Naylor, Bob Blake, Garrett Russell (POS manager), Steve Colavito, Dave Wilz, George Rockstein, and Gennady German

one they were a team. "Metrologic was a hardcore engineering company, [so he had] high standards," Perkowski declared. "If you lied or you were lazy, Harry was ruthless. But [if you were an honest worker,] he was loyal; he nurtured and gave opportunities. There was no time for self-absorbed pity."

The mid- to late-'90s heralded quick changes in the expanding Metrologic. Optical engineer Mark Schmidt was announced as point-of-sale product manager in March 1996. A new ergonomic, handheld, omnidirectional scanner, the "MS-6720" was introduced the same year

The MS-6720 provided flexibility with popular handheld and fixed projection scanner (with 20-line scan pattern) capabilities.

at a price point "between the cost-effective MS-900 series and high-performance fixed presentation MS-700 scanners."[28] The innovative MS-6720 was multi-purpose in that it could be held to scan or stationed for fixed scanning. (Such scanner flexibility was a concept later copied by each of the major competitors, according to Harry.)[29] Also in 1996, holography emerged with much fanfare as the latest innovative development. In May that year, Metrologic debuted the "HoloTrak IS-5700," the company's first use of holographic technology with visible laser diodes, then followed that technology in 1997 with the first modular-designed holographic scanners, the "IS-8000" series.

IS-8000 Series HoloTrak

The company's 1996 annual report discussed the HoloTrak product as one of its more affordable, high-performance industrial scanner offerings. "The HoloTrak line," the report said, "is designed to increase user efficiency and productivity in high volume package-handling situations. The HoloTrak scanners would typically be mounted above work areas and loading doors to allow 'walk-under scanning,' or hands-free, unattended high-speed conveyor belt scanning in industrial and package [sorting] applications."[30]

The holographic scanners were a direct result of a 1994 research agreement between Metrologic and another company, Holoscan, Inc., whose president was Leroy D. (Lee) Dickson. The companies, according to the agreement, would jointly develop holographic scanners, and Metrologic would provide research funding to Holoscan. During 1995, Metrologic acquired Holoscan stock to a point that, by March 1996, Holoscan became a wholly owned subsidiary of Metrologic. Dickson joined the executive staff of Metrologic as vice president of optical engineering while retaining his titles as president and chief operating officer of Holoscan.

Dickson and Harry had become friends when they had served on the FDA's Center for Devices and Radiological Health (CDRH) advisory committee following the 1968 Radiation Control for Health and Safety Act. Harry followed Lee Dickson's career when he was IBM's "holographic guru," as Harry called him. "I looked at that technology and saw tremendous potential," Harry said.[31] Harry spoke to Dickson at a trade show about industrial scanners shortly before IBM released Dickson and allowed him to set up his own company. "I saw a need for a scanner that

From left, Rich Rallison, Chic Naylor, and Lee Dickson at Rallison's holography lab

would cast a beam of scan lines two-and-a-half feet deep," Harry said, "so as a sorter picked up a package, say, for UPS or Fed-Ex, he could just wave the box and it would be read."

Harry asked Dickson if that type of industrial scanner could be designed; Dickson replied that it could. "I trusted him. Together, we forged a design," Harry said. Prior to launching the project, however, Harry sought added expertise from Rich Rallison, a holography consultant near Salt Lake City who had an experimental holography lab using one of Metrologic's cadmium-helium lasers. "Rich opened my eyes up to what holography can be. We connected," Harry said.[32]

Holography could be used to read bar codes, Harry explained, by shining a laser light through a rotating, ten-inch disc with segments around its edge. The tight beam of the laser reflected off of the bar code and bounced back to a mirror which translated the information to a photocell and, ultimately, a computer which interpreted the data. However, getting the first disc made was especially tricky, as were the other disc samples that would serve as "master" discs. Sheets of pocketed, gelatin-like material were poured onto spinning discs that were anti-reflective on one side; the transparent gel scattered throughout the disc. "You can reproduce almost any optical function," Harry said, "by exposing that gel to that optical function to make the master gel. What goes on inside that gel is a technical miracle."

Rallison made the first disc for Metrologic most likely during 1994-1995 in his Utah "HoloLab" built especially for the process. During the several-minute laser exposure of the material, there must be no relative movement of any parts of the apparatus of even a few millionths of an inch. The environment had to be "ultra-stable and ultra-clean," Harry said. Harry quickly realized that a Metrologic holography production effort would require a new building. After seeing Rallison's lab, Harry came back to New Jersey and designed an addition to his Blackwood headquarters.[33]

The new building extension would be located near a busy expressway, so Harry worried about the structure's stability. "I was concerned that the truck traffic on Route 42 might be a problem," he said. Seismic studies were conducted, then Harry designed the bottom structure. "It turn[ed] out," he continued, "that the bed below [was] a good sandy loam, with clay underneath, [so the building was stable]. We then designed double mechanical, filtered [multi-ton concrete] pads on which to mount the master [laser] exposure tables, and the production tables" for laser exposure of individual holodiscs.[34]

Aerial view of Metrologic by Route 42, including holographic addition to total about 115,000 square feet

(continued on page 214)

The Power of Holography in Industrial Scanning
by C. Harry Knowles

Before HoloTrak, package handlers, such as UPS, Fed-Ex, and USPS, used handheld or wearable scanners which had to be manually pointed at each bar code on packages that were handled. This approach slowed sorting and tracking considerably and interfered with the handlers' movements, creating physical ailments.

By contrast, the opportunity of holography in industrial scanning, illustrated in Fig. 1A from original assignee Metrologic's U.S. Patent 5,984,185 (known as Patent '185) is great. Packages of uneven shape and thickness are scanned with minimal manual personal effort. The scanner is fixed, immobile, and out of the way—in this case, overhead.

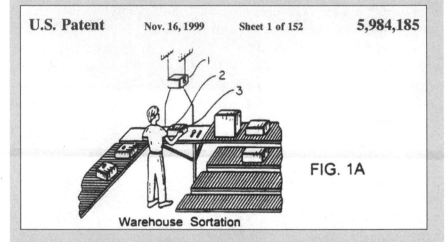

U.S. Patent   Nov. 16, 1999   Sheet 1 of 152   **5,984,185**

FIG. 1A

Warehouse Sortation

To read the bar codes with tremendous speed, the active scanning field needs to be wide and deep. In addition, the scanning pattern within that scanned field must be graphically rich with scan lines and rapidly recurrent. The scanned volume allows every package's bar code to be read repeatedly to provide reliability through redundancy and maximum speed of handling.

This holographic technology is detailed further in Figure 2E from Patent '185 which shows a box providing three sets of scanned lines. Fig. 2A shows the three laser modules and the holographic disc inside the box in 2E.

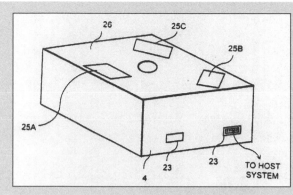

Fig. 2E from '185
(Box inverted from that shown in Fig. 1A)

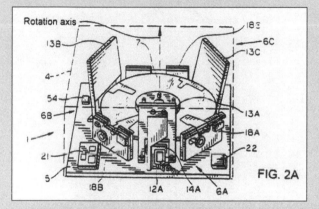

Fig. 2A from '185
(Box inverted from that shown in Fig. 1A)

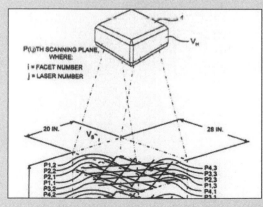

An extract from Fig. 5 from '185 shows scan
lines projected into only one layer.

This one layer, typical of pre-HoloTrak scanners in the industrial market, does not need holography but can be provided by use of a reflective mirror. Such laser scanning can provide 6" to 7" depth of field for typical one-dimensional bar codes used in industry. Thus, for that one layer, any bar code passing within the 28"-wide-by-7"-deep-by-20"-long "tunnel" will get scanned.

HoloTrak came into play by providing a deeper scan volume, in the case of Patent '185, four fields deep, or roughly three to four times deeper than normal mirrored scanners.

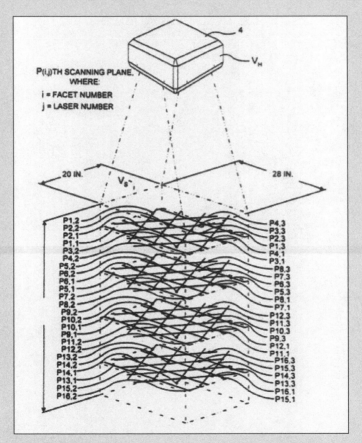

Fig. 5 from '185, showing added depth of field by using holography

The magic lies in using diffractive optics rather than mirrors. The scanning is done by a rotating holographic disc, as shown in the planar view in Fig. 3 from '185.

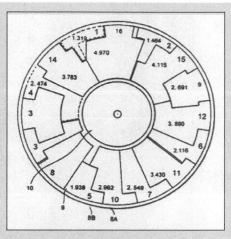

Fig. 3 from '185.

Each of the 16 facets shown in Fig. 3 provides multiple functions: focusing the outgoing beam; scanning the beam along one line at one of the four "layered" distances from the scanner; and gathering the faint laser light from the bar code onto a photocell via a large gathering mirror focusing the return beam onto a photocell. Thus, each facet of each of the three separate laser modules will scan one of the 48 lines in Fig. 5. Four of the facets will scan one "layer" from that laser module.

Another feature provides for keeping optimum signal levels into the photodiodes from each of the layers. In Fig. 3, the large-area facets are for collecting the return scattered light from the layers farthest from the scanner; and the smallest-area facets collect light from the nearest layers.

The production process and, hence, costs are similar to that using photographic emulsions. Further, using holographic diffractive elements in each facet, complex optical functions can be built into the "master" from which each disc is exposed. The optical efficiencies achieved in the production discs were such that 92% of the laser light starting into the disc was projected onto the bar code at within about 2% of theoretical resolution.

The power of holography has been widely unappreciated in regards to its vast potential for growth. As the auto-ID industry has ridden the wave of each breakthrough in technology, the customer has reaped the benefits. With the ever-increasing demand for speed and near-100% bar code-reading accuracy, the power of holography cannot be ignored.

(Rich Rallison was the major source of the holography processing. Lee Dickson and Tim Good provided the diffractive optical design work.)

Harry designed special pads on which to mount the ultra-sensitive holodisc production tables.

Meanwhile, Harry talked with the United Parcel Service (UPS) senior vice president and chief information officer, Frank Erbrick, who managed UPS' engineering efforts. Erbrick visited Metrologic in December 1994[35] and, according to Harry, said he needed 100,000 such holographic scanners. "I told him that I was sure we could build the scanner," Harry recalled. "I even told him they would be less than $1,000 apiece. Lee and I then designed the first holographic scanner and it worked. We built [the] extension at Blackwood for hologram production to handle the high volume for what we believed to be an absolute, assured [UPS] order."[36]

The holographic venture was a faltering one, however. Patent prosecutor Tom Perkowski said that, while Harry was eager to buy Holoscan to attract the larger Fed-Ex-type industrial scanning market, the holographic technology had a key weakness: "It couldn't read two-dimensional bar codes," Perkowski said.[37] It could read linear bar codes, though, so Harry felt a large and profitable market could be found.[38]

One-dimensional, or linear, bar codes, Harry explained, were limited to a length of about 30 characters. "More than that and the symbol gets too long and narrow to reliably and quickly scan," Harry said. While supermarkets originally needed only 10 to 12 numeric characters with the standard UPC, the desire for capturing more information increased; and technology adapted for longer codes. "Therefore," Harry said, "folded one-dimensional codes got designed, and then morphed into 2D codes of various designs [that] can carry 100 or more characters. There are many designs of 2D codes. Some can accommodate thousands of characters. The compromise in size, resolution, speed, depth of field, and orientation all begin to play as choices for each different industry."[39]

With the 1995 Blackwood expansion targeted for holographic products, Harry was counting on the large UPS order. UPS' Erbrick was pushing for production as soon as possible. "We had more than 92 percent optical efficiency on our holographic discs," Harry said. "With 92 percent of the light usefully cohesive, we could scan four feet out. It

TECH 10

was phenomenal."[40] Erbrick, according to Harry, had expressed that UPS wanted Metrologic to meet all its scanner needs for its extensive, nationwide sorting and transfer facilities. Earnest plans, discussions, and holographic scanner testing ensued into the next year, along with the fulfillment of a UPS order for 3,225 Metrologic TECH 10 non-holographic industrial scanners.[41] Thus, a significant amount of Metrologic's attention shifted to landing and serving its potentially biggest client.

Since UPS' first visit to Metrologic, Harry knew of Erbrick's intention to retire in the near future. Then UPS engineering vice president Michael L. Eskew (who would serve as UPS CEO 2002 to 2007) had seemed equally impressed with the holodiscs' potential, according to Harry; so Harry was not overly concerned with the transition.[42] UPS announced the 35-year UPS veteran Erbrick's retirement November 1996,[43] but as his retirement was pending that year, Erbrick's embrace of the new holographic technology dissipated. "Frank's vision disappeared within the UPS organization," Harry said. "At the beginning of October, he came and told me [UPS was] going in a different direction. We had no contract with them. Frank said, 'I'm sorry.' I was disappointed, but we didn't have a contract."[44]

Another drama playing out involved rival Symbol, whose leaders had watched Metrologic file the patents for this exciting new technology of holographic scanners. Symbol's approach for UPS-style customers was to use handheld scanners, according to Harry. The Holoscan products "scared the hell out of them," Harry said.

In 1996, Harry toured Symbol President Tomo Razmilovic through Metrologic's Blackwood facility, including the holographic production areas, during a period of negotiation between Symbol and Metrologic. Since the 1993 lawsuit settlement, the two companies regularly explored opportunities for cross-licensing and adjustment of the settlement which would be of mutual benefit. Razmilovic claimed his company could sell thousands of the holographic scanners, according to Harry, who said, in retrospect, that Symbol merely was posturing.

State-of-the-art holodisc lab at Metrologic

(Razmilovic would, in 2004, achieve fame when he fled to Sweden following the issuance of an arrest warrant in his name for more than $200 million in securities fraud while at Symbol.[45] Regarding the accounting scandal, Symbol reached a settlement with the SEC in 2004 and avoided criminal charges. Co-founder Jerry Swartz settled with his company; the agreement, according to a Symbol press release, included Swartz paying $4 million toward class action lawsuits and $7.2 million to Symbol.)[46]

"Symbol got where it did by throwing money at every problem," Harry said. "They didn't sell any HoloTraks, but Symbol could tell UPS that 'whether you go with the handheld or the Holoscan product, we can supply.' They were hedging their bets.

"Suddenly, our UPS guy fell out," Harry said. "That business evaporated. I had taken money from the profitable part of the company and switched it to this holographic venture. Sometimes, you have to take the gamble."[47]

The outlook was hardly bleak, however. With the strong retail scanner lines and international presence, 1996 sales rose to $46.9 million by the year's end.[48] Revenue growth over the previous year had decreased to 13 percent, compared to 15.6 percent in 1995, but 1996 "included unfavorable foreign exchange fluctuations from the company's German subsidiary," according to the 1996 annual report.[49] International sales, it continued, accounted for 62.9 percent of total sales.

In light of his holographic investment, Harry got creative with strong marketing of the new industrial scanners. In mid-May 1997, when Philadelphia hosted the ID Expo, the premier annual scanner (or automatic identification) industry event, Metrologic transported and toured close to 30 company visitors at the Blackwood headquarters to show off its latest technology. In a *Business News New Jersey* article, Diana Lasseter described the setting:

"CEO C. Harry Knowles saw...such a large industry gathering as an opportunity to strut his company's stuff, and so he arranged a tour of his company's facility. More importantly, plenty of people wanted to listen. At last year's ID Expo in Chicago, Metrologic Instruments unveiled a new technology that promised to revolutionize industrial bar code scanning. During that event, it was named the most important new technology for the industry. At last week's Expo, Metrologic introduced the new-and-improved version of that product."[50]

Metrologic production floor

The new version, the HoloTrak IS-8000 holographic product line, seemed to be attracting a large amount of attention. Although, according to Lasseter's article, Metrologic had yet to sell one of its HoloTrak IS 8000 scanners, the immediate payoff was coming in visibility and increased market rating by analysts. Lasseter reported that Janney Montgomery Scott raised its recommendation on Metrologic stock from "hold" to "buy."

The article also mentioned that Fed-Ex had already spent six months testing HoloTrak in the field and the product was performing well. "Negotiating with the likes of Fed-Ex is a departure for Metrologic Instruments," wrote Lasseter. "The company's niche has historically been smaller-end users....Nearly 80 percent of the company's business comes from standard, point-of-sale products like in-counter and projection scanners and hand-held and wearable scanning devices....All eyes are now fixed on Metrologic's product that promises to replace existing technology."

Thus, insiders in the auto-ID industry saw Metrologic as the moment's industrial darling; the holographic technology was sexy and promised just shy of a scanning revolution. Because holographic scanners bear a long depth of field, according to Harry, "boxes as high as 40 inches on a wide conveyor belt can be read at high speeds of 600 feet per minute."[51] Still, Harry hinted in a *Wall Street Reporter Magazine* article at the flaw, as assessed by Perkowski, concerning lack of two-dimensional capabilities, saying, in 1999, "We can read...normal one-dimensional bar codes. We are rapidly moving into two-dimensional bar codes which store more information and are becoming more popular and other two-dimensional technologies. What this combination gives the customer is reliability and very high scannability."[52]

By the time of the 1999 article, Harry was also talking about building Metrologic's sophisticated form of holography together with three-dimensional image processing. Perkowski echoed that direction in his recollections, saying that Metrologic's holographic emphasis eventually shifted to 3-D photography and linear cameras.[53]

Recalling the Holoscan endeavor, however, Harry spoke about the mood when UPS withdrew its order commitment. "We scared the whole market," Harry said. "We made a lot of industrial scanners, and solved some problems for the Postal Service and Fed-Ex. We had moderate success, so it wasn't a losing proposition. Opportunity is where it cost us in terms of what we could have been doing during that time. We should have spent the time leap-frogging into 2D and iQ—or laser planar light imaging—technology. Holography got us a lot of attention; everyone in the industry was impressed. But UPS bought handhelds from our rival, Symbol, at a significant increase in cost compared to holoscanning."[54]

Symbol and Metrologic did enter into a patents cross-licensing agreement in December 1996.[55] The agreement, which Perkowski helped craft, stipulated certain scenarios in which Metrologic and Symbol would pay royalties to each other in hope of keeping peace between the competitors for some years.[56] Metrologic paid an advance license fee of $1 million at the end of 1996, according to that year's annual report, and agreed to pay another $1 million during the next two years. Symbol, meanwhile, amended the 1993 patent lawsuit settlement "to reduce the maximum aggregate amount payable...by [Metrologic] from $7.5 million to approximately $5.1 million." The 1996 agreement excluded holographic scanners, but a December 1997 amendment allowed Symbol to buy Metrologic's HoloTrak scanners for resale by Symbol under the Symbol label.

While the agreement served both companies, and industry observers made much of the newly cooperative relationship, the bond was tenuous and superficial. The company leaders "played nice" about each other when talking to reporters or in public statements because restraint served their publicity and agreement needs. But Symbol's image was that of Goliath with 1996 revenues of $656 million[57] contrasted with Metrologic as David with its $46.9 million in sales.

In 1997, Metrologic continued its HoloTrak industrial scanner marketing, as well as sales of its vast retail offerings, including the latest omnidirectional handheld scanner, the MS-6720 introduced the previous year. Commenting in February 1997 on the sales of the MS-6720, Harry said, "The growth in sales in the fourth quarter [of 1996] was attributable, in part, to sales of Metrologic's new MS-6720..."[58] By the end of 1997, the number of Metrologic patents topped 30 and total sales increased to $53.4 million, boosted by a record

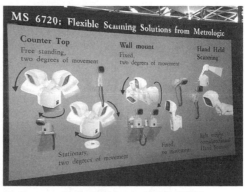

Industry show display of MS-6720

fourth quarter of $14.5 million—the highest level of sales of any quarter in Metrologic's history—prompted by North American and European product demand.[59] During the year, Metrologic entered into an agreement for Rockwell Automation to start selling HoloTrak products under its own brand name, while a Panasonic company in Japan began an exclusive sales arrangement for the Metrologic holographic industrial product line there.[60]

In recognition of Metrologic's success and the commitment of its president and CEO, Harry was chosen that summer as one of Greater Philadelphia's ten Entrepreneurs of the Year.[61] However, the 1997 successes were overshadowed by personal trauma, as Janet, Harry's wife of 25 years, was diagnosed with breast cancer. Harry's initial reaction was shock; he was generally upset with the world for several weeks.[62] Then, his "solver" instincts subjugated his fears. Always one to tackle a problem head-on, Harry researched the illness and, along with Janet, sought the best healthcare available. They turned for advice to their friend and family doctor, Edward D. Viner, then chief of medicine at Cooper University Hospital in Camden, New Jersey, and Harry and Janet's longtime internist.

Viner, whose expertise was internal medicine, medical oncology, and hematology, recommended that Janet see Cooper oncologist and breast cancer specialist Generosa (Jenny) Grana, director of the Cooper Cancer Institute.[63] The Spanish-born Grana had earned an excellent reputation for her skills as a physician but also was known for her empathetic style of care, believing the most rewarding part of medicine was the shared experience with her patients.[64] Janet, in a later breast cancer survivor story, called Grana an "angel."[65] Janet and Harry did check several other facilities and doctors; but, after meeting with Grana and touring Cooper, Janet decided she had found her treatment center. In a Cooper newsletter, Janet commented, "As busy as Dr. Grana is, when you're with her, you feel like you're the only patient she has." Also, Janet found the nurses extremely positive. "I felt like I had my own cheering section," she said.[66]

Janet found that her support network and a positive attitude helped her deal with her cancer and the treatment road ahead of her. She used inspirational books and tapes, a daily journal, and her art (bead jewelry and sculpture) to cope. In 1998, she had a radical mastectomy and chemotherapy. Her chemo infusions lasted six months. "I was with her for almost all of her chemo sessions," Harry said. "I gave her as much love and support as any husband could."[67] As Janet recalled that time in her life for the hospital newsletter, she said, "Hope is what it's all about....I definitely believe that your state of mind makes a big difference on how you heal."[68]

But heal Janet did, and she and Harry determined in their gratitude that they would give back to Cooper, donating nearly $5.5 million toward the hospital's breast cancer program to enhance research, care, and services. In recognition, the Cooper Cancer Institute named the program the Janet Knowles Breast Cancer Center. Janet later volunteered at Cooper and with the American Cancer Society; she also spoke in support of others battling breast cancer.

Harry's relief at Janet's recovery was evident in a May 1998 note to half-brother Bill Penn: "We are both in great spirits and health," Harry said. "For which we thank God. But perhaps as important, we simply love to be together. It seems to almost seal out the rest of the world, but I get so much from her, that I have little drive to move out to the world more than we do."[69]

When Janet returned to Metrologic following her cancer treatments, she worked part time. She had already stepped away from key financial duties; during the years immediately preceding her cancer, she mostly handled accounts receivable and payable and ordered parts.[70]

Janet and Harry

In a similar vein, Harry had begun cutting back on his management duties with the idea that, at age 70, he needed to plot his retirement from Metrologic. His daily routine included a short, early-afternoon nap at the office. The naps, Harry said, started when he was about 60 and allowed him to work more effectively longer in the day.[71] He came a tiny step closer to formalizing an exit strategy in April 1998 when CFO Tom Mills was promoted to executive vice president and chief operating officer (COO). Mills would continue his CFO duties. The Metrologic press release on the promotion explained that Mills was "responsible for most day-to-day operations of the company including marketing, sales, production, quality control, administration and finance." Harry remained president and CEO "with continued responsibilities for research and development activities."[72]

Harry's research time in 1998—a year in which Metrologic spent $4.2 million on research and development[73]—was concentrated on holographic engineering, as his team struggled with the product development's electronic needs past one-dimensional-only capabilities. Harry commented in a May 1998 e-mail:

> I have spent almost every day tightly closed in on the critical problems of optics and the conversion of the optical signal into digital data....We have a good, but not great, team for that kind of electronics, and I have been really stretched trying to stimulate them into reaching the upper levels of electronic capability....I simply am not able to sustain the kind of personal pressure that it takes anymore.
>
> In effect, we are building about 220 individual scanners, mostly high-speed holographic scanners, and some using the same holodiscs, around the tunnel of scanners. We run them over a thick glass plate to read from the bottoms...
>
> I have told our team that if we 1) win a Bridgestone Tire company scanner job, and 2) get part of the USPS tunnel business, then I am retiring....I am going to have to begin to take time off, whether I like it or not. I simply can't keep up with the daily grind, with the daily pressures that are expected of a CEO. Fortunately, except for the area in which I am now involved in engineering, we are in very good management shape.[74]

Harry used sketchbooks to plot out his solutions to engineering problems, as these drawings from 1995 illustrate.

At this juncture in product development, Harry was serving as engineering manager, as his teams of engineers shouldered more responsibility. Those leading the way included the highly inventive development science engineer and research manager Xiaxun (B.J.) Zhu (whose specialty was computerized image processing) and production manager Joe Sawitsky. Harry's focus always lay in completing the job however he could—filling the gaps where needed. "My quirk is I don't like organizational charts," Harry said. "I recognize the need for a reporting line, but I emphasize teamwork. Everybody's job is everybody's job. Let's work together to get the damned thing done."[75]

Although Harry recognized the need for more rest and less stress, even his personal pastimes tended to be technical and scientific in nature. One such interest in astronomy led to his search for a telescope for his 4,800-square-foot weekend home in Avalon, New Jersey. Harry asked his close friend and Harvard physics professor Costas Papaliolios for advice on what to buy. Papaliolios then asked Harvard astronomy professor Josh Grindlay, who recommended a Meade 16-inch reflecting telescope he hoped to buy for his department. In the end, when Harry discovered that Grindlay didn't have the funds to buy one for teaching his students, Harry bought two telescopes at $20,000 each—one for himself and one for Harvard. The telescopes would have cost much more if Harry had not designed the

Harry bought Meade telescopes for his Avalon home and Harvard Science Center on Harvard Square.

critical mounts himself and enlisted Metrologic colleague Chic Naylor to construct the mounts.[76] Harvard installed the new instrument on the roof of its
Science Center on Harvard Square and dedicated it
as the "Knowles Telescope" in May 1998.[77]

That June, Metrologic celebrated its 30th anniversary with an open house. Veteran inventor Harry
could be proud of the hard-fought milestone. That was not the only
Metrologic milestone to celebrate that year. By the end of the year, total
sales were $65.6 million, compared to $53.4 million in 1997 and $46.9
million in 1996.[78] In 1998, the company had 534 full-time employees
and 53 U.S. patents, with another 26 pending patent applications, as
patent prosecutor Perkowski continued to guard Metrologic's intellectual property.[79]

A promising new product was introduced at the Retail Systems
Conference in New Orleans in June of that year: the "Orbit MS-7100,"
a compact, omnidirectional presentation laser bar code scanner. The
1998 annual report described the Orbit as "lightweight and designed for
applications where counter and workspace [are] limited. Orbit can be
used for many applications, including point-of-sale applications in retail and specialty stores."[80] A Metrologic press release boasted of its at-
tractiveness and ease of use, saying that the product's "contoured design
makes it comfortable for the end user to handle where Orbit may need
to be picked up or when scanning large or bulky items."[81] The Orbit unit
list price of less than $1,000 was between the MS-6720 handheld and
MS-700 series.

Also, at the time of the Retail Systems Conference product launch,
Orbit was *targeted* to be Metrologic's first point-of-sale scanner to feature the holographic technology found in its industrial product line, using holography, according to the release, "to precisely shape the scanner's laser beam, providing reliable performance and high efficiency."
However, Harry said holography was dropped from the final Orbit
product marketed to clients when he found hidden faults in that application of the technology. Instead, normal optics replaced the holography. "We had to redesign around the problem with the holographic
components," Harry said. "That cost us several months of delay and
great expense in market introduction."[82] Still, once introduced, Orbit
enjoyed tremendous reception.

According to Tom Perkowski, Mark Schmidt played the key role in the Orbit scanner's ultimately successful development. Schmidt, who had progressed from optical engineer to point-of-sale product manager in the mid-1990s to marketing manager in 1997, recommended the hiring of an industrial design firm, Bressler Group, to assist with the product's housing appearance. One of Bressler's designers, Sung Byun, was impressive enough that Metrologic hired him away. "Sung and Mark Schmidt took Metrologic out of the box style to fashion design," Perkowski said.[83] The Orbit scanner later won four industry design awards.

Metrologic's Orbit debuted in 1998. The popular presentation scanner won four industry design awards.

The era was marked by Metrologic's driven pursuit of new products—handheld, fixed projection, and holographic scanners—for its end users, distributors, and value-added resellers.

Only with new products, increased sales efforts globally, and reduction of manufacturing costs could Metrologic continue to compel higher and higher profits. "Harry created wealth by making things, not by making money," Perkowski said. "What was once innovative becomes a staple. You have to keep creating things."[84]

"Once you get on that track," Harry said, "you can't get off of it. You have to keep running."[85] Metrologic certainly kept a running pace throughout 1998. That year's other items of note for Metrologic included investment banker Bill Rulon-Miller's addition to the five-member Board of Directors; a joint venture to form Metrologic do Brasil to increase Metrologic's Brazilian market;[86] the addition of Omni-Quest IS-6520, a new scan engine, to its OEM (original equipment manufacturer) product line;[87] and the purchase of HoloTrak scanning workstations by Emery Worldwide (later part of UPS) for its Dayton, Ohio, North American freight processing center.[88]

IS-6520

Sales grew phenomenally the next year, jumping almost $15 million, to a year-end 1999 total sales figure of $80.1 million. The cost of those sales was $46.7 million, with net income rising slightly above the previous year to $4.9 million. Almost 58 percent of the sales were international; products were shipped to more than 90 countries.[89] Accompanying those sales were 76 Metrologic U.S. patents and 16 foreign patents.[90]

The number of full-time Metrologic employees climbed to 600 in 1999. Many U.S. corporations were moving the bulk of their manufacturing jobs overseas where labor costs were much cheaper; but Metrologic, for the most part, had kept its production workforce at home. Harry's sense of loyalty to his Blackwood work family had been a continuous compass for the company CEO, as had his fierce protection of U.S. intellectual property. With such rapid growth and immense demand, however, Metrologic was bound for transformation. Harry decided to get in front of the inevitable change and proposed what he considered an intelligent growth strategy in China while maintaining the Blackwood headquarters' integrity.[91]

Metrologic already had opened a regional sales office in Singapore; thus, Harry was familiar with the current Asian market and manufacturing capabilities. After evaluating sites worldwide, he proposed a new facility in Suzhou, China, 60 miles from Shanghai, in the China-Singapore Suzhou Industrial Park (later referred to as the Suzhou Industrial Park, or SIP). According to Metrologic's October 4, 1999, announcement of the opening of Metro (Suzhou) Technologies Co. Ltd., the new Metrologic facility would be "dedicated to research and development and the manufacturing of laser scanners..."[92] (During the evaluation period, Harry also had quizzed research manager B.J. Zhu's visiting parents, who were familiar with the industrial park. Zhu's mother reassured Harry that the Suzhou park was created to solve a problem Harry feared— dealing with a multitude of Chinese governmental agencies.)[93]

Harry and the Zhus

Harry declared his perspective on the opening, saying in the release, "The company believes that it can achieve significant cost efficiencies related to the development and manufacturing of certain new products in China. However, the company's 113,000-square-foot manufacturing facility in Blackwood, New

Jersey, which is also Metrologic's corporate headquarters, will remain the company's primary manufacturing plant."[94] At the time of the announcement, Metro (Suzhou) Technologies employed 16 people, with additional personnel yet to be hired.

Celebrating the 1999 opening of Metro (Suzhou) Technologies

In discussing why Metrologic chose Suzhou, Harry said, "Our decision was based on many factors, including the proximity to the growing Asian market, the quality and stability of the engineering talent pool, the attractive tax incentives, regionally available quality schools and universities, the cultural environment and the satisfaction expressed by many high-technology American companies already based in the Singapore-Suzhou Industrial Park."[95] (One of the American companies already located in the park was a production facility established by Harry's half-brother Hugh Knowles for his company, Knowles Electronics. Harry said that reference was most helpful for his research and to gain the trust of local Chinese authorities.)[96]

In a 2010 retrospective report prepared by Villanova University business professor and consultant Stephen J. Andriole, Harry is characterized as the primary proponent of the Suzhou site despite disagreement among company executives. "Cost and quality control requirements," Andriole said, "helped to drive the need for off-shore manufacturing....While rivals Symbol Technologies and PSC/Datalogic established manufacturing presences in Mexico and Eastern Europe, Metrologic...located in Suzhou, China. The selection of Suzhou was pushed by Mr. Knowles over the objections of his senior managers and advisers, but the selection of Suzhou proved brilliant."[97]

Andriole continued: "The objection to Suzhou stemmed in substantial part to the fact it was, by then-prevailing standards in China, a high labor cost area. Mr. Knowles determined that the advantages of Suzhou (ready access to a well educated workforce, especially engineers, proximity to Shanghai, a vital technology, education and transportation center, and substantially reduced governmental headaches as a consequence of locating in a giant international industrial park), far outweighed the comparatively slightly increased labor costs [still enormously less than U.S. costs] over what were available less populated areas."

Summarizing, Andriole said, "The decision to create a significant engineering presence in Suzhou with Chinese engineers created a two-continent design and manufacturing center capacity...offering competitive advantages: during the years of Metrologic's most explosive growth, most of its sales were international."

In a November 1999 *Wall Street Reporter Magazine* interview, Harry repeated that "the quality of engineering that is available out of China fits our profile perfectly."[98] Indeed, Metrologic was already recruiting a dozen graduates of China's top schools to come to the U.S. for training, while lining up 20 more for the next year. Harry had discovered during his years at the helm of Metrologic that even top college graduates lacked the advanced math and science skills needed to succeed at his company. As a result, he had put in place the elaborate Metrologic PGET, or post-graduate engineer training program, which provided free classes in subjects such as digital electronics and statistical analysis at the Blackwood headquarters.[99] The investment paid off for the technical staff—in the form of advancement potential—and for Metrologic in the form of quality and invention.

"At Motorola [in the late 1950s and early 1960s], and later at West inghouse," Harry said, "we had no problem hiring plenty of good engineers, well schooled in science and math....But, when I started to hire them in the mid-'70s [for Metrologic], I found [they] were not well grounded. That situation seemed to get worse through the '80s." Using Kelly College from his Bell Labs days as a model, Harry launched PGET.[100]

However, the root problem, Harry was convinced, was that these engineers—and most U.S. students—had not had adequate math and science education throughout their schooling. Harry was frustrated with the end result of new hires lacking critical skills, but he held an even deeper concern at the prospect of U.S. students falling increasingly behind other nations. He remembered the glory days at Bell Labs "where the place dripped with Nobel laureates-to-be." Harry was not content to tolerate American mediocrity. He determined that, if he could generate enough money, he would start a national program to foster better science and math teachers.

From its first laser kits for science teachers to its textbook-like catalog inserts, Metrologic had a long history of involvement with education. Each engineering session or product introduction became a chance to teach. Harry annually supported high school physics competitions for many years, funding the American Association of Physics Teachers Physics Bowl. In 1996, he established a professorship at Auburn University to honor his beloved mentor and college physics professor, Howard Carr, and his wife, Carolyn. By the late 1990s, Harry could follow his heart to do more.

After Metrologic went public in 1994, Harry could see the huge potential for Metrologic to increase financial status and the subsequent growth of his and Janet's personal stock portfolio. "I began to see where we [personally] could generate perhaps $100 million," Harry said. "I also felt that we could generate $5 million per year from the investment in perpetuity."[101]

In 1998, Harry wrote a preliminary draft for the establishment of the Janet H. and C. Harry Knowles Foundation, with the help of an attorney friend, David Brandt. Brandt also introduced Harry to Scott McVay, retired executive director of the Geraldine R. Dodge Foundation, one of the country's major philanthropic

Scott McVay organizations. McVay would prove invaluable to Harry's vision and the stated intent of the Knowles Foundation: "to nurture a better cadre of science and math teachers in the U.S."[102]

"Even though, at the time, Metrologic was worth a total of only about $20 to $30 million, I had the audacity of convincing Scott that we could get our $100 million in short time, with perhaps a little left over for Janet and me to live on," Harry said.[103]

Since a bulk of Harry's money was tied up in Metrologic stock, the attainment of a $100 million endowment for the Knowles Foundation would be a lengthy process. As the majority Metrologic stockholder, Harry could not endanger his company's value with hasty stock transactions. Therefore, his strategy was to grow Metrologic to increase its stock value, then gradually transfer stock to his foundation. In the meantime, Harry would seed his philanthropic efforts from personal Knowles funds.

Harry's original plan included a somewhat naive retreat concept as part of his financial encouragement for good science and math students to enter the teaching profession. Recruited as the first addition to the fledgling foundation's Board of Directors, McVay assumed the task of setting up a nationwide search for an executive director of what, in 1999, officially evolved into the Knowles Science Teaching Foundation, or KSTF. The KSTF executive director search took the better part of a year, but ended with the 2000 hire of

Angelo Collins

Angelo Collins, an associate professor at Peabody College at Vanderbilt University who held a Ph.D. from Wisconsin and an impressive list of credentials—including shaping Interstate Teacher Assessment and Support Consortium (INTASC) science standards and serving as the associate director of the National Center for the Improvement of Student Achievement in Mathematics and Science.[104]

Collins spent her first year traveling the country, visiting with experts in science and math education among the roughly 80 organizations she identified as relevant to Harry's strategy for KSTF. As the former director of the National Committee on Science Education Standards and Assessment, Collins was uniquely familiar with education professionals nationwide. She used those relationships to shape an astute sense of what trajectory KSTF would need to take to effect real change in the U.S. education system. In a discussion of KSTF history on the foundation web site, Collins' conclusions from her year of research were described: "Her findings on how best to cultivate and support high school science and mathematics teachers led to the creation of the foundation's signature program, the KSTF Teaching Fellowships, in 2001."[105]

The Knowles fellowship program would ultimately attract the best college-level or recently graduated engineering, science, and math majors to pursue high school math or science teaching careers. Instead of making more money in the private sector, excellent students were encouraged to make a difference as teachers. In turn, KSTF provided stipends that were renewable for up to five years and an in-depth support network which energized and mentored young teachers to not only stay in the profession, but to inspire their students and colleagues in high schools across the nation.

In 1999, however, KSTF was in its infancy on its way to fuller development with the help of McVay and Collins. Harry, as founding board member, funding source, and visionary, would do all he could to enable his dream of quality high school math and science education. The shaping of that dream would be made in concrete steps in coming years, in parallel with the growth of Metrologic.

Metrologic's own education effort, PGET, escalated engineering expertise within the company. Several of the PGET-trained staff members advanced into key leadership roles for Metrologic. One in 1999 was Mark Schmidt, who was promoted to vice president of marketing. That same year, Joseph Sawitsky advanced to vice president of manufacturing. Optical engineer Schmidt, whose talents already had resulted in successful Metrologic products, was former Metrologic POS product manager and marketing manager. Sawitsky, an aerospace engineering graduate of the U.S. Naval Academy and former nuclear submarine commander, joined Metrologic in 1998 as production manager.[106]

In March 1999, Executive Vice President and Chief Operating Officer Tom Mills, who was already overseeing most day-to-day ad-

From left, Stan Meltzer, Rich Close, and John Mathias

ministrative operations, was added to Metrologic's Board of Directors as he took on increasing visibility and responsibility.[107] The board, in October, expanded from five to eight members, adding three business executives as outside directors: Richard Close, then-president of Polaroid Graphics Imaging; John Hsu, owner and managing director of several large companies in Taiwan, Singapore, and China that employed more than 5,000 people; and John H. Mathias,

chairman and CEO of JPM Co., a 50-year-old wire and cable company based in Lewisburg, Pennsylvania, with annual sales of about $130 million.[108]

In addition to Mills, Close, Hsu, and Mathias, other members of the board included outside directors Stanton L. Meltzer and Bill Rulon-Miller, Janet

John Hsu

Knowles (who still retained her Metrologic vice president of administration title as well as served as secretary and treasurer of the board), and Chairman Harry Knowles.

The chairman's recent research concentration—Metrologic's HoloTrak product line—enjoyed increased success in 1999, as the first patent (of at least 17 holographic patent applications) covering HoloTrak scanners was issued in September for Metro-

Metrologic's HoloTunnel employed its holodisc technology for six-sided tunnel scanning.

logic's unique holographic technology. The patent bore the title, "Holographic Scanning System with High-Resolution 2-D Scanning Field Steerable Within 3-D Scanning Volume." Corporate counsel Nancy Smith indicated further holography patents would follow, since the U.S. Patent Office had allowed the filings.[109] Metrologic already was planning to display its "HoloTunnel" at the industry's Scan Tech show in October.

Metrologic's holographic architecture was embedded in the company's HoloTrak 8000 series, as well as its HoloTrak C series, which enabled the HoloTunnel's scanning. The HoloTunnel, which Harry called "the culmination of our industrial scanner market strategy,"[110] provided six-sided scanning with parcel dimensioning and weighing for high-speed, high-volume industrial needs. The HoloTrak design used the Metrologic-designed "holodisc" instead of conventional rotating polygons, resulting in more effective, long-depth scanning for hands-free, walk-under, or conveyor applications.

The company's release explained that the holodisc contained "up to 24 holographic elements that focus a laser beam, sweep it across the bar code, then receive the reflected light back from the bar code. As the holodisc turns, it focuses several laser beams into multiple focal planes to create thousands of scan lines per second, resulting in a very large, dense scan field...to deliver more effective, reliable scanning performance...."[111]

Vital to the protection of Metrologic's inventions and its $80 million in annual sales

Rotating holodisc

was vigorous diligence concerning its patents. Harry had learned the hard way during the Symbol patent litigation to safeguard his company's intellectual property. Thus, when other companies stepped on Metrologic's patents through the years, those entities faced certain legal action, such as in 1999 when Metrologic sued PSC, Inc. for patent infringement with several of its products. At times, lawsuits were dismissed; sometimes they were settled. Others, such as the case with Symbol, seemed to last forever. But in the corporate world, particularly that of auto-ID, lawsuits were ubiquitous. In a statement concerning the PSC lawsuit, Harry said, "Metrologic has over 30 years of experience in the bar code scanning industry, and we have spent a great deal of time and effort in developing a patent portfolio with respect to the technology used in our bar code scanners. We fully intend to vigorously protect our rights in our patents."[112]

While Metrologic had corporate counsel Nancy Smith on staff, it was outside patent prosecutor Tom Perkowski who had, since 1990, meticulously built for Metrologic one of the industry's strongest patent portfolios. Perkowski recalled a mentor reminding him that "an invention is defined by its claim."[113] Perkowski's devotion to his craft was guided by that overarching principle. Before his relationship with Metrologic would end, he would file about a thousand patents for the scanner company.

Many of those patents contained Harry's name. Harry said that U.S. Patent Office guidelines encouraged companies to note each person involved in the creative aspect of a new idea or product as a co-inventor on the patent filing. This thorough approach often included Harry, who was key to virtually each new Metrologic product.[114]

Metrologic patent wall

"A patent attorney," Perkowski explained, "uses words to define an invention. That patent is a deed." Inventions precede patents, however, and Perkowski marveled at the Metrologic CEO's rate of production. "Harry really loved what he did and was a great engineer," he said.[115]

The admiration between Perkowski and Harry was mutual. "Tom does happen to be about the best damned patent prosecutor I have ever encountered," Harry said. "A patent prosecutor is one who files for patents...not at the litigation end. He takes a good idea and then builds an offensive and defensive armament around it in many different directions. Few patents are worth a damn. His are monuments that withstand tornadoes."[116]

Metrologic products were sold in more than 100 countries with subsidiaries around the globe, including Metrologic HQ in Blackwood, New Jersey; Puchheim (Munich), Germany; Suzhou, China; Caracas, Venezuela; and Singapore.

As the new millennium was ushered in, a new age also dawned on Metrologic. More than 900 people now worked for the manufacturing company worldwide, while its products were sold in more than 100 countries.[117] Subsidiary locations included Germany, China, Brazil, Italy, France, Spain, and England. Sales reached $91.8 million (up $11 million from the previous year), according to the year-end annual report, which numbered Metrologic patents at 128 domestic and 16 foreign. Metrologic's momentum was astounding.

The New Jersey Inventors Hall of Fame agreed, inducting Metrologic in the corporate category into the 2000 Hall of Fame at its ceremony February 17. Metrologic was recognized for its "overall contribution to technology since its inception in 1968, a corporate culture that fosters a spirit of innovation, contributions to the economic development of New Jersey, and excellence of products."[118]

The new age at Metrologic included a major change at the top of the corporate structure, as COO Tom Mills was promoted to president and chief operating officer effective February 9, 2000.[119] Harry remained chairman and CEO. "Tom's promotion was part of the plan," Harry said.[120] Harry hoped for a gradual exit which would leave his company strong and grant him flexibility of schedule and involvement.

In the official press release on Mills' promotion, Harry commented, "This promotion represents the continuing progression of Metrologic's management structure, which has been ongoing due to the doubling in sales over the past four years and our plans for continuing growth. Now, as president, Tom will have improved visibility both inside and outside of Metrologic."[121]

Other management changes that year included an increase of responsibility for Kevin Woznicki, who, instead of continuing as vice president of North American sales, was asked to add the markets in Central and South America. His new title became "Vice President, Sales –The Americas," according to the July release. Dale Fischer, who formerly handled South American sales, would continue as vice president of international sales with special emphasis on the Asian markets.[122]

The complex network of managers reflected expanding offerings of products as Metrologic introduced several new scanners in 2000. A new handheld laser scanner, the "MS-9540 Voyager," featured a new Metrologic "Code-Gate" push-button data transmission technol-

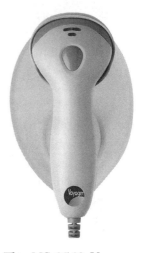

The MS-9540 Voyager included a CodeGate data transmission button which avoided violating Symbol's activation trigger patent.

ogy.[123] Since Harry's re-invention of handhelds in 1990 to a triggerless design, the appearance of a button on a handheld could have invoked memories of the Symbol lawsuit. However, because Voyager had a data-transmission switch and *not* an activation switch, the design cleverly did not run afoul of Symbol's trigger patent.

In the Voyager, the laser was activated by an infrared sensor; the user positioned the highly visible laser line over the bar code and then pressed the CodeGate button to transmit the data. The scanner also

acted as a "fully automatic presentation scanner" when in its stand. The company's press release compared the Voyager to the favorably received MS-7120 Orbit, because the Voyager had "equally aggressive performance, er-

Several of Metrologic's popular scanners: back, from left, MS-9520 Voyager (model without the CodeGate technology), MS-7120 Orbit, MS-6720, MS-951; and, front, MS-6220 Pulsar.

gonomic design and attractive styling."[124] Applications included retail point-of-sale, library, pharmaceutical, inventory, and others.

The boxy MS-900 evolved into the Voyager, according to Perkowski, who said Sung Byun designed the housing and Mark Schmidt also helped with the facelift.[125] Business consultant Stephen Andriole proclaimed that Voyager "became the best-selling device of its kind in the world." A decade later, it was still listed as one of the owner's top three products.[126]

Other scanners to debut in 2000 were the "MS-6220 Pulsar" and "MS-6520 Cubit," both entry-level products. The Pulsar was a single-line handheld designed to compete with low-cost charged-coupled devices (CCD), while the Cubit was a compact, omnidirectional, fixed scanner.

Metrologic's persistence within the package-shipping market paid off with customer orders for its industrial scanners by Lockheed Martin for the U.S. Postal Service and by Canada's Purolator Courier. After Lockheed Martin won a $15.5 million contract from the U.S. Postal Service to install its automatic airline assignment (AAA) systems, Lockheed turned

MS-6520 Cubit

to Metrologic to supply the scanner company's "TECH 8" industrial bar code scanners for 220 AAA systems.[127] The Purolator Courier $1.8 million order secured for the parcel shipping company Metrologic Holo-Tunnel systems (with HoloTrak C-series holographic scanners) for hubs across Canada.[128]

Refinements in the research and product development process (a $5 million investment) at Metrologic in 2000 had organized the company's efforts into two distinct departments—advanced development and new product development. As the company's annual report explained, advanced development's vision was long-range, "driving technological breakthroughs and working on technologies, products and processes not already marketed by the

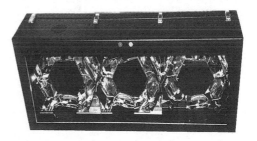

The HoloTrak C-series scanners for high-speed conveyors could contain multiple holodiscs.

company."[129] New product development was just that—getting products through the engineering necessary to get to market in a timely manner. The staff in new product development, having successfully debuted Voyager, were queuing next year's product launches and developing products for the Suzhou operation, along with refining current product lines. Advanced development personnel already were working diligently on vision-based technologies (which would become a new "iQ" series of products), laser-doppler imaging, and advanced holography.

To boost vision-based development, Metrologic, in December 2000, announced its purchase of Cambridge, Massachusetts-based Adaptive Optics Associates (AOA), a United Technologies subsidiary which had a successful pedigree of sophisticated laser vision systems as part of its advanced optical and mechanical product lines.[130] Harry's friend Harvard physics professor Costas Papaliolios had introduced Harry to AOA years earlier. In fact, Papaliolios' relationship with AOA management,  according to Harry, led to mutual respect between the companies and Metrologic's ultimate purchase. With AOA revenues projected to be $21 million in 2000, Metrologic's purchase price of $19 million was determined to be a sound investment. Analysts expected Metrologic stock to rise five cents per share in the coming year based on the AOA purchase alone.

"Acquiring AOA is a significant opportunity for Metrologic to combine AOA's vision-based expertise and technical resources with Metrologic's laser-based technology to better serve our industrial scanning customers," Harry said in the company press release. The CEO further highlighted AOA's role as a top supplier to the semiconductor industry. AOA also had strong government, scientific, and parcel-industry customers. "AOA brings us," Harry continued, "convergent technologies… in high-speed, automated image and data capture…and accelerates our capabilities in the growing industrial…markets."[131]

Perkowski found AOA reticent about patents because he said their history of military contracts caused them to be somewhat secretive. But Harry was especially happy about acquiring AOA, according to Perkowski, because AOA brought their Fed-Ex account with them. Additionally, with a new company, the patent attorney said, came "projects that empowered the teamwork of engineers."[132]

The team that was Metrologic had grown exponentially with offices and subsidiaries (including a new one in Japan) spanning the globe. Manufacturing now occurred in New Jersey and China, with the global workforce still topping 900. Annual sales exceeded $100 million for the first time in 2001, with 2001 sales by year-end totaling $113.6 million—more than double 1997 sales of $53.4 million. (2000 sales had been $91.8 million.)

The acquisition of AOA was a bright spot, credited for the year's sales increase. Foreign sales were 55 percent of total sales. Research and development costs in 2001 totaled $6.5 million; while the patent portfolio continued to expand, with patent totals, as of the annual report filing, at 133 U.S. patents and 27 foreign.[133]

The annual sales number was impressive, but the 2001 cost of those sales was $83.5 million. That cost, along with lower industrial scanner sales (prompting a large write-down of inventory) and some lower scanner unit prices, combined with an unfavorable foreign exchange rate to contribute to a 2001 net loss of $7.7 million. In contrast, the year before had seen $2.7 million in net income.

The lower industrial scanner sales stemmed from Metrologic falling short in sales goals for the laser and HoloScan industrial scanners, according to Metrologic president Tom Mills.[134] "When the strategic decision was made to switch to camera-based industrial scanning, and therefore the acquisition of AOA, the related inventory of laser-related parts, HoloScan parts, etc. needed to be written down in accordance with generally accepted accounting principles," Mills said. In other words, falling sales values translated to the dropped value of Metrologic inventory being recorded as an expense.

In light of the year's net loss, Metrologic was negotiating with its lenders for a new credit agreement which would be asset-based. Harry was surprised lenders were not more understanding of his company's losses, considering that the large inventory write-down lowered Metrologic's tax burden and had "zero effect on cash flow."[135] However, timing was not in Metrologic's favor, since 2001 had shaken the entire U.S. economy to its foundations with the September 11 terrorist attacks on Washington, D.C., and New York City. Citizens and businesses alike were struggling to regain their footing, and banks were skittish.

"Since the adjustments," Mills explained, "were a non-cash charge, which did not impact current liquidity, we believed we would have had a more proportionate response from our friends in the banking industry given the real and current liquidity issues that many other companies had at the time in responding to 9/11 and the tech-bubble-induced recession….[I]t seemed as though every high-tech company was experiencing similar issues and…inventory write-offs. With regard to the banks, they seemed to all be 'pulling in their oars' from a loan perspective during that time."[136]

Under Metrologic's current credit agreement, lenders could declare all debt immediately due. Since Metrologic did not have enough liquid assets to pay the full debt, the company would be forced to sell assets to raise cash if the debt were called. While Metrologic most likely could raise the funds if needed, there was no guarantee. Thus, the manufacturing company pursued alternate terms with its banks.[137] In sophisticated corporate circles, such high-level financial wrangling was typical but still burdensome. Publicly traded companies suffered added scrutiny. Certainly, chairman and CEO Harry Knowles and president and COO Tom Mills felt that pressure from employees, board members, and stockholders.

Harry noted other factors contributing to revenue shortfalls, such as the declining euro, "nagging component shortages and related increased costs, and the economic malaise in the U.S."[138] He and Mills already had decided to accelerate production in Suzhou, China, to increase profits. In addition,

Suzhou production floor

Mills said that they had increased sales prices in Europe, tightened operating budgets, cut management jobs, and increased production automation. The engineering staff in China had been trained; indeed, with AOA added to the Metrologic fold, the number of Metrologic engineers had grown to 140. "That increase," Harry said in a company statement, "should accelerate our introduction of new products and entry into new markets."[139]

Despite the stressful financial picture, Metrologic personnel were busy innovating. Several promising scanners were introduced in 2001, including Metrologic and AOA's first joint project: the "iQ-180," a camera-based imaging system targeted for the parcel-handling industry. The iQ-180 offered linear and two-dimensional bar code reading, as well as "OCR [optical character recognition]-compatible image lift," speed detection, and parcel dimen-

PLIIM scanner for grocery stores and other high-end applications

sioning in a single unit which was mounted overhead.[140] However, the scanner could also be configured for tunnel-style, multi-sided imaging if needed.

In support of the iQ, Metrologic announced later in the year that it had renewed its licensing agreement with Omniplanar, Inc. for Omniplanar's high-speed bar code reading software, "SwiftDecoder." Swift-Decoder decoded two-dimensional, linear and postal bar codes and was integrated into Metrologic's iQ-180 product, saving Metrologic time and resources, according to B.J. Zhu, who had been promoted in 2001 to director of research and development.[141]

The iQ technology was also known as a PLIIM system, or a planar laser illumination and imaging system. PLIIM would result in numerous patents for Harry, Zhu, Metrologic engineer Tim Good, and others. While initially the aim for PLIIM simply was reading codes, the laser technology also had the potential to revolutionize scanning in coming years with its amazingly high resolution over long distances at high speed. According to Harry, ultimately, with PLIIM, the client not only could get a three-dimensional picture of the item going through the scanner, but could read all materials on the package and identify them including date codes, batch numbers, and other critical information without the need for a bar code. By shining sheets of light onto the product, the scanner could reproduce an image off rows of receivers with thousands of photocells that would relay the image to a computer chip. As the technology developed, information from five or even six sides could be read. Harry said that, for about the same cost as the limited, standard rotating polygon scanner, a user could get the superior PLIIM.[142]

(continued on page 244)

The Revolution of PLIIM Scanning

by C. Harry Knowles

Modern AutoID in retail stores requires that not only normal one-dimensional (1D) codes such as the UPC found in most retailing be read, but that 2D codes be read (Image 1). Reading common printed text materials, e.g., date codes, batch numbers, etc., is also desired and, in the future, as technology develops, mandatory.

Image 1, 1D bar code and 2D bar code

Such media may be recorded with adequate resolution in 2D in two ways. The most common method is with a 2D camera similar to the common digital camera. The Achilles' heel of one-shot, 2D imaging is getting adequate light onto the scanned region. To give the optical sensor adequate reflected light for each pixel, along with an adequate depth of field, a bright, usually flashing, broad-area illumination must be used. Users of such a system, that is, both workers and customers, have a low tolerance for such irritation.

The alternative technology is to use a 1D photo array (Fig. 1V1) and to repeat the exposure rapidly enough to get enough resolution in the direction of the motion of the code area, relative to the scanner. In this method, the object code array area is illuminated with a thin planar array of light, known as a planar laser illumination beam array, or PLIA, comprising a plurality of planar laser illumination modules, or PLIMs. Fig. 1V1 from original assignee Metrologic's U.S. Patent 6,631,842 shows the basic idea of planar laser illumination and imaging, or PLIIM, systems. In Fig. 1V1, two sources (one can be conditionally sufficient) of light illuminate the bar code region with overlapping, thin sheets of light (7A & 7B); light is reflected off the region to be scanned, i.e., the bar code, into a lens and linear sensor whose field of view (FOV) is coplanar with these sheets of light illuminating the object (3), providing a one-dimensional digital image in the image processor (5) with a given single exposure. As multiple images are recorded and stored, a 2D image is processed from the multiple exposures.

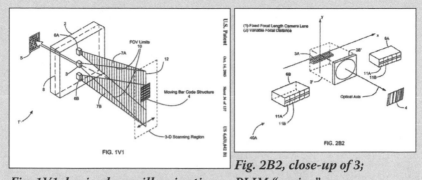

Fig. 1V1, basic planar illumination

Fig. 2B2, close-up of 3;
PLIM "engine"

Thus, the light shines only where needed, particularly if one uses lasers, and can be quite bright—bright enough to provide adequate illumination of each pixel in the linear array and still tolerant for the eye and not broadly spread. Yet, the laser light provides enough photons in each pixel for rapid, repeating, sequential exposures. Note that a 2D array would require the area to have about the same intensity of the line; thus, for 1,000-pixel vertical resolution in 3A, one would have to provide roughly 1,000 times the light energy.

Depending on the depth of field required by the specific application, accommodation for adjustable focusing of the lens 3B in Fig. 2B2 above may be needed.

Lasers, as compared to LEDs or other forms of incoherent light, have the particularly valuable advantage of spatial coherence. In other words, laser light can be projected easily into a thin narrowly directed plane and illuminated over long distances such that the light shines only where it needs to be, and with remarkably effective density distributions.

However, a major obstacle in using lasers in PLIIM is the optical noise, i.e., "speckle," resulting from the chromatic (single-wavelength nature) coherence of laser light. The noise from a single laser is typically about 25 to 30% of the magnitude, making recording the edges of light and dark regions on a code quite troublesome. This noise can be reduced by using many lasers for the lighting and "averaging" the noise component of each laser. The noise component is thereby reduced by the root mean square of all laser beams. Thus, if one uses, for example, 10 lasers, the noise is reduced by a factor of 3+; if one uses 100 lasers, all shining on the same surface, the noise would be reduced by 10.

Alternatively, one can reduce the noise from a given laser by changing the "mode" of that laser with two principal methods: 1) during the time of a given exposure, high frequency modulate (HFM) the current through

241

the VLD, changing the beam wavelength (i.e., the color changes) during the exposure (Fig. 5J2); and 2) optically multiplex (OMUX) by spatially displacing the beam from a given laser into separate coherence sections such that each beam is spatially not coherent with any adjacent beam. Tim Good provided the important idea of the OMUX.

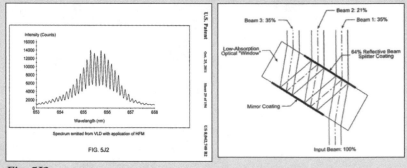

Fig. 5J2

PLIIM scanning satisfies a broad array of scanning needs from large industrial package sortation to handheld, presentation, and engine scanning to high-speed, five-sided supermarket scanning to lifting images and reading text (such as with optical character recognition/OCR). It is effective to design the PLIM elements—both the lasers and optics—and the linear sensor and optics, along with the electronics needed, into an "engine" that is a modular element that can be made separately and in volume apart from the particular scanner application. Fig. 5X4 from U.S. Patent 8,042,740 B2 (known as Patent '740) shows a PLIM "engine," that is, the basic elements of the lasers. While the figure shows six in this particular case, as few as one or two may be suitable.

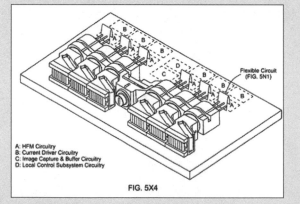

Fig. 5X4, PLIM engine for handheld or supermarket

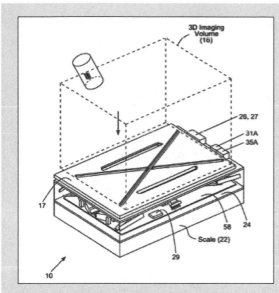

Fig. 2 from U.S. 8,042,740 B2, supermarket PLIIM scanner

Note that in Fig. 2 from Patent '740, there are six separate scanner engines, each one imaging all materials, including text, 1D and 2D bar codes, date codes, batch numbers, and other desired media, on all sides except the top. The resolution can be fine, and the speed as fast as operators can move materials. Since the signal return paths are thin, because of the high light density at the code area, the scanner can be quite thin even for six-engine scanning. Note that in a PLIIM supermarket scanner, there are no moving parts.

Fig. 3J2 from U.S. 6,913,202 shows a special configuration of a PLIIM scanner, where the scanned plane is swept across the target field. The high intensity that can be designed into such a scanner allows for high-speed imaging of a scanned document or package. A designer can reduce PLIIM time-for-imaging by a factor of ten or more over non-coherent lighting.

As many as 40 to 50 lasers may be employed to cover the long throw distances of a meter or so that may be needed for large boxes moving at high speeds, or for scanning very large fields.

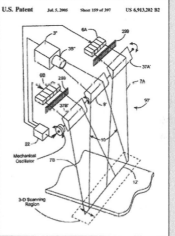

Fig. 3J2, PLIIM scanner

PLIIM's laser technology carries the potential to revolutionize the scanning marketplace. With PLIIM's high resolution, long depth of field, and high speeds, a vast amount of product information may be accessed with each scan. In addition, PLIIM offers the superior power for about the same cost as the limited, standard rotating polygon scanner.

243

In November, Metrologic's "MS-5145 Eclipse" handheld laser scanner debuted. A miniature version of the Voyager, the Eclipse used the CodeGate push-button data transmission technology introduced the previous year in the Voyager.[143] The mid-level scanner was designed and developed in Suzhou; its smaller size and low price targeted worldwide retail markets.[144]

B.J. Zhu at far head of conference table running R&D meeting

Also occurring in China was the attraction of new business. Although seven years away, China already was gearing up for the 2008 Olympics and was determined, according to Harry, that expected throngs of tourists be greeted with impeccable airport passenger and baggage handling.[145] Harry was working closely and personally with the Civil Air Administration of China, which ordered a Metrologic baggage handling and security scanning tunnel system for an airport in Guizhou Province. The six-sided Metrologic tunnel system, according to the release, was the first of its kind combining the company's holographic technology with the new iQ-180 camera and vision-based technology.[146]

In addition, China Shenzhen Airport Group ordered its fourth Metrologic baggage scanning system.[147] Another 2001 foreign order of note originated from Littlewoods, a United Kingdom catalog-shipping company, for more Metrologic IS-8300 HoloTrak industrial scanners. By replacing handheld scanners with HoloTrak, Littlewoods' distribution facility increased capability to 50 million packages annually.[148]

Other products introduced in 2001 included the "MS-7220 Argus-Scan" fixed, omnidirectional scanner for point-of-sale applications; the "ScanPal 2" entry-level, batch portable data scanning terminal for such tasks as inventory control, tracking, and price checking; and a retail, automated "ScanVue" price verifier with full-color graphics.[149]

After the acquisition of Adaptive Optics Associates, Metrologic expanded its research and development organization to include not only departments of advanced development and new product development, but also of optical systems. Metrologic also promoted Jeffrey Yorsz to

AOA president and general manager.[150] In December 2001, AOA delivered a component to Lockheed Martin for its airborne laser missile defense system. The AOA "CP/CM Wavefront Sensor" was designed for the missile system's beam and fire control function and was part of a $5.7 million AOA contract with Lockheed. The wavefront sensor, said a company release, was used "to correct for any atmosphere-induced turbulence in the high-energy laser beam...[allowing] the beam to be tightly...focused on its target."[151] Since much of AOA's work required an extremely high-level security clearance (which was made more complex by the events of September 11); Harry said that, with his inadequate "top-secret" clearance, he did not have the opportunity to collaborate much on AOA projects.[152] Still, he was proud of the AOA team.

Metrologic's web of subsidiaries, sales locations, and global manufacturing were all strategic components of Metrologic the corporation. At its core, however, Metrologic's success revolved around Metrologic the man—Harry Knowles—and that man's vision. As the company closed its 33rd year, Metrologic still reflected Harry's drive for discovery. At every opportunity, new products blossomed. The chairman still could be found in consultation on the production

Harry in his office

floor or grappling with an engineering dilemma with his researchers, although his workday was shortening. Harry provided a palpable strength, a sense of guiding purpose to Metrologic. That strength, however, could prove to be Metrologic's weakness. In the inevitable evolution of the New Jersey company, Metrologic the corporation and Metrologic the man were on a collision course.

Chapter 10

Money Matters

(2000-2004)

Sorting the company finances assumed priority status in 2002, as Harry, Tom Mills, and the board continued their negotiations with lenders to work toward an asset-based arrangement. Technically, Metrologic was in default on its loans. Metrologic's banks, led by PNC Bank, notified the company of such on April 9, 2002.[1]

The trouble with PNC Bank could be traced back to fall 2000 when Metrologic was first putting together the deal to buy Adaptive Optics Associates (AOA). According to Harry, in September 2000, a PNC Bank account manager told Harry that it would be no trouble to complete the $19 million purchase of AOA by the end of that year. Tom Mills and Harry put down $2 million of Metrologic's preciously short cash with AOA's then owner United Technologies Corporation to secure the agreement. "PNC decided to bring in another bank, then another one," Harry said. "I sensed deep trouble at PNC. At the last minute, they switched the basis on which the bank loan would be made. It was incredibly complicated, and Mills and I didn't fully appreciate it. We already had $2 million in, so could not back out."[2]

By the end of the deal, Metrologic, in January 2001, had arranged $45 million in credit—$20 million in a term loan and $25 million in a revolving credit line.[3] While stressed by the changing loan terms, Harry still thought his company was stable with more than enough assets on the books to cover the high credit amount. (Metrologic had ended 2000 with $81.8 million worth of assets.)[4] The banks didn't see it that way. Although the outstanding loan balance was down to $18 million and the revolving credit line was down to $11.4 million (with part of the credit facility borrowings personally guaranteed by Harry and Janet Knowles) by the end of 2001, Metrologic also ended that year with a net loss of $7.7 million. Metrologic had violated specific provisions of the credit agreement, prompting the April 2002 default notification.

"The banks said that the assets would sell for far less if we were to

Metrologic executives and board members spent much of their time dealing with financial challenges. This board meeting photo, snapped by Harry in November 2000 before the AOA purchase, included: on left, Janet and Bill Rulon-Miller; on right, from back, Nancy Smith, Joe Sawitsky, Dale Fischer, Tom Mills, and controller George Daulerio.

go into bankruptcy," Harry said.[5] "By spring 2002, the banks wanted a cash-out. They needed the cash. The banks had too much leverage. I wrote to our local senators, congressmen, newspapers, and television stations complaining. I got zero response. I felt that the banks shouldn't be allowed to have such influence on a business."

Rather than complying with the banks' desire for a cash-out, Harry and Metrologic executives instead tackled the situation by generating cash quickly. Harry explained: "We went to key customers and got rapid payment on accounts receivable. Then, I placed $8 million of the cash into a separate bank. PNC was furious." Harry recalled that a PNC representative demanded the $8 million from Harry. In response, Harry said, "Fine, I don't want you to call the loan." Unknown to PNC, Harry already had bankruptcy papers drawn up. "I had our attorney, Arthur Abramowitz, on standby ready to take us into Chapter 11. I showed him [the PNC representative] the Chapter 11 papers and he said, 'Let's settle.' That kind of intimidation is an example of how rotten banks can be."

By July 9, 2002, a new credit agreement was in place, and the banks withdrew default notification.[6] In a Metrologic press release following the default withdrawal, Harry commented, "This was not a financial health issue, but instead involved extended negotiations with our banks concerning the terms of the agreement. The agreement waives all existing defaults and allows for a reclassification of a portion of short-term to long-term liabilities. Taking into account the payments provided for

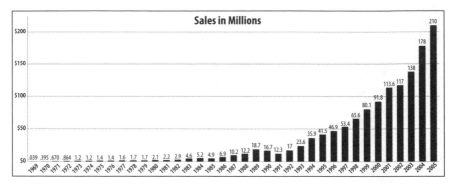

Metrologic sales, shown by year in millions, rose from $39,000 in 1969 to $210 million in 2005 and a projection of about $250 million in 2006 before Harry's tenure with the company would end. Although Metrologic sales increased during the years of intense credit agreement negotiations (2000-2002), negative net income in 2001 made banks nervous. Also note the jump in sales in 1994, when Metrologic went public, and in the 2003-2004 timeframe, after the company would issue a second public offering in October 2003.

in the agreement, Metrologic's net bank debt balance [is now] $17.9 million, compared with $29.4 million at December 31, 2001, an $11.5 million decrease."[7]

Linked to the new $14 million revolving credit line was a requirement for applying daily company receipts as payments. Likewise, cash requirements were funded through "daily borrowings." Investment banker and Metrologic board member Bill Rulon-Miller explained that while it was "not unusual for re-alignment of loans, especially bank lines," the added requirements of applying daily receipts and borrowings were "cumbersome. That's a bank saying, 'I don't trust you,'" Rulon-Miller said.[8]

By January 2003, the credit agreement was amended again, providing for a $13 million credit line, a $4.5 million term loan, and an extension of the agreement to 2006.[9] Metrologic had sought proposals from other banks; but, in the end, remained with PNC, despite its continued requirement for daily postings. In a 2003 press release about the restructured bank debt facility, CEO Harry reflected none of his angst about the bank, providing only a positive image of company finances.

"PNC offered to eliminate the other banks included in the previous bank facility," Harry said in the release, "offered much lower interest rates and fees, and offered the most flexibility and expediency to restructure and reduce our other subordinated debt. I believe this new facility provides Metrologic the best opportunity to continue to further reduce our debt, while providing sufficient financing for the company's working capital requirements."[10]

In the release, Harry addressed Metrologic's financial performance, saying, "Metrologic generated $30 million of positive cash flow from operations over the past 24 months and has restored the company to profitability, which has resulted in reduced bank debt of $10.3 million at the end of 2002."

Metrologic sales in 2002 by year-end totaled $117 million, up by several million over 2001.[11] More importantly, however, net income was back in the positive at $1.7 million in 2002, compared to the $7.7 million loss in 2001. The major improvement in the company's financial picture was the decline in cost of 2002 sales to $74.4 million (down from $83.5 million in 2001) after Metrologic executives had streamlined operations and increased sales prices in Europe and production in China.

Meanwhile, the U.S. perspective of the world scene was hardly a docile one following the terrorist attacks of 2001. President George W. Bush, whose two-term, eight-year presidency began the year of 9/11, led a nation which had lost its innocence regarding evil's reach. Before the two-year anniversary of 9/11, the U.S., in its war on terror, would topple the Taliban government of Afghanistan and depose Iraqi President Saddam Hussein. While the Iraq War would continue for more than eight years and the Taliban insurgency remained in Afghanistan (and spread into Pakistan), the U.S. homeland resiliently carried on— including manufacturers such as Metrologic that constantly battled the tremendous economic effects of world events.

With international sales accounting for almost 52 percent of total sales in 2002, Metrologic was continuing its worldwide market appeal with vast product lines. As of the annual report filing, patents totaled 173 U.S. patents and 35 foreign. In 2002, Metrologic produced 500,000 products (sold in more than 100 countries) with its workforce of 852 full-time employees.[12]

The year 2002 brought new products and significant orders for Metrologic's ever-expanding offerings. Two Metrologic omni-directional, hands-free scanners debuted at the January National Retail Federation Trade Show: the "MS-7320 InVista" and the "MS-7600 series Horizon." The InVista fixed-mount presentation scanner boasted a large scan area, while the Horizon was Metrologic's next-generation, in-counter, mini-slot scanner.[13] The MS-7120 Orbit remained the top seller among Metrologic's fixed-projection scanners; hands-free scanners accounted for 15 percent of total revenue. Handheld scanners, however, generated 39 percent of revenue in 2002.[14] Both hands-free and handheld scanners fell into Metrologic's retail, or point-of-sale (POS),

MS-7320 InVista

scanner category. The other three product classifications for Metrologic were: original equipment manufacturer (OEM) scan engines, industrial products and scanning systems, and advanced optical systems.

MS-7600 Horizon

OEM scan engines were laser-based components for integration into other companies' products (such as price-checker systems, robotics, reverse vending machines, etc.) and included such Metrologic products as the IS-6520 Cubit and ScanQuest lines. The industrial products and scanning systems, meanwhile, were marketed under the AOA name and were laser- or camera-based. Laser-based scanners in this category included the HoloTrak series and TECH series; while camera-based imaging systems (which did use laser light as an illumination source) included the iQ series. The camera-based systems had become the preferred product mode, as the annual report for year-end 2002 attested:

"CCD camera-based or vision technology is rapidly becoming the predominant system sought by companies in many industries including pharmaceutical and parcel and postal handling industries. Camera-based systems offer more functionality and features versus lasers including increased bar code read rates, capable of decoding 1D and 2D bar codes, image capture and optical character recognition (OCR) capability."[15]

The final category of Metrologic products, advanced optical systems, accounted for 14 percent of total revenue and included lithography tools and other laser beam delivery systems, as well as wave front sensors and optical metrology (measurement) systems with applications in atmospheric optics, laser communications, missile defense, and retinal imaging. Such vast Metrologic prowess cost about $6.9 million in research and development in 2002, as the company worked on introducing its new products and developing improved versions of the iQ series and its most popular handheld scanner, the Voyager. In addition, Metrologic kept pace with emerging technologies such as Bluetooth wireless communications by helping to craft standards for the auto-ID industry.

The Voyager became Burlington Coat Factory's scanner of choice in May 2002, when Burlington selected Metrologic to supply Voyager handheld POS scanners to each of Burlington's approximately 300 retail stores.[16] Another Metrologic product order that year was a $1.9 million contract for the iQ-180, the camera-based imaging system introduced in 2001 as a joint development between Metrologic and its then newly acquired Adaptive Optics Associates (AOA). While the March 2002 Metrologic press release only identifies the $1.9 million contract awarder as a "Fortune 500 company," the release goes on to say that the award was a portion of a larger quote.[17] AOA's orders that year included opto-mechanical design and production work for Lawrence Livermore National Labs' $2.25-billion National Ignition Facility project, as well as a $2.5 million field service contract and a $1.8 million order for electro-optical system upgrades.[18] Another impressive accomplishment for AOA came in November 2002 with an influx of $1.73 million—the beginning of a $6.8 million Lockheed Martin contract to provide about 125 data collection subsystems for the U.S. Postal Service.[19]

"One of North America's largest department store chains," according to a May press release, chose to supply its stores with Metrologic's MS-6220 Pulsar handheld laser scanners as well as the ScanPal 2 portable data terminal (PDT) for "inventory control data collection."[20] By December 2002, the retail chain had expanded its order commitment to $5.6 million.[21] Another interesting venture for Metrologic was the September 2002 $1.4 million order from RedDotNet, an innovative company supplying in-store musical CD readers. With the integration of Metrologic's IS-6520 Cubit bar code scanners, RedDotNet multi-media preview stations al-

ScanPal 2 PDT

251

lowed customers to scan unopened CDs to listen to song selections. Stores with these devices, called "Dots," suddenly had a whole new way to convince customers to buy.[22]

In recognition of the company's growing complexity, Metrologic had hired Kevin Bratton that August to serve as chief financial officer, a position which Tom Mills had held in addition to that of president and COO. Bratton, a former CFO at Pennsylvania's JPM Company, according to Mills, had "a proven record as a senior financial manager [and had] successfully negotiated bank debt financing,...prepared SEC filings, and...participated in merger and acquisition transactions."[23]

Other key executive shifts had occurred in March 2002. Nancy Smith, who joined Metrologic in 1996 as corporate counsel, was promoted to vice president and general counsel;[24] and AOA President and General Manager Jeffrey Yorsz was appointed vice president of industrial systems.[25] Yorsz would oversee all of the new product development, marketing, and sales for Metrologic's industrial systems business worldwide under the AOA corporate name and from AOA's facilities in Cambridge, Massachusetts.

Jeff Yorsz

Metrologic's global customer needs were immensely diverse, as even a superficial perusal of new contracts in 2002 indicates. The year had been an exhausting one for Harry, who would have preferred to spend his time on technological innovation without the financial distractions. Of necessity, Harry, Tom Mills, and other key executives and board members focused on the company's labyrinth of continuing fiscal challenges. Ending the year with a positive net income and beginning January 2003 with another credit agreement were significant steps toward stability.

The new January 2003 credit agreement released Harry and Janet from their personal guarantees. However, Metrologic then borrowed $4.26 million from the couple; they mortgaged the Blackwood headquarters property, which they owned, to lend the money. According to the 2003 SEC Annual Report, "In January 2003, the Company entered into a $4.26 [million] subordinated note payable with C. Harry Knowles, its Chairman and CEO and his spouse, Janet Knowles, a Director and Vice President, Administration. The subordinated note bears interest at 10% and requires 60 monthly principal payments of $36,000 with the balance of $2.13 [million] due in January 2008."[26] The loan from Harry and Janet, which would be paid early and in full in October 2003, allowed Metrologic to take advantage of an early payment agreement with United Technologies Corporation, from which Metrologic had purchased AOA.[27] In exchange for accelerated payments to United, Metrologic received a $2.2 million discount on the total cost of the acquisition. In under two years' time, Metrologic had reduced its total debt, according to Harry in a January 2003 press release, from "a high of approximately $50 million" to "below $20 million on a pro forma basis" at the end of 2002.[28]

Harry and Janet's personal finances clearly were woven into the fabric of Metrologic's successes and failures throughout the life of the company. Indeed, in 1985, when Metrologic faced bankruptcy, the Knowles family home hung in the balance along with the fate of the corporate entity.[29] Of course, the intricate lines of power and culpability necessarily shifted when Metrologic became public; there were, after all, demands for accountability by investors as well as the copious regulations of the Securities and Exchange Commission. However, as CEO, chairman, and dominant stockholder, Harry remained not only the foundational force of Metrologic, but the one with the most to lose.

Because Harry and Janet owned the Blackwood factory and its land, Metrologic leased both from the Knowles couple. Harry occasionally allowed the company to postpone those payments if Metrologic's available funds were low. In fact, under the terms of the new credit agreement, rental payments were deferred. At the end of 2002, accrued lease payments due to Harry and Janet totaled $340,000.[30]

"What brought Harry down were the financial issues," Metrologic patent prosecutor Tom Perkowski commented. "Metrologic was able to be adaptive [for so many years] because it was one man; it was not run by committee. Going public was horrible for Harry because he couldn't be Harry anymore. He had to listen to investors."[31]

Bill Rulon-Miller, speaking from many years of investment banking experience, explained the inevitable evolution of a company succinctly: "You grow or die." Continuing, he said that if a company grows, it needs capital. "You can go public, sell out, merge, or try a combination of all. The minute you sell a share, you give up control. You answer to individ-

Early Metrologic Stratos unsuccessful prototype with holodisc, December 2000, two years before a non-holographic product introduction of the final Stratos

uals and companies who own stock. Harry was well aware of that."[32]

Stockholders most likely were pleased with Metrologic's progress, marked by five new products debuted at the January 2003 National Retail Federation trade show in New York City. There, Metrologic introduced "Stratos," a high-volume POS scanner targeted to meet the demands of high-speed checkout at supermarkets and discount mass merchandisers. Stratos, according to the company press release, was "the world's first six-sided, 360-degree bi-optic in-counter scanner with below-counter dimensions of...four inches."[33] Such space-saving distinction proved important in world markets that preferred seated cashiers.

Two newly introduced products were renditions of the popular Voyager handheld scanner. "VoyagerBT" was the Bluetooth wireless version for point-of-sale and light warehousing markets, while "VoyagerPDF" provided two-dimensional bar code reading for moderate-volume applications such as

Stratos, which debuted in January 2003, boasted a space-saving, four-inch below-counter depth.

pharmacies and driver's license verification. The trade show also saw

Voyager BT

Metrologic product additions "Navigator" and "microQuest." Part of the portable data terminal (PDT) line, Navigator featured a back-lit screen displayed on bottom and single-handed operation. PDTs were battery-powered devices that incorporated scanning, a keypad, software, and memory in one mobile unit. Falling under the OEM, or original equipment manufacturers, category was microQuest, a new, small linear laser scanner engine with low power consumption.

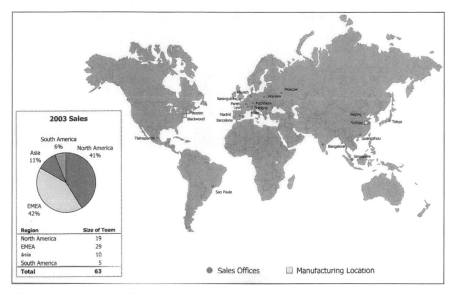

2003 Sales

Region	Size of Team
North America	19
EMEA	29
Asia	10
South America	5
Total	**63**

● Sales Offices   ☐ Manufacturing Location

Metrologic's sales offices around the globe and sales percentage by region.
Most of the company's sales were outside North America.

Metrologic's AOA introduced three new industrial products the following month, in February, at the Chicago Promat trade show. The "iQ-160," "iQ-170," and "iQTunnel" were extensions of Metrologic's iQ-180, introduced in 2001 to provide vision-based scanning for the warehouse and shipping industries. The iQ-160 scanned smaller parcels with the power of the iQ-180 but in a more compact format, while the iQ-170 was an even smaller, lower-cost scanner for flat packages. The iQTunnel provided the iQ-180 and iQ-160 products in a tunnel configuration of two- to six-sided scanning. All the iQ products could be used for one- and two-dimensional bar code reading and optical character recognition.[34]

The push of new products contributed to a record first quarter in 2003, with sales at $32.3 million, an increase of 17.3 percent compared to the same period in 2002. The 2003 first-quarter sales and net income of $1.9 million marked the largest amount of sales and net income for any quarter in Metrologic's 35-year history.[35] The start was a good omen for the year as a whole. By year-end, 2003 sales would total $138 million, with cost of those sales at $79.7 million.[36] A new sales and support office was opened in June in Moscow, Metrologic's first in Russia, recognizing a decade of Metrologic conducting business there.[37]

Net income was an impressive $13.9 million by year-end, com-

Harry speaking at Metrologic's 35th anniversary celebration, Blackwood, May 3, 2003

pared to $1.7 million in 2002. The patent portfolio quadrupled to 250 patents in five years, reflecting Metrologic's prolific product debuts and fierce protection of its intellectual property. Metrologic owned 216 U.S. and 35 foreign patents as of the annual report filing, with another 200 patent applications pending.[38]

Metrologic marked its 35th year in business in 2003 with a May 3 anniversary celebration at its Blackwood headquarters for employees, their families, and special guests. Since founding the company in 1968, Harry had shepherded Metrologic into an expansive global force in the industry. He was still motivated by loyalty to his Metrologic family and the thrill of innovation.

"In the past few years," Harry commented at the time of the 2003 celebration, "we have brought to market some of the most exciting new products in our industry....Being a part of the Metrologic organization has been an absolutely incredible and rewarding experience over the past 35 years. We have seen many triumphs during that time, from the first product we shipped, through our successful initial public offering almost 10 years ago, to our present leadership position in the auto-identification and imaging field....The drive, creativity, and dedication of the many employees we have had over the 35 years [have] been at the core of Metrologic's success."[39]

Metrologic had "transformed itself,"[40] in the words of the CEO, from the company's financial shortfalls in 2001 to a position of fiscal strength. New products were being engineered at every opportunity with accompanying market and profit expansion. The cost of sales, or the cost of manufacturing the products, was 57.7 percent of Metrologic's total sales in 2003. Indeed, as a percentage of total sales, the *cost* of sales had *declined* steadily from 74.6 percent in 2001 to 64.2 percent in 2002 to 57.7 percent in 2003.[41] Naturally, cutting costs helped the bottom line, as did a strengthening euro and a decrease in royalty fees. Metrologic had gotten leaner.

One way Metrologic had cut costs, according to its annual report, was by increasing production in Suzhou, China, where labor costs were

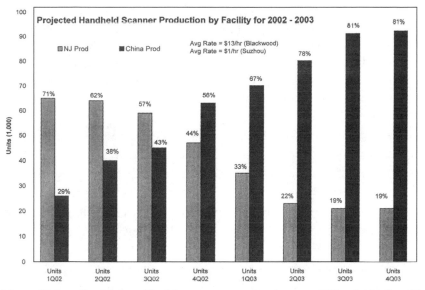

Most of Metrologic's handheld scanner production would be shifted to China, while Harry aimed to keep industrial scanners and product launches in the U.S. Chart source: C. Harry Knowles Collection

less than in the U.S. (by a factor of about ten, according to Harry).[42] The Metrologic workforce had been reduced slightly in 2002 to 852 from a 2001 level of more than 900 employees; but the numbers were back up in 2003 to 924 employees worldwide, 531 of them working at the Blackwood facility.[43] When the Suzhou facility opened in 1999, Metrologic had about 600 employees at Blackwood. Since then, production of the bulk of Metrologic's handheld scanners, which were lower-cost and higher-volume devices, shifted toward China; while industrial scanners and many of the newer products continued to be manufactured in Blackwood. "We intend to increasingly add manufacturing of other low-cost, high-volume products to Suzhou, China," stated the 2004 annual report (for year-end 2003), "to take advantage of lower costs."[44]

In an overview of the manufacturing facilities within an April 2003 e-mail to key executives and board members, Harry said:

> Strategically, we *are* planning on expanding domestically. Blackwood will continue to be our major headquarters, administration, marketing, engineering, and central manufacturing facility....We will expand administration, engineering, sales, and marketing into [some of the] spaces now occupied by manufacturing.

257

Joe [Sawitsky, manufacturing vice president,] is planning on using Blackwood production for the heavy tech items like iQ, Stratos, and all initial production of significant new products to get tight marketing feedback, quality and configuration control, and plan automation. We will maintain this posture, over the next several years, while we are establishing tighter controls at Suzhou.[45]

The critical need to cut costs to maintain financial stability while protecting a loyal workforce made for a daunting and unenviable task. CEO Harry did a better job at it than most, still holding numbers at Blackwood relatively high in 2003; but the manufacturing labor growth was targeted for Suzhou. In fact, Metrologic was scheduled to begin construction at the end of that year to double the size of the China factory from 20,000 to 40,000 square feet. Nevertheless, the U.S. facility in Blackwood dwarfed the Suzhou facility in size with 116,000 square feet, 82,000 of which were dedicated to manufacturing. Both facilities, according to the annual report, were leased until that status changed in December 2003 when Metrologic purchased the Blackwood facility from Harry and Janet Knowles for $4.79 million—less than the appraised value—to lower long-term operating costs. Plans also were made to purchase the Suzhou facility and additional land for expansion when that construction was complete.[46]

Harry's comprehensive approach to manufacturing attempted to tap into the advantages of doing business in China, while shielding his

U.S. workforce. Harry said that China's pluses included its labor costs at one-tenth that of the U.S. and an unlimited supply of well-grounded engineers. However, Harry recognized his nation's interests, specifically taking aim to protect sensitive intellectual property from loose Chinese patent laws by keeping early

Harry in Shanghai, March 2003

product development—and, thus, patents—at home in Blackwood. With key engineering and complex pilot production in the hands of top U.S. engineers, Harry thought he could protect current American workers and navigate the troubleshooting necessary to turn around new, quality products quickly. He also felt the U.S. was stronger than China in marketing those new products.[47]

"It was my decision in 1999 to open China operations," Harry reflected in 2010. "My strategy was for intelligent growth in China and to keep invention, product launch, and control at Blackwood, from where we would parcel individual jobs to Suzhou."[48] In 2003, however, Harry could not anticipate how soon he would agonize over job losses at home in the U.S. For now, he kept pushing hard to capture more of the market; new products meant more revenue to safeguard the company's viability and, thus, the employees' jobs.

An influx of cash via a second public stock offering provided another option for more financial breathing room. Board member and investment banker Bill Rulon-Miller, who had managed the 1994 IPO, proved indispensable, according to Harry, in negotiations with underwriters to prepare for a second offering. Rulon-Miller caused the others "to rise to another, much higher level of expectations, performance, and integrity," Harry said at the time.[49]

Metrologic administrators, wanting to take advantage of the company's rising stock status, filed paperwork with the SEC in July and September 2003 to offer for sale 1.5 million shares of common stock.[50] In the final quarter of 2002, Metrologic's split-adjusted share price on the NASDAQ had a high price of $2.94.[51] By the October 2003 offering, the shares would be priced at $34.50 per share.[52] In the first quarter of 2003, according to Harry, the number of Metrologic shares changing hands averaged about 15 to 20,000 per week; by June, that number was more than 200,000.[53] With increased volume resulting from a June three-for-two stock split approved by the Metrologic board[54] and the July 9 announcement that Metrologic had been included in the Russell 2000 and 3000 fund indexes[55]—which meant investment managers automatically would turn to the company as an option—the volume of Metrologic shares changing hands soared to 1.4 million by the second week of July.[56]

Metrologic leaders were gratified to see the piqued public interest. Some Metrologic board members had been nervous about how potential investors would respond to a 74-year-old CEO. At the June 19, 2003, board meeting, directors (including Harry and Janet) closed the meeting's afternoon session to non-directors and discussed the sensitive issues surrounding Metrologic's critical need for capital.[57] Without enough money on the books to sustain major product line launches until profits resulted, cash flow always would be a precarious dance. Directors asked themselves several questions: Would a second public offering generate enough funds? What effect would the issue of CEO succession have? Since Harry's eventual departure was a given, should Metrologic explore other options, such as selling the company to secure its long-term finances? The board kept options open and voted unanimously to investigate the possible sale of the company. Such an exploration, while fiscally respon-

sible, was risky. If news got back to employees that Metrologic was shopping itself around, morale would be devastated. Key executives would be included in the loop; but, for the most part, specific explorations would be kept quiet during the course of the next two or so years as leaders considered and discarded various buyout options. Following the

Harry, shown here with Rose Eife at a 2003 employee awards program, worried about honoring the trust of his employees as he and the board investigated the possible sale of Metrologic.

June meeting, as Metrologic leadership moved cautiously ahead, Harry wrote of his discomfort in a confidential e-mail to his inner circle of directors:

"I am extremely uncomfortable at having this discussion with anybody," Harry wrote, "without our being able to let those around us being in on the possibility. First, it simply is not my way of operating. I trust those around me, and they in turn have been very trustworthy, in my opinion. Second, with as many folks as will know about it knowing, the circulation of this type information is not likely to stay secret. Our credibility is at stake, and I value that commodity almost to the limit. Once broken, it is irreplaceable."[58]

The required level of energy for the second public offering, however, kept company leaders preoccupied for the most part. The board and executives had been preparing for months. While discussions about beginning a CEO search had taken place that spring; by the June board meeting, any search was deemed a distraction and postponed. However, Harry met concerns about his age by hitting the training circuit—lifting weights, walk-

The 75-year-old CEO tackled the 2003 road show with renewed vigor, selling potential investors on the value of Metrologic stock. The second public offering provided nearly $56 million in net proceeds.

ing, dieting, and meeting with a trainer three times a week. Writer Scott Goldstein chronicled Harry's transformation in an article for the weekly New Jersey business journal, *NJ Biz*: "By the time Knowles turned 75 [in] August, he had lost 20 pounds and gained tons of energy. He promptly took off on a three-week, 20-city tour to tout Metrologic stock to institutional investors, who liked what they saw and heard."[59]

The road show was hugely successful. By the time underwriters purchased additional shares, the October offering resulted in the sale of 1.725 million shares for net proceeds of $55.5 million.[60] (In contrast, the initial public offering in 1994 had netted $14.5 million with the same number of shares; but the 1994 shares had sold at $9.50 each.) The near $56 million influx in 2003 allowed Metrologic to purchase the Blackwood property from Harry and Janet and pay down debt to only $5.5 million by year-end. Because investors responded so favorably, the Metrologic board approved an October 30 two-for-one stock split after the close of the public offering. As Harry commented at the time, "this stock split reflects...our commitment to expand our shareholder base [and]...is part of the company's strategy to make Metrologic's shares more available to investors."[61]

Having more working capital gave Metrologic more flexibility with large clients such as Sears and Safeway. "It takes financial strength to go after those customers—we don't get paid until 53 days after delivery of the whole package," Harry explained in a December 2003 *Investor's Business Daily* interview. "When you chase a $10 million to $20 million deal, you've got to cut the big guys some slack. The cash reserve means we can afford to wait a little longer for payment from big guys."[62]

Metrologic attracted its share of noteworthy orders in 2003 as it marched toward its $138-million sales year. United Airlines ordered $3.7 million worth of Metrologic's IS-8500 HoloTrak scanning stations and tunnels for its baggage handling systems at its five major U.S. hubs in Chicago, Denver, Los Angeles, San Francisco, and Washington, D.C.[63] A major retailer, identified only as "one of the nation's largest department stores" in a November 2003 press release, contracted with Metrologic to provide another 8,000 Voyager MS-9520 handheld scanners. The department store chain added to 5,000 Voyager scanners installed earlier in the year.[64] Point-of-sale scanners constituted 81.7 percent of 2003 revenue for Metrologic.[65] In China, 4,000 Pulsar POS handheld scanners, manufactured at the Suzhou facility, were ordered by a cosmetics company for its stores throughout that country.[66] Rising market growth in China added to Metrologic's international sales, which accounted for almost 58 percent of the scanner company's total sales.

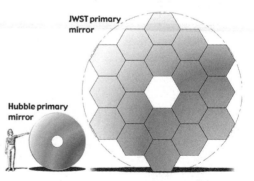

Also in 2003, Metrologic's AOA expertise attracted a contract to provide a complex electro-optics alignment subsystem for NASA's James Webb Space Telescope, the successor to the Hubble Space Telescope.[67] Jeff Yorsz, AOA president, commented on the estimated $1 million contract from Ball Aerospace and Technologies: "We are proud to be part of such an important

Comparison of Hubble and James Webb Space Telescope's primary mirrors. As part of its contract with Ball Aerospace, AOA provided an alignment system for the unique mosaic of 18 hexagonal mirrors making up one 21.3-foot, primary mirror that the Webb telescope, when launched, would use to collect light to peer deep into space.

Photo courtesy of NASA

scientific endeavor. While AOA has been providing this type of leading-edge, electro-optic solution for years, the James Webb Space Telescope requires some novel imaging concepts and also provides us with the environmental challenge of space." Other substantial AOA awards included an airline order for portable bar code reading stations for tracking U.S. mail[68] and a recurring $2.2 million field service contract.[69]

Auto-ID industry opportunities were everywhere, and Metrologic was poised to take advantage of them. Legislation such as the Health Insurance Portability and Accountability Act (HIPAA) of 1996 had prompted patient confidentiality and safety measures throughout the medical community. HIPAA's administrative regulations went into effect in April 2003. Bar codes could streamline many of the needs at hospitals by matching bar codes on patient wristbands with bar codes on medicines, charts, samples, etc. Metrologic's customized scanners and software for hospital applications earned the company a major hospital operator's order for more than 7,500 MS-9520 Voyager bar code scanners for improved patient care.[70] Additional scanners were planned for purchase, especially in light of a proposed U.S. Food and Drug Administration rule to require drug manufacturers to include bar codes on most prescription drugs. (The FDA issued its final ruling February 25, 2004, requiring such bar codes.)[71]

In speaking of the hospital operator's Voyager order, Metrologic Strategic Sales Director Greg DiNoia said, "This application is a great example of the growing need for bar code scanning in the healthcare industry....Drug manufacturers are beginning to bar code single dose medications, while healthcare facilities, pharmacies, and doctor's offices will be using the bar codes to identify, protect, and track documents, lab samples, and patient medications."

Metrologic increased market share with products such as the well-received Stratos high-volume, in-counter scanner. NCR, PSC, and Symbol all made competing devices, but Metrologic's was priced as much as 25 percent less than the rival products, according to Harry, who discussed his product strategy with journalist Peter Benesh in a December 2003 *Investor's Business Daily* article.[72] A *Philadelphia Inquirer* article, written by Wendy Tenaka in August 2003, also referenced Metrologic's success during this period compared to its competitors. "Recent accounting scandals," Tenaka wrote, "and management shake-ups at ri-

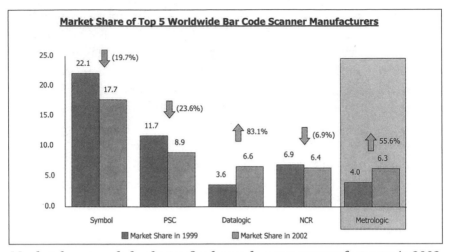

Market share trends for the top five bar code scanner manufacturers in 2002. Metrologic increased market share in 2003 with lower-priced products.
Chart source: C. Harry Knowles Collection (Venture Development Corp. and Metrologic)

vals Symbol and PSC, Inc. also have made Metrologic a more attractive stock...In June, Symbol's former chief accounting officer pleaded guilty to criminal charges of manipulating the company's financial results; and PSC is just emerging from bankruptcy."[73]

Brian Arena, then a portfolio manager with the New Jersey Division of Investments, when interviewed by Tenaka, said, "Competitors have been stumbling, and Metrologic is more advanced in some of their products. [Metrologic] got beyond its balance-sheet problems in the last year, and cut their debt level. They always had some potential. Just recently, everything seems to be clicking."

Even seemingly endless royalty and patent litigation between Metrologic and Symbol had taken a small turn in Metrologic's favor in 2003 when the U.S. District Court for the Eastern District of New York dismissed in March certain counts of Symbol's complaint that Metrologic had breached the 1996 cross-licensing agreement which detailed royalty scenarios between the two parties. Then, in December, the U.S. Court of Appeals for the Second Circuit dismissed Symbol's appeal. The glimmer of resolution would be short-lived. Despite court-compelled arbitration, Symbol continued to claim royalties were due and patents were infringed upon. Arbitration attempts stalled. Meanwhile, Metrologic had filed suit in June against Symbol for patent infringement and breach of the license agreement.[74]

"Symbol was a constant toothache," Harry said. "All the legal is-sues—all that wasted energy...But they were also a stimulus for new products just to beat them."[75]

Harry's venom for Symbol was as constant as his love for Metro-logic. As Bill Rulon-Miller commented, Harry looked at Metrologic as "his baby."[76] The 75-year-old CEO knew some questioned whether he would be able to let go. Harry had tried to step back from the reins several times in different ways. In 1982, he gave up the presidency to concentrate on scientific discovery; but the 1985 bankruptcy pulled him back in charge. Taking the company public in 1994 introduced the ele-ments of new board members, investors, and regulators. During the last decade, he had gradually released control of many functional details as he named vice presidents of manufacturing, sales, marketing, and finance. Then, he elevated Tom Mills in 1998 when he added the COO and executive vice president titles to Mills' duties as CFO. Mills became the heir apparent in 2000 when he was promoted to president and COO with the continuing responsibility to manage daily operations of Metro-logic. Still, as 2004 rang in, Harry retained the CEO title.

Janet Knowles, who had limited her work involvement since her breast can-cer in 1997, wanted her husband of 31 years to retire. Harry had cut his daily hours in the office from eight to six and included a mid-day nap, but he was a constant, guiding presence in the engi-neering labs. He also often worked dur-ing the middle of the night at home via computer with Metrologic's Germany and China offices. The frenzy of 2003's second public offering would have been

Janet, at home in Moorestown

difficult for Metrologic to navigate without Harry at the helm. Harry was Metrologic's visionary and public face.

Since Harry dominated as such a key strength, the impact of his eventual departure could be viewed as Metrologic's biggest weakness. "This company depended on Harry Knowles," board member Rulon-Miller said. "It wasn't unusual then for a company to be reliant on an individual or two. One person can't handle it all. When Tom came in as

Bruce Harrison

CFO, he looked like he had a lot of potential. It was a question of how Harry was going to build his management team. Will the trusted person grow into the role of CEO? I wasn't prepared to hand the reins over to Tom from Harry. I was prepared such a person existed."[77]

Attorney Bruce Harrison, an expert in labor law who would have an almost 20-year association with Metrologic, said, "Harry *was* the business."[78] Harrison first came to know Harry in the 1989-90 timeframe when Metrologic was still in the old Bellmawr house before the operation moved into its headquarters in Blackwood in 1990. A lead attorney with Capehart & Scatchard (a large regional business and litigation law firm) in Mount Laurel, New Jersey, at the time, Harrison had been retained by Metrologic for help with environmental and labor issues. Harry, fresh from his experience as a witness at the Symbol-Opticon trial, had little trust in the law when they met, according to Harrison. However, through the course of working on Metrologic cases over the years, Harrison became one of Harry's most trusted friends.

"The relationship between Tom [Mills] and Harry was excellent," Harrison said. "Harry was the visionary, not finance. Tom was a CPA, a detail guy. Tom was integral to the second offering. No one will invest in a company without a professional financial presence. Tom allowed Harry to really be Harry in engineering."

However, several years had elapsed since Mills had been named president, and the passing of the CEO title had yet to happen. Mills had seen the CEO search delayed at least once (at the June 19, 2003, board meeting), although the issue of succession remained prominent on board agendas. Thus, he must have been, at the least, weary of the wait and, more likely, suspicious that he would not be the chosen one after all. The comments he could read from Harry in the press were less than encouraging.

In a February 9, 2004, *NJ Biz* article, Harry talked about his reticence to retire. "First of all, I'm having fun," Harry said in the interview. "Second, I want the company not only to survive, but to thrive, and I think I can [help it] do that more effectively than anyone else."[79]

Although well liked, Mills was not seen as the Harry-style visionary. Following such a dynamic leader as Harry would be difficult for anyone, especially when Harry still actively steered the company's course. Mills decided he needed a break from his pressure-cooker role. On February 10, 2004, Metrologic announced that the president and COO had given notice of "his intention to take a year-long sabbatical of independent study and extended travel with his family."[80] Mills' resignation as an officer was effective as of February 27 and as a board director as of February 18.[81] He had become president four years earlier on February 9, 2000. Having joined Metrologic as its chief financial officer in May 1994, Mills helped in the process of taking the

Tom Mills at a dinner and roast in his honor, Philadelphia Four Seasons, February 25, 2004

company public and saw sales increase from $36 million his first year to $138 million in 2003. With Mills' resignation, Harry resumed his role as president, CEO, and chairman.

"It was a difficult personal decision," Mills said in the press release, "given the significant current and long-term opportunities that Metrologic is now beginning to realize. I am very confident with the Company's financial and product strength, and the direction in which the Company is headed. I have the utmost faith in the capabilities of the management team that is carrying forward Metrologic's market-driven focus."[82]

In the release, Harry said, "We have reluctantly accepted Tom's decision to leave and recognize the personal and family sacrifices he has made. Tom's departure is entirely personal in nature, and his decision is not related to Metrologic. We greatly appreciate Tom's contributions over the last 10 years, which have been important to the growth of the company. He will be missed by all of us. While I have agreed to resume the role of President and CEO, it is critical to emphasize that the current leadership structure in place at Metrologic will [e]nsure the continued growth of the business."

Privately, Harry reflected years later that Mills left because Harry "didn't make him the real president."[83] While Mills most likely resigned for a combination of professional and personal reasons, Mills himself professed the key reason for his departure was wanting to be a better husband to his wife, Lorie, and father to his three daughters. In a July 1, 2004, *New Jersey Business* magazine article, journalist Anthony Birritteri painted a picture of Mills' Metrologic life: "He was working late hours, was usually stuck in traffic, used the cell phone early in the morning or late at night to call company offices in Europe and China, and even took a laptop with him on vacation. The 44-year-old executive began to realize he wasn't the father or husband that he wanted to be."[84]

"I was out of balance," Mills said in the Birritteri interview, "and spent way too much of my waking moments thinking about, worrying about, and dealing with work issues. In my mind, I was justifying what I was doing....You could only do it for a period of time before you have to take a break or go stark raving mad....There was never a good time to leave Metrologic, but things were going well; and, if there was going to be a time to go, this was it."

Mills experienced an epiphany, according to the *New Jersey Business* article. "The breaking point for Mills," Birritteri wrote, "came when he missed his 10-year-old daughter Deborah's piano recital by 10 minutes because of traffic (the average commute to and from Blackwood to his home in Downington, Pennsylvania, was one-and-a-half hours). Prior to that, he missed his daughter Rebekah's 13th birthday while away on business in China. There were also the annual promises to his wife... that he would take a summer off. That never happened." While Mills did not rejoin Metrologic after his sabbatical, he later became CEO and president of the Dallastown, Pennsylvania-based Gichner Systems Group, Inc., a weapons systems division of Kratos Defense & Security Solutions serving defense contractors and the U.S. military.[85]

Mills left behind the Metrologic corporate conundrum in favor of his family; but, as founder and company visionary, Harry would find his own departure a much more entangled process.

Chapter 11

Endings

(2004-2009)

Harry in one of Metrologic's experimental scanning facilities

With Tom Mills out of the running for the CEO job, Metrologic leaders began meetings on who would succeed Harry. As recently as December 2003, analysts had lauded Harry's leadership. In Peter Benesh's December 1, 2003, *Investor's Business Daily* article, he wrote: "Analysts see [Knowles] as one of the company's great strengths. 'He's unusual,' said James Ricchiuti of Needham & Co. 'Most companies wouldn't see a founder stay at the helm. Knowles is still going strong. He's got a passion for the business.' Analyst Chris Quilty of Raymond James & Associates offers a similar view. 'He's made that crossover from founder to chief executive,' he said."[1]

Now, in 2004, there was added urgency to nail down a plan for Metrologic's future. In March, Metrologic promoted a number of its vice presidents to senior vice presidents in a move to "strengthen its management structure and address the issue of CEO succession," according to the release.[2] Benny Noens was promoted to senior vice president of EMEA sales, Joe Sawitsky to senior vice president of manufacturing and operations, Mark Schmidt to senior vice president of worldwide marketing, and Jeff Yorsz to senior vice president of industrial operations; while Greg DiNoia was promoted to vice president of North American sales and Edward Rock to director of sales administration.

"For over a year," Harry said in the release, "our Board has been evaluating the Company's overall management structure with a view towards strengthening the organization for my eventual retirement. The promotion of these key executives is a significant step in implementing this plan of CEO succession." Harry also said that the board would consider internal and external candidates.

In a May 16 e-mail to Metrologic leaders, however, Harry commented on what he felt was the undue distraction of the succession issue:

> In my opinion, the concern, while it has validity, is excessively negatively emphasized by the Board....I do not intend to retire, but to continue my slow back away from day-to-day management. I plan to continue to specifically penetrate specific problem areas, for example in [Fed-Ex Ground], *where I and those around me, feel it is appropriate.* Those exercises are positive, and highly productive, if chaotic.
>
> By my backing away, which to me is methodically being executed, management is growing and getting individually stronger. The company is increasingly working by internal organization, with little interference or guidance from me....If something were to happen to me, I have strong confidence in our Board in stepping in...and selecting at least an acting CEO from among the several candidates. And knowing the strengths of those individuals, I have total confidence in their ability to quickly shoulder the harness of those minimal things that I really do, and to do them even better than do I. [T]hey would be done differently, but that is what change is all about.[3]

The larger context of Harry's e-mail was actually a discussion of potential buyers for Metrologic. On May 19, 2004, the board met with the stated purpose: "to make a decision on the continued viability of Project Meteor," the code name for the board's investigation into selling the company.[4] UBS Investment Bank had been drafted in March to canvass interested parties; UBS gave its report on May 18. Fifteen parties were contacted. Several expressed some interest in "Meteor," including Danaher, Honeywell, NEC, and Siemens; but only one submitted a formal letter of interest with an offer of $18 to $22 per Metrologic share. With only one interested party and no competitive bargaining position, as well as the disruption to Metrologic operations a buyout would cause, the board voted to reject the offer. Harry had serious concerns about selling to the interested company, which recently had laid off 100 employees in another buyout. Pursuit of a Metrologic buyer would continue (with UBS assisting Metrologic with presentations to

more interested parties that year and beyond); but, for now, no clear direction emerged.

For the May 27 shareholders meeting, Harry, board members, and executive staff prepared for tough questions from Metrologic investors about more than succession.[5] Metrologic's stock price had fallen from about $32 a share at the beginning of the year to about $15, despite strong sales numbers the first quarter of the year (the second-best sales quarter in company history). Since sales were going well, the stock drop was perplexing; but some suggested the price was artificially deflated after short sales (when investors made transactions in anticipation of a decrease in share price).

Of course, the share price decline followed soon after the February 2004 departure of Metrologic president and COO Tom Mills; so the transition may have prompted a perception of instability. However, Harry felt he had underplayed profit predictions for 2004 and that may have affected stock price.[6] Or, perhaps the stock was volatile after so much activity with the second public offering and splits.

Still, materials from the board meeting, held the same day, indicated a company rich with contracts and prospects.[7] Household-name retail accounts active in 2004 included: Abercrombie & Fitch, Burlington Coat Factory, Crate & Barrel, Sears, Safeway, Movie Gallery, Family Dollar, Chico's, GNC, and new accounts Sunoco and Sherwin-Williams. Several other accounts were listed as pending, but it is unclear on most whether "pending" equated to imminent contracts. They included: KB Toys, Albertson's, Ralph Lauren, Party City, Target (which would contract with Metrologic in 2005), Circuit City, Whole Foods, Michael's, and Publix.

On the industrial side, Metrologic was expecting additional business from automated package handling leader Fed-Ex Ground, the ultimate "big fish" for tunnel scanner sales, potentially totaling about $27 million worth of orders in 2004, 2005, and 2006 as part of its $1.8 billion automation program. Metrologic's 2004 Fed-Ex Ground scanner installations were a test and training for future installations. If Metrologic won over Fed-Ex Ground, any resulting contract announcement probably would raise Metrologic's stock price, as well as spur other package handlers—such as USPS, UPS, DHL, and others—to follow suit. In a May internal e-mail, Harry discussed the extreme delivery and product demands of the Fed-Ex deal, along with the expectation of losing money during fulfillment of the first part of the contract in order to land the profits from the remainder of the Fed-Ex award. Nonetheless, Harry's characteristic enthusiasm was clear in the memo, saying, "This is the most exciting single piece of business that we have ever seen. It looks like we can do it...and we will!"[8]

In addition, Metrologic's AOA could boast of its National Ignition Facility (NIF) contracts (going through 2008) from Lawrence Livermore National Labs, including the most recent $2.8 million contract for light source launcher assemblies announced in February[9] and the ongoing $6.3 million output sensor package production contract. The NIF, located in Livermore, California, housed the world's largest laser system, which not only advanced basic science and fusion energy research, but allowed safe evaluation of U.S. nuclear weapons systems. The $270 million-dollar facility was managed by the National Nuclear Security Administration and the University of California's Lawrence Livermore National Laboratory but resulted from the collaboration of agencies, laboratories, universities, and industries nationwide.

A month prior to the board meeting, Metrologic had introduced the "IS-3480 QuantumE," a new combination omni-directional and single-line scan engine for original equipment manufacturer (OEM) devices.[10] This product offering was followed up later in the year with the October introduction of "MS-3480 QuantumT" at the National Association of Convenience Stores Tradeshow. The QuantumT, Metrologic's first hands-free, omni-directional bar code scanner with capability for single-line scanning, replaced the MS-6520 Cubit and was targeted for outlets

QuantumT

such as convenience stores and pharmacies.[11]

Thus, despite the succession distractions, Metrologic was busy with normal operations, taking its scanning products to market in more than 110 countries through its 17 offices worldwide.[12] Since 2000, Metrologic had introduced 16 new products as of the annual report filing and would spend $7.5 million on research and development by the end of 2004. In November 2004, Metrologic an

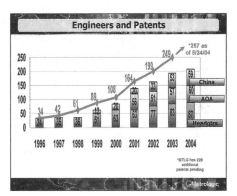

Patents continued to climb—to 257 in May 2004, but they would reach 300 by November of that year.

Chart source: C. Harry Knowles Collection

nounced it had received its 300th patent from the U.S. Patent and Trademark Office;[13] by March 1, 2005, that total would be 263 U.S. patents and 53 foreign patents, with more than 225 other patent applications on file with the PTO.[14]

With more than a thousand full-time employees—about 600 of them at Blackwood and almost 200 in China—helping fuel Metrologic, the company achieved a significantly improved sales year. Metrologic's year-end 2004 sales totaled $178 million compared to $138 million in 2003, with a 2004 net income of $22.7 million. The cost of 2004 sales shot to $96 million (compared to $79.7 million in 2003).[15] Sales offices expanded in 2004, with Metrologic announcing the opening of new sales offices in Bangalore, India, and Warsaw, Poland, and a third office in China in Beijing—heralding Metrologic's operation of offices in 14 countries.[16]

However, in the spring of 2004, the board expressed heightened concern about the company's future. "The board was scared," Harry said. "I was in my 70s. They said, 'We need an exit strategy for you, Harry.' I wanted to give the senior vice presidents more testing time, but the pressure was on. Prematurely, I appointed a president."[17] On June 22, 2004, Metrologic announced the promotion of Benny Noens, formerly senior vice president of EMEA (Europe, Middle East, and Africa) sales, to president and CEO and his addition to the board of directors. Harry remained as chairman of the board.[18]

The six-foot-three Noens had been the driving force behind phe-

273

Benny Noens

nomenal sales growth in Europe, leading EMEA sales to nearly $56 million in 2003 from $3.5 million in 1991, the year after joining Metrologic as the German subsidiary's sales manager. He also had served as board member and director for several subsidiaries throughout Europe. "The European operation was a juggernaut under Benny," attorney Bruce Harrison said. "He spoke seven or so languages and was extremely well liked."[19] Taking Noens' EMEA responsibilities would be Mark Ryan, who was promoted to the position of director of EMEA sales.[20]

"This 'changing of the guard,'" Harry said in the Noens press release, "is a part of Metrologic's long-range strategy of building a solid basis for the Company's continued growth....Benny was selected from a talented group of excellent senior management. His proven record of intelligent leadership, integrity, sales growth in Europe and his handling of strategic acquisitions are impressive." In turn, Noens commented that his "top priority is to continue the vision that Harry started over 36 years ago. Under his leadership, Metrologic has grown into the strong company it is today."[21]

Handing the baton brought deeply mixed feelings for Harry. Investment banker and board member Bill Rulon-Miller said, "Some thought that Harry was not good at training other people to run the company—that he was not willing to let go. Harry had no problem delegating to the CFO or to an engineer. But the next step of delegating to a CEO to take his place was much harder."[22]

In one sense, Harry was still mid-stride directing Metrologic when he named Benny CEO. Harry had continued to enjoy the challenge and, even at age 76, had proven perfectly able many times over. When asked whether he found himself spread too thin running Metrologic, Harry responded, "I never looked at it that way. I thoroughly enjoyed it. I found the challenges satisfying."[23]

Harry especially relished the scientific discovery involved in the product development process. Virtually all of the 300-plus Metrologic patents had his name on them. He had attempted to mitigate the distracting noise of the accounting issues along the way by delegating daily operations and spending as much time as possible with the research engineers. No one could love Metrologic more than the founder, who had taken one idea in 1968 and grown it into a global powerhouse—not to mention a livelihood for more than a thousand people.

However, the pressure to name a successor had become too intense, and Harry acquiesced. He could maintain a guiding role as chairman of the board and back away from daily appearances. In fact, Harry said he was essentially staying home when Benny took over. Harry welcomed the flexibility of hours, as did Janet after several years of nudging her husband towards retirement. Harry wasn't exactly walking away from Metrologic; but he did recognize he would have more time to focus on his newest treasure, the Knowles Science Teaching Foundation (KSTF), which he and Janet had established in 1999 to support high school science and math teachers. In fact, in April, Harry had gifted one million shares of Metrologic to KSTF, which already held more than 600,000 shares.[24]

When Metrologic threw an October 2004 retirement party for its founder, guests gathered in New Jersey from all over the world to honor Harry. Harry was astounded and gratified by the money represented in

Friends, colleagues, and employees gathered to honor Harry at a retirement dinner October 21, 2004. The roomful of guests included: top left, Herb and Claire Gottlieb; center, Harry and Metrologic board member John Hsu; and top right photo, from left, Lucy and Boyce Adams, Hella and Scott McVay, and Carolyn Carr (daughter of Harry's mentor, Auburn physics professor Howard Carr).

the room, especially that held by employees who became millionaires through the value of their Metrologic stock options. "There were 24 or so Metrologic employee millionaires," Harry said, "another 20-plus half-millionaires, and 30 or so vendors who had made millions. It was a rewarding experience."[25]

Harry had first found a little cash source for Metrologic in 1969 when he launched helium-neon laser kit sales from a *Popular Electronics* cover appearance. That educational line was a mainstay for the struggling company for many years until finally it, too, "retired" from Metrologic the same year Harry did. In November 2004, Metrologic sold its educational laser products line to Tempe, Arizona-based Industrial Fiber Optics.[26]

Metrologic's impressive sales numbers in 2004 received a considerable boost from an acquisition process begun earlier in the year with Omniplanar, a leader in two-dimensional imaging software such as "SwiftDecoder," which Metrologic had licensed since 2000 for its iQ industrial vision-based line. Metrologic announced September 27 it had acquired 100 percent of Omniplanar's stock for $13 million.[27] Not only would Metrologic save on licensing fees and gain proprietary software, but the Princeton, New Jersey-based company brought with it an impressive clientele, including Fed-Ex, UPS, USPS, Lockheed, Siemens, and Northrop. Within a week of the acquisition, Metrologic promoted its product marketing director Garrett Russell to general manager of Omniplanar.[28] In April the following year, Omniplanar added another giant—Adobe—as a licensee of its in-demand Swift-Decoder bar code software.[29]

Following the June 2004 appointment of Benny Noens as president and CEO, chairman Harry, naturally, was less involved in the company's engineering development and abandoned his role as primary Metrologic spokesman. Noens became the prevailing voice for press releases and the public face for appearances—such as on September 29, 2004, when Metrologic celebrated the 10-year anniversary of its NASDAQ listing and Noens opened the day's NASDAQ stock market.[30] Still, Harry, concerned about all the unfinished projects, was a stern taskmaster for Noens and was a dominant force in the board room as chairman. In 2005, Harry controlled about 44 percent of Metrologic's stock and, according to the annual report, had "significant influence over the ability to determine the outcome of all corporate actions requiring shareholder approval."[31]

Metrologic faced triumphs and challenges in 2005 on its way to surpassing $200 million in sales for the first time in corporate history. Sales totaled $210 million by the end of the year (compared to $178 million in 2004), with the 2005 cost of sales at $120 million. New sales offices were opened in Thailand, Taiwan, Australia, Korea, and China (its fifth). Patents, which had tripled in the past five years, numbered more than 365, with 195 patents pending. Research and development expenses were $8.5 million. Net income amounted to $17.8 million in 2005, down from $22.7 million in net income in 2004. There were two main reasons for the decline: the fall purchase of Omniplanar inflated the 2004 figure; and, in 2005, Metrologic was hit with $12.6 million in Symbol litigation costs.[32]

When the court system had dismissed Symbol's appeal in 2003, Symbol had followed with a June 26, 2003-filed claim that eleven of Metrologic's products were royalty-bearing (under the 1996 license agreement between Metrologic and Symbol) and that, alternatively, those products infringed upon Symbol patents—even though these were the same products found to be outside the license agreement by the U.S. District Court for the Eastern District of New York and the Court of Appeals for the Second Circuit.[33] However, Symbol's dogged persistence was rewarded in August 2005 when, after an arduous arbitration process, the final ruling declared that three Metrologic products (of the eleven in Symbol's claim) were royalty-bearing, including the MS-9520 Voyager and MS-6220 Pulsar. A February 2006 ruling by the U.S. Federal District Court in the Southern District of New York affirmed the arbitrator's ruling, prompting Metrologic's requirement to pay past royalties and interest totaling $14.4 million through December 2005.[34]

Meanwhile, Metrologic had filed two separate suits against Sym-

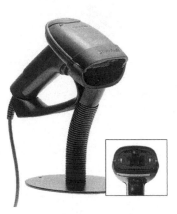

Metrologic shifted from lasers to cameras with the MS-1690 Focus, adding two-dimensional capability.

bol, one in June 2003 and another in May 2005, claiming patent infringement and breach of the royalty license agreement. Symbol answered with two more patent lawsuits (in September 2005 and March 2006) against Metrologic; the suits named products found previously by the arbitrator to be outside the existing cross-license agreement.[35] The Metrologic-Symbol relationship—or lack thereof—was a nightmare.

"Symbol was combative and confrontational," Rulon-Miller said, "in their defense of intellectual property and all their assets. Symbol was the thorn that never went away."[36]

Another longstanding exchange of patent lawsuits between Metrologic and PSC, Inc., resulted in an August 2005 settlement, in which Metrologic received a $2.25 million cash payment. The parties dismissed all claims, agreeing not to sue each other under defined parameters.[37] That peace continued for less than a year. Resolving all pending litigation would prove elusive, if not impossible, for any large company; but Metrologic's lawsuits with Symbol were particularly entrenched and posed a hindrance to potential buyers of the company.

Despite the licensing agreement problems with Symbol, in August 2005, Metrologic entered into another cross-license agreement—this one with Intermec IP Corp., a division of Intermec, Inc.[38] Intermec held more than 145 patents related to one of the auto-ID industry's newer expanding technologies: radio frequency identification, or RFID. The agreement provided the two companies access to each other's RFID technology. While reliability issues were still being addressed, the RFID "smart labels" had distinct advantages compared to the standard UPC label: RFID could read and write more information and labels could be read in batches instead of as individual item scans. Smart labels would enjoy increasing use in the future in applications ranging from cattle tracking to consumer products, inventory control, and pet identification and would spark a fierce debate concerning the privacy rights of consumers.

Metrologic was highly proactive in its pursuit of new technology and products. In 2005, several products debuted, including Metrologic's first handheld imaging product, the "MS-1690 Focus," which was introduced at the January National Retail Federation trade show.[39] Two-dimensional vision-based instead of line-oriented laser-based, the MS-1690 Focus incorporated Omniplanar's SwiftDecoder software, allowing omni-directional reading of linear and two-dimensional bar codes, as well as photo capabilities. "With Focus, the product line was rounding out," patent prosecutor Tom Perkowski commented. Perkowski said that Focus could be considered a landmark product for Metrologic, marking an engineering shift for Harry from lasers to cameras. (Focus would later evolve into the camera-based "Genesis" product line.) "It was a fertile time," said Perkowski.[40]

When the engineering prototype for Focus had been developed almost two years earlier, in Spring 2003, Harry commented that Focus, "our mega-pixel, two-dimensional imaging handheld," was Metrologic's "best bet" to combat speed problems being experienced by their Quantum scanner. "Focus will soon break down into a spectrum of products," Harry predicted, "from low-cost, 1D ruggedized and miniaturized engines, through the present concept of Focus, all the way up to industrial-caliber, two-dimensional image capture engines. The main cost and performance criteria [and] barriers will be in the speed and breadth of the power of the [p]rocessor capturing and manipulating the image."[41]

The line-oriented "MS-2200 StratosS," part of the high-volume, POS Stratos scanner line, also was introduced in 2005, becoming Metrologic's first five-sided, bi-optic in-counter laser scanner that June.[42] On July 22, 2005, Metrologic announced that United Kingdom retail giant Tesco was testing the Stratos line in its stores for a possible order of 2,000 scanners.[43] (The pilot would prove successful, with Tesco increasing

Tesco Stratos

the potential order to 3,500 scanners in 2006 and placing an order for 1,300 MS-2220 StratosS scanners for Central European Tescos.)[44] In September 2005, Metrologic debuted the "SP-5500 OptimusS" portable data terminal as part of its handheld mobile computer

OptimusS

line.[45] New products often took time to impact the

marketplace, but Metrologic's Focus caught industry attention quickly. By August, Target had signed an agreement with Metrologic to provide MS-1690 Focus scanners to its retail stores.[46]

Other significant product orders included AOA's ongoing proprietary contracts, such as a $5.4 million bump on an existing contract which, over the course of several years, represented a $25 million commitment to Metrologic's optical systems subsidiary.[47] AOA also continued to attract increased funding from Lawrence Livermore National Laboratory for the National Ignition Facility construction project. Additional orders to Metrologic in 2005 included more contracts for handheld scanners—3,000 MS-5145 Eclipse scanners for Canada's 2005 elections and 10,000 Voyager series scanners for a European retailer.[48]

Although Metrologic attracted its share of new business, orders declined by 24 percent in its industrial product lines (mostly because of the end or loss of contracts), and retail handheld and projection scanners experienced lower-than-average selling prices in European markets.[49] Added to the mix were the year's ongoing legal costs. Thus, on June 16, 2005, Metrologic revised its revenue projections for 2005 downward and announced unspecified staff reductions to cut costs.[50] While Metrologic ended the year actually meeting its original revenue projections with a $210 million sales year, its $17.8 million net income fell short of projections.

Under constant investor pressure for profits, companies often adjusted their income projections from quarter to quarter. Now, CEO and President Benny Noens had his turn feeling that scrutiny in his first full year at the helm. "Management is committed to building a strong, profitable company that will improve and maximize shareholder value," Noens said in a September press release announcing the appointment of a corporate development director tasked with finding new business.[51] The corporate-speak masked what would prove to be Noens' growing discomfort as chief executive.

As the Metrologic leadership headed into 2006, major changes were on the horizon. The board continued to consider buyout options. Chairman Harry Knowles was well aware of the challenges to demonstrate profits, settle lawsuits, and continuously adjust to industry and manufacturing shifts. Despite some cuts, Metrologic employed 1,400 full-time employees worldwide that winter.[52] Internal 2006 reports numbered employees between 600 and 700 at the Blackwood, New Jersey,

As this slide from the Metrologic June 2006 shareholders meeting indicates, expansion was planned at both the Suzhou and Blackwood, New Jersey, plants. However, handheld and projection scanner manufacturing had shifted mostly to China.

headquarters and more than 500 in Suzhou.[53] The Suzhou, China, facility, now doubled in size with 46,000 square feet, manufactured close to 70 percent of handheld and projection scanners for the company. More expansion was planned in China, where labor costs were less; but upgrades were also planned at Blackwood, where advanced engineering, prototyping, and automation efforts dominated and the basic intellectual property rights would remain on U.S. soil.

Coming out of the prototype phase in February 2006 was a new product in the handheld Focus scanner line. Metrologic debuted the "MS-1633 FocusBT" at a healthcare trade show in San Diego, marking a combination of the two-dimensional Focus "with the flexibility of Bluetooth wireless technology."[54] The healthcare industry was an expanding market for Metrologic, which announced an agreement with EnovateIT in February to provide bar code scanners in hospitals and an agreement with patient monitoring company Spacelabs Medical in March to have Spacelabs sell Metrologic scanners.[55] Another agreement also came in March for Metrologic to provide identification card specialist Intelli-Check with a customized version of Focus scanners for its encoded ID card software that serviced the producers of driver's licenses and military identification cards.[56] Also that spring, Metrologic began serving Systeme U, France's largest co-operative retailer, which had begun an installation of more than 9,000 bar code scanners in its stores. Metrologic would provide a range of products, including the Stratos, VoyagerBT, and Orbit scanners to the French company.[57]

Harry at a KSTF meeting, circa 2005. While Harry attempted to shift more attention to his Knowles Science Teaching Foundation, that would prove difficult in 2006 when Metrologic crises demanded Harry's presence.

While Metrologic attracted new customers and debuted new scanners in 2006, the products represented had been shepherded through engineering and prototype development some time before—when Harry was CEO. As chairman, Harry worried that engineering and strategic planning were beginning to lag. However, he was trying to balance his active concern for Metrologic with planning for his future. As part of his estate planning, he announced plans to sell about 400,000 shares of his and Janet's Metrologic stock over the next six months. They owned 8.1 million shares, from which they, according to the February press release, were donating another one million shares to their foundation, KSTF. KSTF, with the latest Knowles gift, would own 2.5 million shares but planned to sell about 400,000 shares.[58]

Harry's gradual withdrawal from Metrologic was about to hit a wall. First, vice president and general counsel Nancy A. Smith resigned, effective March 10, 2006.[59] Weary from work overload, including the ongoing Symbol battles, Smith ended her ten-year service to Metrologic. Harry asked attorney Bruce Harrison to step in as general counsel. "Nancy was a plain-spoken, good person—capable and honest," Harrison said. "Her leaving led to my employment. I knew that the company was for sale. Harry was open about the challenges, but I [am] a challenge junkie. I knew and had affection for the people and the company. I was 59. I hoped it would be my last job."[60] With such critical litigation pending, Harry said it was "such a relief" when Harrison agreed to fill the vacancy. "Bruce worked with Metrologic at the most difficult times," Harry said.[61]

The difficulties didn't end there, as board members and CEO Benny Noens reached a battleground. Noens, according to Harry, wanted to settle with Symbol for a percentage (possibly four percent after a Symbol starting offer of seven percent) of *all* gross sales; while Harry and fellow board members saw that concession as inconceivable. Noens, whom Harry had recommended for the CEO job, was widely recognized as one of the company's pioneers in building European sales since he had joined the company in 1990. However, as board member Bill Rulon-Miller said, being "good at sales alone doesn't make a CEO."[62]

On April 20, 2006, after less than two years, Metrologic announced Noens' resignation from the position of CEO and president for "personal reasons."[63] "I am pleased with the success that Metrologic has achieved during my tenure as chief executive officer and president....I regret having to make this decision at this time in the company's history," Noens stated in the press release. His resignation would be effective July 1, but his oversight of the company had ended.

The April statement detailed the formation of an "Office of the Chief Executive," consisting of Harry, Noens (until he left in July), and newly promoted executives: Mark Schmidt, promoted to executive vice president of strategic initiatives; Joe Sawitsky, promoted to executive vice president of operations; and recent addition Frank Zirnkilton, executive vice president and chief administrative officer (whose position would be eliminated by August). The group would "manage the company through this period of transition" while looking for a replacement for Noens. The press release also announced Bruce Harrison's appointment as vice president and general counsel and board director Richard Close's appointment as chairman of the AOA board.

Management by the Office of the Chief Executive was "awkward," Harrison said; but, effectively, Harry was CEO again. (He was named interim CEO in July when Noens' tenure ended.) "There was one guy in charge—Harry," said Rulon-Miller. "There are many ways to create a succession plan. To some degree, [the Office of the Chief Executive] was done to give the board a closer look at potential CEOs."[64]

Reaction to Noens' surprise resignation was swift. Metrologic's stock price fell from $21.90 per share the day before the announcement to $18.80 per share the day after.[65] By May 10, shares dropped to $16.41 after an announcement that 2006 net income was projected to be 30 percent less than previously forecast. The February 28 court ruling which had stipulated that Metrologic pay $14.4 million in past royalties to Symbol also added to the cumulative market reaction. Yet, sales and income were both up from 2005. With the year's revenue still forecast to be 20 percent more than 2005's $210 million, analysts did not seem alarmed. A May 11, 2006, *Philadelphia Inquirer* article quoted JP Morgan Chase & Chase analyst Paul Coster as concluding that Metrologic's revenue line "was good...which suggests to me that the changes being made are being made from a position of strength. It is much worse when you're reacting to a situation, but they seem to be in command."[66]

Harry, shown above in 2006, found resuming CEO duties a challenge as he explored viable options for Metrologic's future without him.
AU Photographic Services

The Philadelphia Inquirer's April 22, 2006, coverage of Noens' resignation offered a peek at the scenario which may have played out behind the scenes at Metrologic. Harry, according to the Jane Bergen article, said that "Noens may have chafed under increased supervision by the board of directors because it cramped his independent style, which had been instrumental in expanding the company. 'Our margins were dropping, and the board felt it was time to make some strategic moves,' Knowles said....In July 2004, Noens returned from Europe to become the chief executive, and his independent management style permitted Knowles to retire effectively from the company, confident that the company would grow, Knowles said. 'Benny strategically organized Metrologic to get the place running without my daily attention,' Knowles said." The article also mentioned that Harry said the board played a more active supervisory role as a requirement of the 2002 Sarbanes-Oxley Act regulating corporate governance. "I think Benny probably found it a little constraining," Harry said in the interview.

The Metrologic founder, back in as CEO, looked at the options for his beloved company. "Reversing Benny's presidency was messy," Harry reflected in 2008.[67] "I had stopped physical training I'd done in 2003. If I'd been in physical shape, I wouldn't have had a problem. I was in a panic on how to get out." No simple solutions existed that would enable Harry to disengage. He could not sell much of his Metrologic stock in the public arena without initiating a heavy market pressure to sell and causing the share price to drop precipitously.

"I entertained the idea of a private buyout," Harry said. "There was a financial model for buying out public stock. By going private, we could get rid of $2 million a year in overhead. But the real, underlying reason was, as a private company, we could strategically invest without the demand for immediate profit, quarterly results. Also, there was flexibility to work with other companies. The model was fantastic, but, at my age, I didn't have the credibility with banks to borrow the $200 million needed."

Bill Rulon-Miller

Bill Rulon-Miller, commenting on the 2006 situation years later, said that if Harry didn't sell Metrologic, he would be forced to sell. "In my investment banking profession, selling was the outcome I expected one day. It was Harry's idea to sell. The advice from the board was to sell. Harry did everything he could to ensure the transition was as smooth as possible, especially for the employees. [We were] very concerned with getting as good a price as possible. There was an obligation to shareholders, employees, and the community."[68]

Harry and the board had tried to shop Metrologic to other manufacturing companies since 2003, but the succession problems and lawsuits kept most buyers at bay. When two parties had expressed interest, Metrologic had decided not to sell. Faced with the growing urgency to sell, Harry turned to private equity firms. Private equity firms are specialists in raising capital, usually through debt, from investors to acquire the private assets of a company, thus gaining ownership. One typical approach of private equity firms is to borrow money to take public companies private, restructure, then sell the acquired company at a profit—which can be an extremely large return on their actual invested equity.

One of the world's largest technology-focused private equity firms, Francisco Partners, was interested in Metrologic, as was hedge fund Elliott Associates. Metrologic and Francisco had first discussed possibilities in October 2005, but Metrologic had rejected a December 2005 Francisco indication of interest as too low.[69] Harry contacted Francisco in June 2006 to resume talks. "Within weeks, we were down the chute with Francisco," Harry said. "The board supported it. In less than six months, we had conceived the approach and completed the sale. Francisco effectively owned the company."[70]

Bruce Harrison

On September 12, 2006, Metrologic announced the agreement to be acquired for $433 million cash[71] by a group of investors, led by Francisco Partners and including Harry and Elliott Associates.[72] In other words, Francisco (and its investors), Harry, and Elliott had put up the money to buy out Metrologic and turn the public company back into a private company. "It was stunning how fast it happened," Bruce Harrison said. "It was warp speed."[73]

A special committee of the board, consisting of independent directors, unanimously approved the merger agreement and recommended shareholder approval. "Under the terms of the agreement," the press release stated, "Metrologic shareholders will receive $18.50 in cash for each share of Metrologic common stock....The transaction is expected to be completed in the fourth quarter of 2006..."[74] Along with regulatory approvals, the agreement was subject to shareholder approval. However, Janet and Harry, who controlled about 41.5 percent of the stock with their approximately 10 million shares, and Elliott Associates, with its 7.5 percent, voted in favor. By the completion of the deal, Harry and Janet's ownership in Metrologic dropped to 15 percent.

"We believe that this transaction is in the best interest of our shareholders, customers, partners, and employees," Harry said in the announcement. "Metrologic plans to maintain its headquarters in Blackwood, N.J.," the release stated, "and to continue its sales and manufacturing activities out of its current locations. Metrologic does not anticipate any changes to the operations of the business."

Francisco Partners, Rulon-Miller explained, was a private equity buyout firm. "Francisco was high-end and highly regarded with a good track record," Rulon-Miller said. "They knew how they were going to manage. Investors provided money for a period of time. Their plan was to continue to grow the company, then sell it for investment profit. The board had mixed emotions when the time came to sell. But it was time to do it."[75]

On December 21, 2006, the Francisco acquisition was completed and Metrologic stock ceased to trade on the NASDAQ market.[76] Harry had continued as chairman and interim CEO until the December completion of the acquisition. Then, with the Francisco purchase, the old board was dissolved and a private one took its place. In January 2007, Harry stepped down as chair, although he was placed on the board of the succeeding company and was still serving as interim CEO. He had no plans to stay. Hiring a top national recruitment firm, Harry continued the search for his replacement.

As part of the agreement with Francisco, Metrologic had agreed to sell its subsidiary, Adaptive Optics Associates (AOA). On October 2, 2006, Metrologic—largely through the efforts of AOA board chairman Richard Close—completed the sale of AOA to Essex Corp. for $40.3 million cash, which was applied toward the privatization of Metrologic.[77] Revenue for 2006, according to the second quarter (June 30) projections, was expected to range between $245 and $255 million with net income between $19 and $21 million. Both ranges represented increases over 2005 sales ($210 million) and net income ($17.8 million).[78] Exact figures were not transparent, since Metrologic was now a private company and no corporate annual report was filed with the SEC.

While 2006 had been consumed with the Francisco purchase, other business of note occurred during Harry's final period as CEO of Metrologic. That spring, Metrologic acquired the private Needham, Massachusetts-based firm Visible-RF, which offered distinct radio frequency communications technology and expanded Metrologic's radio frequency identification (RFID) market.[79] The transaction came on the heels of Metrologic introducing its initial line of RFID readers at a Las Vegas RFID trade show—the "SP-5800 Maximus" series and the "MR-600 Impulse" series.[80] In May, Metrologic subsidiary Omniplanar launched new software for its SwiftDecoder two-dimensional engine. "Swift-OCR" provided high-speed optical character recognition, while "Swift-Verify" decoded and verified linear bar code print quality.[81] Finally, in

October Metrologic released its next advance on one of the company's best-selling small, omni-directional hands-free scanners, the MS-7120 Orbit. The "MS-7180 OrbitCG" debuted at the National Association of Convenience Stores show and incorporated patented CodeGate technology.[82]

Metrologic's POS scanners were ranked first in 2006 in a survey of almost 300 value-added resellers by *VSR* (Vertical Systems Reseller), a trade publication.[83] Metrologic scored 22.5 out of 25 possible points and beat out Symbol, PSC, and Hand Held Products. Metrologic won the honor again in 2007. Harry received a prestigious honor himself when he was inducted into the New Jersey Business Hall of Fame at the 2006 *NJ Biz* Business of the Year Awards ceremony.[84] It was a fitting recognition of his entrepreneurial career in New Jersey.

Harry at his induction into the New Jersey Business Hall of Fame, 2006

Harry's last year at the helm, like most years, had its share of litigation. PSC filed a suit May 10, 2006, in the U.S. District Court in Oregon claiming that the Metrologic Stratos line infringed on two PSC patents—which Metrologic disputed.[85] (The 2005 agreement covered products sold prior to March 16, 2005.) In June, however, litigation in Metrologic's May 2005 suit against Symbol was decided in Metrologic's favor, resulting in Symbol owing unpaid royalties dating back to 2004. The June 30, 2006, total due from Symbol was estimated at more than $2.6 million.[86] Still, much of the ongoing Symbol litigation had yet to be settled.

As the Francisco board, chaired by its founder and managing partner Dipanjan Deb, took its place in January 2007, Harry proposed purchasing land north of Metrologic's Blackwood property to outfit a "campus" of sorts for expanding U.S. engineering and pilot production on new products. However, Francisco squelched the idea by denying the purchase. Francisco wasn't interested in adding more expense; as a private equity firm, it was in the business of making money on its investment. Francisco "knew how to buy, hold, and sell," said now Metrologic general counsel Bruce Harrison. "To Francisco's credit, they didn't pretend it was a long-term buy."[87]

In January came layoffs targeted to cut waste. Employees had grown increasingly anxious in 2006 as they became well aware of Metrologic's impending sale to Francisco. Their fears were justified. Harry was distraught for his loyal Metrologic family as cuts began; he argued for the expansion of Blackwood operations. In 2010, he would say the layoffs sparked his final departure.[88] When Harry and Francisco hired a new CEO in March 2007, Harry ended any semblance of daily involvement. By May 2007, he was off the board completely and had liquidated his remaining 15 percent interest (1.5 million shares) in the company. He was retired for the second time.

On March 26, 2007, Darius Adamczyk was named CEO to succeed Harry.[89] A Harvard MBA graduate, Adamczyk was a former president of Ingersoll Rand's Air Solutions Group. He also held two engineering degrees—a master's in computer engineering from Syracuse and a Michigan State degree in electrical and computer engineering. "Darius' management approach was different than Harry," general counsel Bruce Harrison commented. "He hired a vice president of engineering and drove his carefully constructed system, but he was not involved in the products. But he had Harry's corps of engineers. Darius was decisive, unemotional...impressive."[90]

That year, when the human resources director departed on medical leave, Harrison, already deep in litigation work for Metrologic, became HR director by default. "Harry had been there for the first layoff in January, but there were two horrible layoffs after he left," Harrison said. From April to June, hundreds of employees lost their jobs. "We cut long-service, good employees," Harrison said. "Harry had a deep feeling of guilt to the people who lost their jobs. He was generous and compassionate."

Harry's tenure at Metrologic had ended, almost 40 years after it had begun. When asked what he was proudest of, without hesitation, he said, "Building a team of people based on quality thought. We had mutual respect for one another and an atmosphere of truthfulness. You don't build a quality engineering organization without that. The inventors and I had zero clashes. And the people on the production floor had incredible respect for Janet and me. The operators are important. They love you caring, solving."[91]

On the invention side of Harry's Metrologic career, Harry would list six "firsts" as the most important:[92]

1) "programmable" scanners in the sense that the fast, hard-wired transistor-to-transistor-logic (TTL) Metrologic employed in 1975 in its Monitor 101 and Verifier 315 equated to an advanced digitally programmable processor;

2) handheld scanners with built-in decoding of the bar code's product information within the scanner, such as with the 1982 MS-190 series;

3) mini-slot scanners, the MS-260 series, debuted in 1985, which brought the advantage of grocery-store-style, in-counter scanning to smaller retail outlets in miniature form;

4) revolutionary triggerless (automatic) handheld scanners that, in 1991 as the MS-900 series (which evolved into the Voyager), resurrected Metrologic's business after the Symbol lawsuit-induced injunction against Metrologic triggered scanners such as the successful MS-290 handheld;

5) handheld, omni-directional scanners including the MS-6720, which was introduced in 1996 and could be held or stationed for fixed scanning; and

6) planar laser illumination and imaging, or PLIIM, scanners that began with Metrologic's introduction of "iQ" products, including the iQ-180, Metrologic and AOA's first joint project in 2001, a camera-based imaging system targeted for the parcel-handling industry offering linear and two-dimensional scanning. The continuing effort of PLIIM brought powerful potential to both industrial and retail products by providing high resolution over long distances at high speed.

The breadth and depth of Harry's work, in fact, could be seen throughout the products debuted in 2007 and beyond. At the annual New York National Retail Federation trade show alone, Metrologic announced four new products in 2007 and an amazing ten products in Metrologic's 40th year, 2008—all stemming from Harry's genius. "Harry is one of the pre-eminent scientists on the face of the earth," Harrison said.[93]

"He should be extraordinarily proud," Rulon-Miller added, "for providing a livelihood for so many people, a business for the community, and advancement for the state and the country."[94]

Francisco Partners was true to its purpose. On April 28, 2008, less than two years after its acquisition of Metrologic, Francisco announced an agreement for Honeywell International to buy Metrologic for $720 million in cash. Honeywell intended to merge Metrologic with its automation and control solutions business, Honeywell Security.[95] A critical accomplishment paved the way for Honeywell to buy: Metrologic and Symbol, which had been bought by, ironically, Harry's former employer Motorola in January 2007, settled their long-running legal disputes. Metrologic's Bruce Harrison and his counterparts at Symbol/Motorola resolved all pending litigation in December 2007.[96] Meanwhile, Honeywell had bought Hand Held Products (HHP), one of a handful of image-based competitors in the industry, in December 2007. Honeywell needed Metrologic to round out its lines; since Metrologic provided desirable, low-cost scanning products and had, according to patent prosecutor Tom Perkowski, "wrapped up the patents."[97]

"Francisco," Harry said, "had about $125 million of their own money into the ownership of Metrologic. They'd borrowed about $300 million. I had to 'sell' that to lenders. About 20 months later [from September 2006 to April 2008], Francisco sold a $430 million company to Honeywell for $720 million. They'd more than tripled their money invested, receiving $420 million on their investment of $125 million after paying back what was borrowed. They made this outrageous amount of money but were taxed at only capital gains rates."[98] Indeed, the income of private equity firms is often classified as "carried interest"—a form of capital gains—and, thus, taxed at a 15 percent rate, as opposed to the highest salaried income tax rate of 35 percent.[99]

On July 2, 2008, Honeywell completed its acquisition of Metrologic. Metrologic would again be public as a subsidiary of Honeywell and part of Honeywell's Imaging and Mobility line, which would include the newly acquired HHP.[100] In 2009, Honeywell would form a new division for Metrologic and HHP—Honeywell Scanning & Mobility; Darius Adamczyk would serve as its president. "When Honeywell bought Metrologic," Bruce Harrison said, "they had Harry's IP [intellectual property], engineering capability, China, and Darius."[101]

Perkowski bemoaned what could have been, saying, "Before Harry left, he planned to replace all lasers with cameras. That was 100 patents. [Without Harry,] there was no one to shepherd them through. If Harry'd had another year, he could have revolutionized the industry [again]."[102]

The future of camera-based scanners lay in Metrologic's powerful PLIIM, or planar laser illumination and imaging, technology, which, ultimately, could identify all information on a scanned item—from five or six sides—without needing a bar code. However, with Harry's departure, PLIIM's full development into the marketplace languished.

"I miss Metrologic," Harry said. "It was all facts and science and competition."[103]

Facts and science must have sounded awfully good to Harry in 2007, as he left Metrologic behind to begin another chapter of his life with his wife of 35 years. Janet had been encouraging Harry to retire and liquidate their stock. Together, they had picked out a house in Hanover, New Hampshire, almost on the campus of Dartmouth College, with the intention of moving from Moorestown to escape oppressive New Jersey state taxes. With the Hanover home purchase underway, June and the time to move had arrived. Then, according to Harry, Janet told Harry, "I'm not going."

"Janet totally and absolutely out of the blue with no forewarning whatsoever said she was not coming to live with me in Hanover," Harry wrote in a June 2007 e-mail from New Hampshire.[104] "I am hoping she will change her mind, and that we can get to the bottom of her

Harry and Janet in earlier, happier times at Metrologic

mindset. I am asking her and our doctors to see if her meds or [a] physiological change in her cancer…can be at the root."

Harry would find that no illness was causing Janet's hunker-down mentality. Anguished, Harry sought answers. The one conclusion he could draw from talking with Janet was bleak: not only did Janet not want to move; she had no intention of living with Harry anywhere. Confused and deserted, Harry abandoned their planned 35th anniversary renewal of vows at the First Unitarian Church of Philadelphia where they were married. For more than three decades, Janet had worked by Harry's side at Metrologic. Now, he had neither.

Chapter 12

Beginnings

(2007-2012)

Harry's Hanover, New Hampshire, home

As Harry set up house in Hanover that June 2007, he agonizingly examined the year's events for any possible explanation for Janet's extreme change of course and heart. The drawn-out departure from Metrologic indeed was stressful as Janet and Harry left their life's work and watched layoffs of employees who were family to them. However, Janet had urged Harry's inevitable retirement. With the December 2006 acquisition by Francisco and the 2007 naming of a new CEO, Harry was able to withdraw from the board and liquidate the remaining Knowles stock to complete the Metrologic cord-cutting.

Work and Janet had been Harry's anchors for decades. His Metrologic tenure may have ended, but Harry's workdays most definitely had not. Harry planned to move to New Hampshire with Janet, develop some new technologies (including a foldable, lightweight telescope using adaptive optics and with real-time video capability), and devote much of his time to the Knowles Science Teaching Foundation (KSTF) which

On March 3, 2007, Auburn University honored four of its sons with Lifetime Achievement Awards, including, from left, retired Marine Corps Commandant General Carl E. Mundy, Jr., AU Veterinary Dean Emeritus J. Thomas Vaughan, and world-class entrepreneur and philanthropist C. Harry Knowles. AU Photographic Services

he and Janet established to cultivate and support excellent high school math and science education. In fact, the annual summer meeting was scheduled for the following month—July 2007—with full work sessions for KSTF's nearly 90 fellows during an intense three-day gathering in Chicago.

Harry thought that Janet shared his deep passion for improving the state of U.S. education after years of hiring frustrations at Metrologic, where Harry found it increasingly difficult to find top college graduates with adequate math and science skills. That state of affairs was intolerable to Harry, who recalled his country's dominance in advanced scientific thought and breakthroughs during his Bell Labs and Motorola days. Since Metrologic's training program wasn't enough to battle America's education failures, Harry had determined that effecting change in high school math and science teaching was the answer. KSTF resulted in 1999 with funding provided by Harry and Janet, who, in subsequent years, transferred an increasing number of Metrologic stock shares to build their promising foundation. By 2007, Harry and Janet financed KSTF to the level of more than $82 million in assets—almost $68 million of which was in investments.[1]

As Harry searched for reasons Janet had separated from him, he refused to view money as the primary culprit, suspecting that the fabric of Janet's motivation was much more complicated. However, Janet's declaration that she refused to move to Hanover was proclaimed, according to Harry, during an estate planning session, in which Harry discussed his long-standing effort to build KSTF's endowment to at least $100 million. In an August 2007 e-mail to his longtime friend and former Vanderbilt and Bell Labs colleague Phil Porter, Harry detailed how events unfolded: "On June 5th," Harry said, "Janet and I were in

Moorestown, with our estate attorney discussing wills, etc., when Janet stopped the discussion with 'Harry, I want you out of my life.' I thought at first she was in a temporary tiff about some of the discussion. It turns out that she was and is quite serious."[2]

While Janet may have been concerned about Harry's ongoing transferal of their personal wealth to KSTF, she had partnered in the endeavor since the beginning. She was not a selfish or greedy woman, often helping Metrologic employees who were in financial need during her years at the company. But Harry, in retrospect, noted to Porter a gradual shift in Janet's demeanor: "If all of this indeed does sound insane, you might imagine where my head has been!" Harry shared.

> I asked her doctors to make sure there was nothing wrong that they could tell. She did cooperate with her oncologist with a physical; the conclusion is "nothing physically wrong." And she insists that she knows what she is doing, and feels emotionally sound.
>
> To me, this whole situation has made little logical sense, except that she has been most uncomfortable with Auburn, KSTF, and other academic connections. We/she now has enough money to live however she wants, without my "interfering." I believe that Hanover [and, thus, Dartmouth]...was a step too far into academic waters. Until June, I felt that we were about as happy a couple as existed on earth. You will remember our wonderful trip...on the surface, she seemed OK. However, now and in retrospect, she was uncomfortable. She has been becoming more and more remote for the past six months to a year or so.[3]

The trip to which Harry referred was a March 3 journey to Harry's alma mater, Auburn University, nestled in the quaint town of Auburn in East Alabama. Harry, a 1951 Auburn physics graduate, was honored at a formal banquet that evening as an Auburn University Lifetime Achievement Award recipient. Also inducted were fellow Auburn alumni retired General Carl

Harry with his brothers, Bill Penn, center, and Jim Ramsey, at Lifetime Achievement Awards, 2007

Carolyn Carr, left, daughter of Harry's mentors, and Janet at March 2007 Auburn awards dinner

E. Mundy, Jr., former commandant of the U.S. Marine Corps; AU Veterinary Dean Emeritus John Thomas Vaughan; and former alumni leader Earl H. "Buddy" Weaver (honored posthumously).

More than two dozen of Harry's family and friends joined Harry and Janet for the dinner and awards ceremony, including his brothers, Bill Penn and Jim Ramsey, and their wives, Cathy and Ruth, respectively; niece Hope Penn McCarrell and her husband, Bill, and their son, Tim; Janet's daughter, Diane, and her husband, Tom Lynam; six-decades-long colleague Phil Porter and wife Louise; and Auburn friends Dick Webb (whom Harry had known since childhood through Ensley High and Auburn days), Milton Blount, Herman Blagg, Crawford Nevins, and Anne Pilcher.[4] Also joining the celebration was Carolyn Carr, daughter of Carolyn and Howard Carr. Harry's former physics professor and lifelong inspiration, Howard Carr had died in August 2003; his wife preceded him in October 1998.

Although the former physics department head Carr retired from Auburn in 1978, he continued to maintain an office in Allison Hall on campus until a few months before his death, enjoying his interaction with Auburn students and faculty and maintaining relationships with alumni such as Harry.[5] Harry saw Carr intermittently through the years as time allowed. "Janet and I stayed with the Carrs for [such things as] meetings," Harry said. "Carolyn was always taking care of Howard, who had diabetes and arthritis. When he retired, Carolyn was still bouncing around. Then, she had a sudden pain in her leg—cancer. Howard called me and said, 'Harry, I need you.' I came on the next plane.

Harry and the elder Carolyn Carr, who was a surrogate mother for Harry during his college student days at Auburn, at one of the Carr Professorship ceremonies, 1990s

Carolyn was almost gone. It was one of the tenderest times in my life. Death brings on reflection. It was good to just sit and be with Howard. He was such a tower in a personal sense. The outstanding people in your life really make the difference."[6]

Howard Carr, 1990s

Harry's respect for and dedication to quality teaching could be linked to his deep appreciation for the education—in physics and in life—Howard Carr gave him during his years as a young college student. Harry honored both the Carrs in 1996 with the establishment of the Howard and Carolyn Carr Endowed Professorship in Physics.[7] "As you get older," Harry said in a 2005 interview for the Auburn College of Sciences and Mathematics (COSAM) alumni magazine, "you begin to [ask]...'what is the root of my luck?' It is not luck. It is the teachers, and the one who began the whole sequence of incredible respect of teachers for me was Howard Carr."[8]

Harry also maintained his contact with his alma mater through the years in other ways than his personal relationship with the Carrs, serving on the advisory board (as chair part of the time) of Auburn's newly formed COSAM in the late 1980s; offering guidance via the COSAM Leadership Council in 2007 and beyond; and supporting professorships, a physics experiments van which traveled to high schools, and math learning efforts with his donations. In

Harry and the dean, Stewart Schneller, at the COSAM Distinguished Alumnus Award ceremony, 2006
AU Photographic Services

fact, AU's COSAM honored Harry in November 2006 with its Distinguished Alumnus Award—a few months prior to the March 2007 Lifetime Achievement Awards induction.

At the March dinner, Harry thoroughly enjoyed his time with his old Auburn friends and sharing the experience with family. Noticeably absent were his three children, Harry, II, Robert, and Marjorie, who had distanced themselves from their father since they became adults. Still, the evening was one of nostalgia and warmth in Harry's much beloved Auburn. For Janet, Harry surmised in his August 2007 note to Phil Porter, academia had become an increasingly uncomfortable setting.[9] Although Janet did not hold a college degree, her uneasiness with Auburn, according to Harry, seemed more centered on her belief, repeatedly stated to Harry, that Auburn only wanted Harry's money.[10] Janet could not relate easily to the tight-knit community of Harry's alma mater and the love he held for his Auburn University family. In Harry's mind, Auburn had turned a young, confused man into a confident leader. Fostering a love of truth and a thirst for knowledge, Auburn set Harry on his life's course; and Harry would never forget it.

"When I dream, I am still at Auburn over half the time," Harry said in a 1999 interview for his alumni magazine. "That's when the answers came together. I want to encourage teachers who can provide some answers for others as the Carrs did for me."[11]

By the June 2007 separation of the Knowles couple, Janet, according to Harry, had grown weary of earmarking their personal money for KSTF. "The amount of money I have been putting into the Foundation," Harry said in his August e-mail to Porter, "with her apparent cooperation until recently, seems to be part of Janet's frustrations. The situation seems particularly exacerbated, as she is not comfortable with all that academic stuff. The amount of money we have for her and the family is more than any of us ever dreamed about; so I think she feels that she has around her the two kids [and] the pups, and she does not need my irritations."[12]

Janet detailed some of those "irritations" for Harry in a June memo. She complained, according to Harry, that he "kept her from expanding herself, and that I was contemptuous of her, and berated her and called her names." Harry declared the complaints "totally untrue" in an e-mail to a friend discussing the situation. "I have done nothing to bring this on...no infidelity, no abuse of her, nothing but a trail of support," he said. "I am not claiming to be the ideal husband...no way. I can be picky and testy, but not anywhere near 'normal' badgering that we frequently observe around us."[13]

With Janet at the family home in Moorestown, New Jersey, and Harry "tax sheltering" in Hanover, New Hampshire, resolution to the marital woes would not come quickly. Harry struggled to settle into the historic, slate-roofed Hanover house—a home larger than Harry desired but bought because Janet, according to Harry, had insisted on some-thing bigger than a con-do. "Getting the house in shape up here in Hanover is more of a chore than I had assumed it would be," Harry said at the time. "Losing Janet out of the equation, at least tempo-rarily, has made it a lot tougher."[14] Harry was still hopeful that he and Janet would reunite. "On Janet, I think I am better under-standing the situation....

Janet at the Moorestown home, 2000

She is a powerful and wonderful lady, and has her own strong mind. I think it will work out...with help."

Harry could not predict the future of his marriage, but Janet's daughter and her family visited Hanover despite Janet's absence. A half-block from the Dartmouth campus, the Hanover house was lovely; but, in his distraught mindset, Harry barely noticed. Instead, he turned to his life's panacea: work. Zeroing in on Knowles Science Teaching Foundation duties, Harry prepared for the July meeting.

KSTF had matured into a highly effective structure under the guidance of KSTF executive director Angelo Collins, one of the nation's top education professionals hired away from Vanderbilt in 2000 to shape Harry's vision. Collins, who held a Ph.D. from the University of Wisconsin in curriculum and instruction and a master's in biology from Michigan State University, had been a prominent crusader for high standards and student achievement in math and science nationally (having written U.S. science education standards) and served as co-editor of the *Journal of Research in Science Teaching* as well as on numerous national advisory committees. A fellow of the American Association for the Advancement of Science, Collins had countless publications and research efforts to her credit.[15] In short, she had credibility within the national education community but no desire to maintain the status

Angelo Collins and Harry at KSTF headquarters in Moorestown, 2005

COSAM/Auburn University

quo. With KSTF and Harry, she could channel her efforts toward improving math and science education across the country.

After joining KSTF, Collins conducted a year-long study of critical issues and visited with experts nationwide. Then, at Collins' suggestion and with the support of KSTF's board (which included chair Harry and Janet), the foundation was organized around what would become its signature program: the KSTF Teaching Fellowships.[16] The fellowship program invited the best college-level or recently graduated science, math, and engineering majors to pursue careers teaching high school math or science instead of working in the more highly compensated private sector. In return, those inducted as KSTF fellows received stipends (in addition to their normal teaching salary) that were renewable for up to five years, along with a network of support, which included professional development, mentoring, and gatherings with their peers.

Created in 2001, the program awarded its first three science fellowships in 2002. The first mathematics cohort was inducted in 2005 with seven teaching fellows named. In June 2007, the sixth cohort of 27 math and science teaching fellows was welcomed at KSTF's Moorestown, New Jersey, headquarters. Another KSTF program, the Young Scholars Research Fellowship (later called the KSTF Research Fellowship), begun in 2005, supported pre-tenure faculty and others with two-year, $110,000 awards for research efforts studying the "recruitment, preparation, induction, mentoring and retention of high school science and mathematics teachers."[17] By the 2007 summer fellows meeting, held at the Marriott Chicago O'Hare July 26-28, the number gathered included 80 KSTF teaching fellows in various stages of their five-year programs, five young scholars, and the foundation's first alumni group—the original three 2002 fellows who had "graduated" from their KSTF fellowships.[18]

Harry transcended his marital distress as he fed on the energy electrifying the Marriott meeting rooms full of some of the nation's best high school math and science teachers. All he had to do was observe the group to know his foundation was making a difference. The young teachers were defying mainstream dropout statistics that, according to Collins, stated that half of all new teachers leave the profession within the first three years.[19] Not only had KSTF enticed the fellows to make a difference as teachers, they were as excited about learning as the more than 10,000 students they had taught during the 2006-2007 school year.[20]

The stories of the group gathered attested to KSTF's success, such as was the case with KSTF alumni teaching fellows Jennifer Barchie, Ben Buehler, and Lisa Sitek. The three 2002 science cohort fellows hailed from different parts of the country, but each had seen fundamental progress in their schools. At the time, Barchie taught science to eleventh- and twelfth-graders at Mount de Sales Academy, an all-girls Catholic high school near Baltimore in Catonsville, Maryland. "Teaching is exciting every day," Barchie said during the

2002 Science Fellow Jennifer Barchie at a KSTF meeting

summer meeting, adding that KSTF "helped me be a better teacher."[21] Her KSTF colleagues, she said, were people she trusted, good teachers in physics who prompted her to push herself.

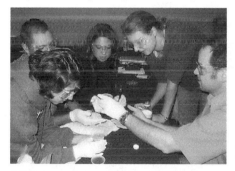

KSTF teaching fellows feed off their networking, such as with these 2004 science cohort members working together to design inquiry-based lessons.

Trust was an important component of the KSTF cohort structure; since lesson plans were presented before teaching cohorts, critiqued, and even videotaped in an effort to improve the fellows' skills. The three-day summer meeting was intense with workshops, roundtable and poster sessions, expert presentations, lesson studies, and sharing of technology. Topics ran the gamut from the physics of light, to chemistry modeling, to group work in mathematics, to meaningful algebra, to assessment, to leadership—to name a few. Former astronaut George "Pinky" Nelson, a three-time veteran to space shuttle flights, gave the keynote address.

KSTF staffers, including more than half a dozen who were experts in education in their own right, shepherded the teaching professionals through the potential of their KSTF fellowships and discussed the requirements of the five-year commitment. For example, fellows submitted portfolios each year, and KSTF program officers visited the fellows' classrooms at least once during the course of the fellowship to provide in-depth feedback. Along the way, KSTF provided mentoring and instructional materials grants, as well as opportunities to attend national professional meetings. To encourage learning from colleagues, each cohort of fellows met twice each year, in the spring and fall, in addition to the summer meeting for all fellows. By investing in their fellows, KSTF was building a community spirit which, ideally, would be contagious for fellow teachers in high schools across the country. The ultimate result would be measured in better learning by high school math and science students.

Ben Buehler, who taught chemistry and physics at Blue River Valley High School in Mt. Summit, Indiana, said, "KSTF has made me want to become a better teacher. It's made me excited about the profession." His 2002 science cohort colleague Lisa Sitek, from Burlington (Vermont) High School, echoed his thoughts:

Lisa Sitek

"I've learned more from this fellowship than I did in any of my education classes. I had taught for three years, then left. But I applied for the KSTF fellowship. I told myself that if I got the fellowship, then I would go teach. I got it, and I'm glad I did."[22]

Sitek elaborated in a fellowship reflection essay for KSTF in 2007, saying that the 2002 cohort members "formed a small community that worked together to improve our teaching and, in turn, improve the education of students in three different states....[T]he greatest gift KSTF gave me was treating me as a professional and making me part of a community of dedicated teachers. I no longer teach in isolation and have the ideas of many other people helping me develop my lessons."[23]

Angelo Collins empathized with the plight of her young fellows: "Teachers feel isolated, unappreciated," the KSTF executive director said in 2007. "They learn new technologies, then end up in schools with no equipment."[24]

As the first KSTF fellows and alumni, Barchie, Buehler, and Sitek "helped shape our organization," Collins explained. When KSTF recruited fellows in 2001, Collins said they received 15 applications; of these, six people were invited for interviews, and Barchie, Buehler, and Sitek were chosen in 2002. Their excellence prompted KSTF lead-ers to expand the foundation's business plan

Angelo Collins

to include an alumni program. As the number of applications and fel-lows grew each year and as cohorts moved into the alumni group, KSTF hoped to keep these top teachers involved in advancing their profession even after their five-year fellowships had ended.

"There isn't anything we're doing here that's new," Collins said in 2007. "What's unique is we're doing it all, and our selection process. I taught high school for 18 years. I thought I was pretty good. It wasn't until my advanced degree that I realized I had a lot to learn. The most satisfying part for me is seeing these young teachers starting their careers knowing they have more to learn."

Buehler talked about this learning process in a video entitled "Thank You KSTF" presented to KSTF in April 2007 as his five-year fellowship was coming to a close: "Four years ago," he said in the video, "at a Knowles meeting, was the first time I saw video of myself teaching. Before I watched the video I thought I was pretty good. After I saw [the] video, I was humbled. I entered the teaching profession to motivate and inspire. I wanted to shift the paradigm of teaching from students taking

Ben Buehler

notes to students generating their own ideas. But, after watching that… video…it was clear that I needed some help."[25]

Buehler, who had been a finalist for teacher of the year in Indiana in 2006, applied his KSTF-honed skills to his classroom and was seeing the results. "Ben teaches in a high school…where few boys go to college," Harry said via e-mail in 2007, "and, until he came, very few took science. Of his chemistry class this year, eight of the 20 students (double the number of three years ago) are not only going to college, but they are majoring in science! Ben says he is now reaching a couple hundred kids per year in physics and chemistry, and it is growing. The three of our first science cohort in 2002...[are] all superior teachers now....In the schools of Jen Barchie and Lisa Sitek...the number of students now taking science has similarly doubled. For Lisa's efforts in physics [and its growing] popularity, they now have 14 classes in science, whereas, four years ago, they barely had 10. Burlington High School has had to add several additional science teachers to handle the additional projected load. I have no doubt that it is because of her influence. With appropriate modesty, each [of the three fellows] says it is themselves that has made the difference in the schools."[26]

Harry reflected in 2007 on KSTF's impact after five years of fellowship cohorts:

> The program that Angelo and staff have assembled is definitely having the impact that we hoped for. I have no doubt that we will be changing the teaching system from the inside out. Is this happening because of our selection process, or because of our mentoring of those select few? Anecdotally, it seems that both are true: we are elevating the effectiveness of the group, but we are generating the environment that keeps the upper echelon in the system teaching! Can we prove that statistically? Probably so, and we are looking for ways to do just that.
>
> But the feedback from this trio confirms, to me at least, the effectiveness of the "whole body process" approach that Angelo has strategized and implemented: recognizing fellows as *professionals*— self-resonant interaction within the KSTF peer groups; financial aid; mentoring by skilled, well-trained, and motivated staff. We are making a difference now...but [it is] a drop in the bucket considering probably several million students in the USA each year that should/would be subject to our influence. What we now hope to do [is]...broaden the influence.[27]

One of the presenters at the July 2007 fellows meeting, Steve DeAngelis, who had not heard of KSTF before that year, became a true believer quickly because of the foundation's approach to valuing teachers. Originally in industry, DeAngelis had been teaching since 1978 and, at the time of the 2007 meeting, was a physics and resource teacher at Maranacook Community High School in Readfield, Maine. "This is the best model of professional development I've ever seen," he said. "The session [I was in] was spectacular. They have first-year teachers videotaping lessons. That's hard to get them to do, but it's self-evaluative and powerful. The energy in the room was palpable. First-, second-, and third-year teachers are feeling empowered, confident, and willing to take risks.[28]

Steve DeAngelis

"What drives me crazy is the best and brightest don't go into teaching or don't stick with it. If we truly value teaching, we have to let teachers know we value them. Society doesn't value teaching. KSTF is going to change that [by] changing the culture of teaching. They're supporting teachers emotionally and teaching how to be leaders. The KSTF model gives teachers a voice and a support group with other teachers—you can't oversell [the importance of] that. This will change retention."

One of the 2006 science fellows, Cathy Tempest, agreed, saying in the KSTF 2007 Annual Report that KSTF had proven to be her "greatest resource as a first-year teacher, not only for academic and financial reasons, but for the support each cohort offers. By sharing personal experiences, advice and resources, this group of fellows constantly reminds me why I am in this profession in the first place, and why I should stay."[29]

DeAngelis gave credit to Harry for his dedication and substantial financial backing of KSTF. "I feel people who make significant money have a responsibility to give back," DeAngelis said. "Harry's obviously doing that. He's pumped about learning. Great teachers are the same way."

KSTF alumnus Ben Buehler thanked Harry and Janet specifically in his video of appreciation: "Harry and Janet," he said earnestly into the camera, "over the last five years, the foundation that you created has transformed how I teach and how I think about the teaching profession. The Knowles fellowship has made me a better teacher, has made me be part of something bigger....Teaching is a lonely job. At times, it can make you feel like a hamster running on a wheel that keeps turning students through. I believe that I would have been a teaching statistic if I had not found KSTF....Your foundation has given me the courage and skills that I need to stay in this profession."[30]

The video continued with clips of students excited about their various science projects and testimonials from them, a fellow teacher, a parent, and even Buehler's wife. Also included was a segment of Buehler teaching after the KSTF fellowship transformed his skills. "The effects of your foundation don't stop with us fellows. They affect every single person that we meet," Buehler explained as he addressed Harry and Janet. "This foundation has caused me to stare at master teachers and ask how I can be more effective in the classroom. Because of the great staff you've put together at KSTF, over the last five years, my teaching has improved. I inspire a little more, and I bore a little less. Because of the thought, the time, and the money that you've used to make us fellows better teachers, there are thousands of students...across the U.S. who are learning a little bit more."

Buehler concluded his video by referencing a key principle of the KSTF philosophy: "Because you view teachers as professionals, I now view myself as a professional," he said. "Harry and Janet, thank you for taking an interest in me and my students. Your support changes the lives of thousands every day."

Harry, October 2004
COSAM/Auburn University

The Knowles financial support for KSTF resulted from painstaking years of Harry growing Metrologic as a public company, so that its stock value climbed. Since he and Janet had been gifting Metrologic shares to KSTF along the way, KSTF grew with Metrologic—exactly as Harry planned. While Harry had not brought KSTF's endowment up to his goal of $100 million yet, the 2007 level of $82.9 million in assets was well on its way following Harry's liquidation of Metrologic shares. That $82.9 million, Harry emphasized, reflected an endowment level amassed over time and was an ever-changing number, as KSTF expenses tapped into available funds and return on investment fluctuated.[31] In 2007, KSTF was working with $6.5 million in revenue from $1.7 million in interest and $4.8 million in unrealized investment sales appreciation. Appropriate annual revenue was crucial, according to Harry; the core KSTF endowment needed to generate $5 or $6 million a year at that time to cover the foundation's costs. KSTF expenses in 2007 were reasonable at $4.6 million, but plans for the non-profit included growing the number of fellows and programs.[32]

Each of the 80 KSTF fellows received a stipend of $1,100 a month in 2007, along with potential (depending on the proposal process) materials grants of $1,000 a year, tuition assistance, professional development funding of up to $1,000 per academic year, and supportive program funding which included mentoring and cohort and fellows gatherings.[33] Harry estimated that KSTF spent $130,000 per fellow during the course of each five-year fellowship.[34]

"In five years, costs will be at $7.5 million a year," Harry said in 2007. "Looking at the numbers, $100 million is a low amount to support this. Is it worth it? Yes. We're going to have a significant effect. The KSTF model indicates that we will have more than 400 fellows in the next 20 years teaching 50 to 60,000 students each year. If you cut a path of affecting one percent of high school students in the country, that's a major effect. We have pretty good data, but we won't be able to measure [the full effect] for 20 years. In my lifetime, I won't see the flow of where this takes science and math teaching. But the investment we're making will exist for the next 50 years and will change this country."[35]

Not one to shy away from challenge, Harry envisioned franchising KSTF programming to reach five percent of U.S. high school students. However, even at its established trajectory, KSTF was delivering impressive results. "KSTF will make as profound a difference as any organization this size in the world," Harry predicted. "We are changing math and science teaching by selecting the absolute crème-de-la-crème who want to be teachers and enabling them to be and stay teachers."

Harry credited Angelo Collins and her KSTF staff. "The program Angelo has put together is beyond my wildest expectations," Harry said at the time. Collins remembered that, at the beginning of KSTF, Harry had an idea of what he wanted to do. "But all he knew," she said, "was his memories as a student. I spent the first year going around the country. We came up with a wild and crazy plan. I conceived the selection process, which is quite rigorous. Harry let us do it on our own and make our own mistakes. I love Harry. He's incredible."[36]

With programming handled aptly by KSTF staff, KSTF board attention was often monopolized by financial issues. In 2007, Harry served as

KSTF meeting after board expansion, 2013. Seated, from left: Harry; Nicole Gillespie (who became the executive director in 2013); and Janet. Standing, from left: Larry Tint; Stephanie Holm, vice president of administration; Paul Kuerbis; Ed Viner; Bill Rulon-Miller; Suzanne Wilson (a national teacher education leader who joined the board in 2013); and Scott McVay.

president of the board, Janet remained as treasurer, and Scott McVay served as a trustee. McVay, who was the retired founding executive director of the prestigious philanthropic Geraldine R. Dodge Foundation, had joined forces with Harry in 1998 toward the 1999 founding of KSTF and had managed the executive director search which resulted in Collins' hire.

"KSTF continues to soar," Harry said in 2007. "It is, and must remain, my absolute priority to lock it into place both financially and in direction and management. [T]he Board of Directors must get organized for perpetuity, and we need to provide a management succession system and people chain."[37]

The trustees previously included the leadership of Boyce Adams, who had founded and served as U.S. president of precision laboratory instruments manufacturer Wayne Kerr, Ltd. Adams had a long history of volunteer service before he died in June 2006. One way Adams gave back to his community was by forming the Moorestown Ecumenical Neighborhood Development (MEND), which built more than 600 housing units at no profit, according to Harry.[38]

The small KSTF board expanded by four in 2008, adding Colorado College education professor Paul Kuerbis, a member of the KSTF Science Advisory Committee; investment manager Lawrence Tint, senior managing director of Cantor Fitzgerald LLP; former Metrologic board member Bill Rulon-Miller, who helped Harry take the company public and, in 2008, served as director of investment banking for Janney Montgomery Scott in Philadelphia; and Ed Viner, longtime Knowles family physician and former Cooper University Hospital chief of medicine. Viner changed the face of South Jersey medicine during his distinguished career, not only as Cooper's chief of medicine for 20 years, but in his national championing of end-of-life care (starting the area's first hospice program) and the establishment of a suburban practice network and a hospitalist system at Cooper. He had recruited several hundred top doctors to come across the Delaware River to Cooper from Philadelphia. A chair of the Cooper Foundation, he worked toward academic efforts in medicine, which, ultimately, led to the creation and 2012 opening of a new medical school, the Cooper Medical School of Rowan University in Camden, New Jersey.[39]

In the early years of KSTF, as Collins was advertising for what would become the first cohort in 2002, the KSTF board of three juggled a panoply of money complications. "One has to put into context," Harry said in a 2007 e-mail, "that all during that time, Metrologic had problems beyond belief, and that several times Angelo, the board, and I met to discuss the possibility that Metrologic might even go under. Angelo, God bless her, kept it going, with the express attitude: 'Harry, you take care of the business and money side, and I will persist in generating a functioning KSTF' with incredibly strong conviction and confidence that matched that almost blind obsession of Janet and me."[40]

Despite the challenges, KSTF thrived. By the 2007 summer fellows meeting, Harry was urging more aggressive financial investing for KSTF

to grow the endowment. McVay balanced Harry's ambition with a touch of caution. "Harry wants the endowment at $300 million," McVay said at the time. "He's pushing for having that one percent [and beyond] of math and science teachers. He feels a deep desire to give back."[41]

With decades of philanthropic service to his name, McVay understood Harry's motivations and admired him. In fact, McVay had introduced Harry at the 2006 *NJ Biz* Business of the Year awards ceremony inducting Harry into the Hall of Fame.

Scott McVay at KSTF 2007 summer meeting

"Harry has phenomenal ability as an entrepreneur, is creative, wonderfully articulate, incisive, and witty," McVay said. "I continue [with KSTF] because I like Harry and respect what he's doing, but also because I believe in the mission. A lot of philanthropy is a soup kitchen. Good foundations effect systemic change. Harry gets that. Harry's greatest legacy will be the foundation."

McVay's prediction regarding Harry's legacy would be echoed in the future by other close observers of the inventor's career. Indeed, Harry himself predicted the same, saying in 2009, "I have no doubt that the foundation will be my greatest legacy."[42] Harry's comment was neither boastful nor dismissive of his Metrologic and technological accomplishments. Rather, Harry's conviction reflected his belief that science and math education in the U.S was critically more important than any personal achievements.

Longtime Metrologic patent prosecutor Tom Perkowski saw complete symmetry in Harry's journey, noting that Harry started his 40-year Metrologic career with education kits on how to build a laser. "Through the foundation," Perkowski surmised, "Harry's going back to where he started. Harry loves science and he loves math. He didn't particularly like the retail industry. He made a brilliant product, but the manufacturing was useful only to continue teaching math and science. You always felt you were in a physics class with him. He was always promoting math and science. At the end of the day, he returns and gives his money back."[43]

Harry, as KSTF board chair, once again worked to secure the future of an organization he had built. Unlike Metrologic, however, KSTF was a non-profit which Harry felt could be preserved with an appropriate succession plan and trusted leaders to carry on his vision after him. Rulon-Miller's addition to the board in 2008 provided critical financial expertise to KSTF operations. His expertise was needed, as Harry's 2007 prediction of KSTF expenses five years out would prove accurate.

The Knowles funding of KSTF provided needed stability during the foundation's infancy. The staff had the luxury of concentrating on programming, not fundraising. However, the KSTF coffers took a hit in the coming months—as would all of the country—when the U.S. joined the globe in financial crisis. While U.S. stocks peaked in October 2007, with the Dow Jones average exceeding 14,000, stocks fell rapidly in the fall of 2008 amid bank failures and bailouts.[44] The Dow sank to about 6,600 by March 2009.[45] KSTF assets, which were primarily in investments, declined as a result. Whereas KSTF net unrestricted assets totaled $82.9 million at the end of 2007, net assets fell from a May 31, 2008, total of $79.5 million to $56.8 million by May 31, 2009. (KSTF converted to a June 1 fiscal year in 2008.)[46]

The stock market did not stay down in 2010 and 2011; thus, KSTF investments also rebounded. By May 31, 2011, net foundation assets climbed back to $77.4 million. "The foundation is in good financial shape," KSTF trustee Bill Rulon-Miller said that year.[47] With program expenses rising only to $5.5 million by that point, Harry's vision was intact—for now.

However, by May 31, 2012, expenses were $6.3 million; and, by the 2012-2013 fiscal year (with a May 31 end), KSTF expenses were expected to reach $7 million (as predicted by Harry).[48] Meanwhile, 2012 assets declined to $71.3 million. While Harry's estate and investment plans included KSTF, those plans and the 2012 endowment level no longer assured permanent funding of KSTF costs. To continue to grow the Knowles vision, KSTF board members added fundraising to their concerns to safeguard the successful foundation's future.

KSTF's impact continued to ripple across the country. By 2008, a new cohort category—biology— was added to the mathematics and physical sciences categories. Nine biology teaching fellows joined  their KSTF colleagues the inaugural year. By 2012, the average number of teaching fellows added each year was 36—12 in each of the three cohort categories—bringing the total number of KSTF fellowships awarded since 2002 to 270.[49] (The September 2012 *active* number of participants totaled 213—149 teaching fellows and 64 alumni.) In the 2012-2013 academic year, about 25,000 students in 38 different states were to be impacted by KSTF teaching fellows and alumni. Unlike the national secondary education teacher retention rate of about 50 percent within the first five years of teaching, the retention rate for KSTF fellows topped 90 percent.[50]

The KSTF model was proving successful due to its complete approach: recruit and financially support excellent potential teachers; respect and encourage fellows by treating them as professionals; improve teaching quality via KSTF's extensive training opportunities; and solve teacher isolation through critical networking with KSTF colleagues. As a result, more than 200 KSTF fellows were in position to be leaders within their educational communities, elevating the performance of not only their students, but their fellow teachers. Executive director Angelo

Collins, who played such a pivotal role in shaping the KSTF model, alas, did not remain at KSTF, leaving the foundation in summer 2011, after 11 years of dedication, to pursue other interests. She was named to the Taft Endowed Chair in STEM Education at East Carolina University in 2012.

Harry credited Collins for her service, commenting on her departure: "She has been the prime intellectual force responsible for creating the teaching fellowship and research programs that are the essence of KSTF. Her guiding vision for our work over the past decade...puts us in a position to continue those programs into the future and explore new avenues of influence."[51]

As KSTF matured, its research and alumni programs both expanded. In 2010, a director for Research and Evaluation joined the KSTF staff to help transition the external research fellowship to an internal division supporting teaching fellowship and alumni programming. The change allowed specific research studies to be conducted by KSTF staff, teaching fellows, and KSTF alumni. An alumni programs director was hired in 2011. By September 2012, KSTF was helping its 64 alumni increase their impact as national leaders in education while continuing their collaboration with the foundation. Alumni could apply for KSTF grants; some grants were used in 2012 to design a two-year physics curriculum, help fellows pursue prestigious National Board teacher certification status, and develop professional development for KSTF and non-KSTF teachers, to name a few. Several alumni, such as Ben Buehler, became KSTF resource teachers, helping KSTF fellows develop their teaching skills.[52]

Bill Rulon-Miller

With Collins' exit in 2011, KSTF board members Paul Kuerbis and Bill Rulon-Miller stepped in as acting co-executive directors.[53] Subsequently, Rulon-Miller joined the KSTF efforts full time in March 2012 after he was hired as president and COO.[54] Nicole Gillespie, who joined KSTF as a senior program officer in 2004, managed the fellowships program in 2012 as director for teaching fellowships. By that summer, the KSTF staff had grown to 24 (and the Moorestown headquarters doubled in size), as the number of fellows in vari-

Nicole Gillespie, 2005

ous stages of their active five-year fellow-ships rose to 167.[55] The 2012 KSTF summer fellows meeting July 26-28 in Philadelphia brought together more than 225 teaching fellows, staff, resource teachers, alumni, and guests. As in 2007, the teachers gathered in 2012 fed off the energy and creative ideas of one another. These educators were thrilled to reconnect with their KSTF lifeline every chance they got.

There were differences, however, in the form of more advanced infrastructure and the ever-growing level of professionalism. Alumni participated fully and interacted with and mentored fellows, but they also had their own meetings to plot strategy. Fellows no longer were required to submit yearly, term-paper-style port-folios to have their fellowships renewed. Instead, KSTF staff monitored the dynamic progress of the teachers in their journeys toward better content knowledge, lesson plans, assessment, and leadership growth. In turn, fellows counted KSTF online communities as one of their tools (in addition to cohort meetings and the summer fellows meeting) to garner feedback and collaboration from their colleagues. Teacher developers (formerly called program officers) on the KSTF staff discussed how best to visit fellows in their schools more often than once during the five years of fellowships—perhaps through long-distance video.

KSTF-supported professional development was simplified for par-ticipants to $3,700 per academic year to apply toward the yearly re-quirement of at least 40 hours of professional development. Monthly stipends for teaching fellows rose from the 2007 level of $1,100 a month to $1,200 monthly in 2012. Total KSTF support per fellow during the five years of a fellowship averaged $175,000 in 2012, according to Gil-lespie.[56]

"KSTF has deepened quite a bit," Gillespie said in 2012. "There is a more cohesive sense of who we are and where we're going. We have such a great staff, and we make some changes logistically along the way; but the teachers carry it." (Gillespie, a U.S. Naval Academy mechanical engi-neering graduate with a master's in physics from the University of Wash-ington and a Ph.D. in science education from the University of California at Berkeley, would be named KSTF executive director in 2013.)

"KSTF's lofty mission is pursuit of scientific truth in our high schools," Harry said during his 2012 summer meeting presentation to a ballroom full of adoring fellows—who honored Harry with two standing ovations. "Our odyssey will cut a major path for scientific literacy in the U.S. and teaching as a profession. We infiltrate the system with excellence from within."[57]

Harry's KSTF actions during this entire period focused on protecting and growing his foundation to effect, in perpetuity, as great an improvement as possible in U.S. math and science education. The preservation of KSTF, however, was not a given back in 2007—especially in light of Harry and Janet's separation. If the marriage ended in divorce, the freely given *joint* support to KSTF also would end. Of course, Harry bemoaned his personal loss deeply.

"Make no mistake of it, I am totally devastated," he had written to a friend June 17, 2007. "The thought of being without her, just as our lives have progressed to the point where we have money, time to be together without pressure, freedom from Metrologic, and KSTF and our other foundations moving very productively, and generally good health....I cannot believe that she really wants to go through with this. But the kids and her memos to me indicate that she is serious."[58]

With the emotional upheaval and abrupt change in his life's course, Harry sought to address his health soon after his move to Hanover. To regain strength and balance—both physical and mental—he entered into a regime of physical training at a local gym with a personal trainer and sought counseling. The enormous success of the KSTF 2007 summer meeting bolstered Harry's spirits, as did the exercise and support of friends and family. Harry ricocheted between believing that his marriage was truly over and that it could be saved. The conflicting feelings were understandable; as Harry said, "35 years is a lot to throw away."[59]

"What are the possibilities that Janet and I will resolve our issues?" Harry posed in an e-mail to friend and family physician Ed Viner.[60] "Given her firm statements...I am not optimistic....Janet has firmly said, and made it evident for some time, that she simply does not like being around me. Yes, she 'loves' me...but that is not a substitute for *liking* and wanting to be around. [Also,] she has made it clear that she wants more money than can be had, as of now, given the commitments we have made.

"That leaves my reaction. I cannot build much of a future on hoping that Janet will change…and I realize it takes two to meet in the middle. But, money aside, if she simply does not like me, then what? Can I change in the ways that will make her actually like me? I do not know.…I know the disparity in what is apparent hopelessness and [the] need to try to save 35 years of mutual and, to me, apparently happy marriage. I cannot resolve it, but my sense of self-preservation does kick in."

In August 2007, Harry headed south to Alabama to celebrate half-brother Bill and sister-in-law Cat's 65th wedding anniversary. He also spent time with step-brother Jim, who had been diagnosed recently with melanoma, and Jim's family. Harry's enjoyment of his visit sparked the beginning of homesickness for his native environs. While Hanover was exciting and beautiful—an "almost fantasy world," as Harry put it— New Hampshire was not home. "It is good to feel Alabama hospitality from friends and family again," Harry said. "There is something rich about 'coming home.'"[61] He found himself drawn back to Alabama and to the people who knew him and loved him regardless of his successes or failures. If he had known Janet's divorce plans, Harry would not have committed to the Hanover move; but he was locked in there at least through the end of the year when his tax obligations to the state of New Jersey ended.[62]

Harry's move to New Hampshire had forced Harry into a degree of isolation. As Harry considered his situation further that fall, he knew his heart was not given to making Hanover a permanent harbor. "My contacts with my family and friends are pulling me back to my Alabama roots," Harry said that November, echoing his earlier comments. "Being there makes me realize that, at my age, my comfort level in being 'home' is more important to me than the excitement level I get at Hanover."[63]

Harry eventually would sell his house in Hanover and add homes in Birmingham—next to his brother Jim Ramsey's abode—and Auburn. He also would purchase a condo in

Harry at the mailbox of his Auburn home

Moorestown for easy access to his foundation and his network of friends there in New Jersey. His work and family relationships would keep him traveling among his residences.

In September 2007, however, Harry remained in Hanover while his mindset turned definitively forward. He had accepted that reconciliation with Janet was not going to occur. As he closed that door emotionally, he and Janet discussed disentangling their assets. "I hope that by November we will have it mostly sorted out," Harry said. "I also hope that I can have my own life better sorted out, and find out who the hell I am. Gaining that knowledge is fun most of the time, exciting…and frustrating some of the time."[64]

Despite the unknowns of what lay ahead, Harry suddenly had a chance for previously unconceived adventures. That fall, he attended a pilots' convention with an old friend and considered options for renew-

Robert

ing his pilot's license. More importantly, in September, Harry's son Robert visited him.

In the past, Robert had gone long periods of time without seeing or talking to his father—sometimes as long as a decade. The relationship of Harry with his three children was strained to the extreme. However, Robert called the Moorestown, New Jersey, home August 15, 2007, for his father's 79th birthday and discovered from Janet that Harry no longer lived there. Robert arranged to see his father in New Hampshire the following month.[65]

Robert, who graduated in business from the University of Maryland and earned a CPA certification, had established a good career for himself with the Metropolitan Area Transit Authority in Washington, D.C. At the Metro, he worked his way up through database operations, then cost accounting, to his position as an automatic fare collection engineer. His confidence was hard-fought. With the mature eyes of a near-49-year-old and a heart harboring childhood pain, Robert tentatively re-established a relationship with his father in Hanover that September 2007.

"He was a different person," Robert said of his father. Following Janet's rejection of Harry, Robert continued, there was "a whole sea change." Robert's 36-hour Hanover visit allowed an airing of hurts and a layer of healing. "I told Dad, 'I was scared to death of you,'" Robert said. "Janet enabled him in many ways."

With the split from Janet, Harry discovered that the thick wall between him and his children began to slowly dissolve. Harry's marriage and the accompanying stress of the blended brood of offspring, in some ways at least, had helped push Harry's children away through the years. However, circumstances and Harry's own harsh behavior toward Harry, II, Robert, and Marjorie were dominant causes of the estrangement.

Harry's skewed view of his parental obligations had deeply bruised his children who, according to Robert, grew up with little to no self-esteem after years of instability. Harry, II, Robert, and Marjorie all suffered major delays in their college education and careers as they endured their alcoholic mother, Phoebe, and unreliable support from their father. Eventually, Phoebe successfully navigated alcohol rehabilitation and reconciliation with son Robert, who, in 2007, had been the one overseeing his mother's care for several years.

Robert, who cared for his mother in her later years, and Phoebe in Baltimore, July 2008

"I want a father, but I maintain my independence," Robert said in discussing his own thoughts about the reunion with his father.[66] When Robert was young, "Dad didn't tolerate weakness. I learned to be stoic. My happiest time with Dad as a child was the summer I was 13 and it was just us and we had a lovely vacation to Sherwood Lake. He would be affectionate maybe once or twice a year.

"I can't go back in time. He hurt me in a lot of ways. He didn't step up to the plate for his kids. I always felt he kept me at arm's length. I think Dad realizes what he missed out on when we were kids. I guess I did forgive him. I see him trying to make changes. He's more vulnerable now."

Indeed, an agonized Harry lamented the lost time with his children, saying, "My biggest disappointment in life is not having done enough with my own kids."[67]

Former Metrologic vice president and general counsel Bruce Harri-

Harry, shown here with Robert at a Phillies baseball game in 2012, attempted to make up for lost time with his children.

son, a decades-long friend of Harry, also witnessed changes in Harry during this time. "I think [Harry's] separation and ultimate divorce [have] been liberating," Harrison said. "He is more introspective... more capable of acknowledging to himself and others self-doubt and examples of failure, more willing to listen to views contrary to his own, and much more family-centric. At his age, to acknowledge life's failures and frustrations and to...attempt to modify his personality and to remedy past perceived failures shows great strength and courage."[68]

Strength through vulnerability would have been anathema for the old Harry. However, Harrison's assessment was correct. Only through the humbling experience of Janet leaving him could Harry begin anew with his children. In the past, when challenges arose, Harry powered through them with bravado and intellect. Now, he found that rebuilding relationships with his children required a gentle, patient love, which sometimes ran counter to Harry's solve-it-now psyche. Still, Harry was determined to redeem himself as a father and found re-birth in the opportunity.

Harry's sense of renewal that fall encouraged him to focus on sorting his life. "I have thought across the spectrum of how life will go from here," Harry wrote. "At 79, one's options do begin to dwindle, even with the resources that I have. Ultimately, it is one's health, energy, intellect that matter...and how long one can count on them." He talked of where he would live (possibly Auburn or elsewhere in Alabama) and with whom—saying, "one cannot live in isolation."[69]

Harry and Janet's separation progressed; by November 2007, Harry said, they had settled all of the key issues on asset allocation and were ready for their lawyers to formalize the split. The couple had spent extended time together on several occasions for recent KSTF board meetings. Harry found the meetings, on the surface at least, cordial and productive and noted that Janet seemed comfortable in her divorce decision.[70] Harry recognized that "the forced [cessation] of our marriage, as disturbing as it has been, may turn out to be a blessing."[71]

Predictably, divorce proceedings were anything but seamless as lawyers sought to protect their clients' interests. Included in the stakes was the $30 million more that, according to Harry, he and Janet had jointly promised KSTF. Adequate funding would prove vital in 2008 and beyond, as U.S. investments suffered from bank and stock crises. Even before stocks spiraled downward in the fall of 2008, however, Harry anguished about the assets battle. "It is enough to almost destroy KSTF, or me, or both…but that is a battle that I will be fighting."[72]

In the end, Janet and Harry both compromised to bring the divorce to a close. However, it took more than two years to complete, with final divorce proceedings filed January 21, 2010. Most importantly to Harry, estate plans regarding KSTF emerged protected. Harry and Janet even managed to remain civil, as Janet continued to serve on the KSTF board.

In a note to his friend, Phil Porter, in November 2007, Harry not only talked about the split with Janet, but the departure from Metrologic the same year: "Metrologic and I are totally separated. As traumatic as that was for me and for many employees, it is done. Some close friends still call but not much. One or two are coming for a visit, but only casually. I have no idea, other than through patent applications, which are still continuing…what is going on."[73]

The most positive side effect of all the changes for Harry, obviously, was the tentative reconnection with his children. Years earlier, Harry set up trusts for each of his offspring, but he now hoped for much more than a financial connection. He, happily, was maintaining contact with Robert after Robert's visit that fall of 2007. With the pending divorce between Harry and Janet, Robert's twin, Marjorie, and first-born Harry, II, also opened to the possibility of a relationship with their father. Their journey would be fraught with stalls and starts. Harry, II, and Marjorie had sought occasional, non-personal contact with their father through the years, but 2008 transformed their interactions to deeply personal.

In January 2008, Harry, II, was hospitalized for complications rising from years of addiction, principally to alcohol. Harry, II's life experiences had sent him on a steep downward spiral. That winter of 2008, father Harry feared his son was on the edge of death. As the oldest Knowles son battled his demons and entered a hospital, father Harry stepped

Harry, II, 2010

in to help as he could—and as Harry, II, would allow. Harry visited his son at rehab and ached with the knowledge that he was powerless to slay this threat to his child. Only the patient himself and caring doctors could carve a way back to the living.

Harry, II, continued seeking treatment during the coming years and, ultimately, emerged from his fight "clean" in April 2009 and turned toward completing his college education.[74] Along the way, he and his father invested time in each other and re-built a bond from the ground up. On June 2, 2012, Harry, II, graduated from Community College of Vermont with a degree in psychology and a plan to pursue his Ph.D., research, and a career in addiction counseling. Harry, II, wanted to help others climb out of the hell that had imprisoned him for all those years. Dad Harry could not have been prouder.

The 2008 crisis served to reintroduce Harry to his daughter, Marjorie, who had been a doting sister to tortured Harry, II, for some time. Marjorie, who held a bachelor's degree from the University of Maryland, worked as a botanist at the Smithsonian in Washington, D.C., but, subsequently, transitioned from that career to artistic ventures—particularly in textile applications. Harry understood that the father-daughter reconnection was a fragile one and required frequent reviews of past hurts. Still, the process was a step toward some measure of much-needed healing for Marjorie.

In February 2008, Harry discovered he was the one in need of healing when his longtime internist and former Cooper University Hospital chief of medicine Ed Viner delivered the bad news that Harry had an aggressive strain of prostate cancer. The diagnosis was confirmed during medical tests

Pursuing her textile art interests, Marjorie examines one of her quilts.

prompted by Harry's pursuit of the comprehensive physical exam required to renew one's pilot's license. A radical prostatectomy was scheduled for early March at Cooper in Camden, New Jersey. The prognosis was good, however, due to Harry's otherwise excellent health and the fact the cancer was caught early. Immediately, family and friends offered to help. After the successful surgery, niece Hope Penn McCarrell (brother Bill's daughter) cared for Harry at the hospital, followed by Harry's daughter, Marjorie.

Marjorie and her father in Hanover, 2008

Marjorie continued her time with her father at his Hanover home following Harry's release from Cooper Hospital. "The reunion with Marjorie is incredibly delightful," Harry said at the time. "I have misjudged Marjorie and neglected our relationship far too long [resulting in] heavy loss on both sides."[75] Harry commented that "after our separation of 30-plus years" words could scarcely describe how he felt about "ignoring her very delicate position during her growth and needing my help."[76]

Having Marjorie with him no doubt accelerated Harry's recovery. The experience could have drained him emotionally; instead, he was buoyed and motivated by the positive family interaction from all sides. Harry did not waste this new-found opportunity to tell his children he loved them. That March, Marjorie reciprocated, telling her father she loved him and forgave him. On the wake of this redemption, Harry's recuperation proceeded seamlessly. Sadly, in future years, the relationship suffered much emotional upheaval, and Marjorie again distanced herself from her family. However, at this point in 2008, Harry's heart was much lighter concerning his children.

Harry's health returned in time for a major event that spring—the presentation by Auburn University of an honorary doctor of science degree to one of her most accomplished graduates. The fact that Harry

Crawford and Beverly Nevins at the graduation celebration

Shirley and Dick Webb and Marjorie

would be given an honorary degree by his alma mater was no surprise to the many following his career, such as then College of Sciences and Mathematics Dean Stewart Schneller, who had nominated Harry and placed Harry's name before the board of trustees for approval. Harry was humbled as his university family, relatives, and close friends gathered in Auburn, Alabama, for the May 10 ceremony.

Included in the day's celebration for Harry were several Auburn University dignitaries and old friends—Crawford and Beverly Nevins, Anne Pilcher, Dick and Shirley Webb, and Carolyn Carr (daughter of Howard and Carolyn Carr). The event also was a veritable family reunion, with attendance by half-brother Bill Penn and his wife, Cat, and their daughter, Hope; step-brother Jim Ramsey and his wife, Ruth; and two of Harry's three children, twins Robert and Marjorie. Robert and Marjorie had seen each other for the first time in five years only recently and were being introduced back into the family fold after decades of absence.

For Harry, it was a culminating, joyous event, soon after which he commented, "You cannot imagine the high that I have enjoyed for the past few days. Being with Robert and Marjorie and seeing them being enveloped by the family and my friends has been an unbelievable experience."[77] Robert and Marjorie, for their part, seemed to enjoy their journey south and learning about their father and family. Later, Robert reinforced his father's recognition, saying, "He did change retailing. My father's honorary doctorate was deserved."[78]

Indeed, the Auburn honorary doctorate resulted from Harry's entire lifetime of work. His career success was littered with brilliant inventions, scrappy survival skills, and a dedication to learning and the purity of knowledge. He had more than 350 patents to his name (with enough pending that he approached 400 patents within a few years), a feat which placed him in the top ten of all U.S. patent holders and certainly marked Harry as one of the "nation's most prolific living inventors," according to a Metrologic retrospective report.[79]

Marjorie and Robert at the Ramsey home in Birmingham looking at family photos

The path to those patents was built on Harry's education and his work experiences. Beginning with Bell Labs in 1953, he had joined the explosion of technological genius after the birth of the transistor with his own contributions—via germanium transistors—to Project Vanguard, the nation's first satellite, and the Nike Zeus anti-aircraft missile system. His germanium mesa transistors served the significant computer models of the late 1950s and 1960s and were a major product line, along with silicon transistors, at Motorola when Harry worked there 1958 to 1962. While at Motorola, Harry patented the universally recognized "2N2222" star transistor, an industry workhorse which would be manufactured in the billions. During his tenure at Westinghouse, Harry developed and presented, at the Institute of Electrical and Electronics Engineers conference in 1964, the basic concepts of the renowned Moore's Law forecasting model for the semiconductor industry (which was published in 1965 by his friend, Gordon Moore).

His rise to fame, however, was not assured until he left the semiconductor industry to make lasers and form his own company, Metrologic Instruments, to eventually deliver his products worldwide. A born visionary, Harry pioneered the world's first handheld laser bar code scanner with built-in decode; mini-slot scanners; triggerless handheld scanners; handheld omni-directional scanners; and planar laser illumination and imaging scanners. Metrologic produced more than 40 different types of scanners for an almost endless number of uses by retailers, distributors, and in industrial and delivery applications. Harry used an array of technologies in his advanced scanners from lasers to holography to camera-based systems to radio-frequency identification and, with those technologies, changed the face of retailing for all.

Along the way, he employed upwards of 1,500 people in the U.S. and abroad and was recognized for his contributions to the regional and national economy with numerous awards, including induction into the New Jersey Business Hall of Fame and two presidential ("E" and "E Star") awards for export success. Harry's genius as a scientist was unquestioned; but his compassion for his employees was not fully evident until he fought bankruptcy, destructive lawsuits, and relentless public market stress to keep his company and his people afloat for the better part of 40 years.

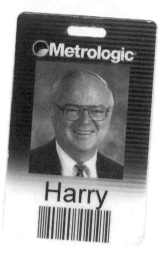

"Harry Knowles is a pioneer," longtime Metrologic patent prosecutor and friend Tom Perkowski said. "He got patents in bar code scanning, but he could have invented anything. What mattered was the creativity. He was truly skilled at his art. He was daring, always on the edge of discovery."[80]

Perkowski agreed with many others who said that the Knowles Science Teaching Foundation would be Harry's greatest legacy. After teaching science to his employees for most of his career and supporting education efforts for decades through donations to Auburn University, Physics Bowl competitions, and his own in-house training programs, KSTF was a natural outgrowth of Harry's focus and concerns for math and science education in his country. In fact, the American Association of Physics Teachers awarded Harry its Distinguished Service Citation in 2002 for exceptional contributions to physics teaching.

"His real legacy will be the foundation," Harry's brother Bill Penn said in 2007. "I am so proud of this guy. This is Harry Knowles: he funded a physics chair [at Auburn]. He didn't name it after himself. He named it after Howard Carr. That showing of appreciation gets to me. Harry knows you get happiness by giving [the money] away and creating happy situations for others."[81]

Harry's other brother, Jim Ramsey, emphasized

Bill Penn

324

that Harry's dedication to education was long-standing, going back to his college days, and that the KSTF dream grew out of what Harry saw as a critical decline in American education. While others may have wrung their hands in frustration, Harry sought solutions via KSTF. "If Harry wanted something, he had the drive to go out and get it," Ramsey said. "Most anything he's taken on as a dream, he's accomplished. I don't think Harry's had many obstacles he hasn't overcome."[82]

Jim Ramsey

KSTF trustee Bill Rulon-Miller said that Harry's "extraordinary intelligence and energy" balanced well with his "compassion and sensitivity to other people." Rulon-Miller said the best entrepreneurs are altruistic. "The best of the guys like Harry are the opposite of narrow-minded businessmen. They have tremendous intellect and advance their fields. They also advance their country and give significantly back."[83]

Thus, Auburn University honored one of her sons May 10, 2008, with an honorary doctorate for his brilliance as a scientist and inventor, his career-long success as a businessman, and his valiant philanthropic efforts to lift U.S. math and science education. However, Harry knew his success had come at a high cost to his family. As he basked in his alma mater's recognition, he was thankful to the core that he had been given another chance with his children. With Robert and Marjorie watching from Section 31 of the university coliseum, where graduation was taking place, Harry felt the peace of their forgiveness in his heart as he stepped to the podium to receive his degree and address the audience of new graduates.

Auburn President Jay Gogue attaches the doctoral stole on Harry as COSAM Dean Stewart Schneller observes.
Photo courtesy of COSAM/Auburn University

Harry, doctoral stole encircling his neck, thought of how fiercely he had desired a doctorate while at Bell Labs. While his new designation as "Dr. Knowles" was well earned and the recipi-

325

ent was pleased and proud to bear the title, Harry knew his fulfillment didn't reside in the achievement. What brought true success and what made one happy? These were apt questions for the eager, cap-and-gown-clad youngsters poised to enter the job market who were now seated before Harry.

After thanking Trustee Paul Spina, Dean Schneller, and Auburn University President Jay Gogue, Harry spoke to his fellow graduates:

> Congratulations to each of you. Today is a milestone in your long journey of learning. Condolences to those who feel you are leaving your closest friends behind. However, fear not; they will stay with you forever. I have many, many here today.
>
> My three-minute message today is not new, however, it is simple. In your endeavors, you MUST follow your DREAMS. DO WHAT YOU LOVE TO DO. Pass up the seduction of money, popularity, and expediency. In pursuit of success, you WILL FAIL, as I have, many, many times. You need to love what you do from dawn to dusk to pick up the pieces and put the next day together with the kind of enthusiasm it takes.
>
> I have an illustration, if I may. I hereby publicly confess to a towering failure beyond anything that any of you have experienced, I hope. I am personally responsible for giving the City of Birmingham a big shove down the slippery slope from its economic pinnacle of the 1940s.
>
> Let me set the stage: it was early August 1945, about the time of Nagasaki and Hiroshima, and just before VJ Day. I was a 16-year-old photo-chemistry nerd, working for Lollar's at the time, the South's largest mail-order photofinisher. I had done so for several summers. We were located on the third floor of the Lyric Building, which still stands across 3rd Avenue from the Alabama Theatre.
>
> To further describe the impending events: directly below us, on the second floor, was Birmingham's largest fur storage facility. [T]housands of Birmingham's most elegant furs were stored there. The gold-gilded lobby of the Lyric Theatre was on the first floor.
>
> My job was to process hundreds of rolls of film each day that were logged in from the early-morning mail. I had to develop, fix, and wash them with huge quantities of running water. Naturally, I arrived late each morning and was one of the last to leave each day, having processed the film from the day before.
>
> Coming from my home near Legion Field on this particular

August morning, I jumped off the street car at 17th Street and innocently bounced up 3rd Avenue. Approaching 18th Street, I could see a crowd standing outside "my" Lyric building, along with fire trucks and stalled traffic. Getting closer, I could see fellow workers standing on the street and could hear the Armenian furrier sputtering and swearing. Approaching even closer, I could see a flood of water flowing from the Lyric lobby out across 3rd Avenue.[84]

At rapt attention, the graduation audience anticipated calamity in Harry's tale.

"A terrible chill ran up my spine," Harry said, slowly emphasizing each word for effect. The coliseum full of people laughed. He continued:

Harry during his commencement address on the campus of Auburn University, May 10, 2008
COSAM/Auburn University

As I approached, Bill Lollar himself sidled up and, with an unforgettably eerie tranquility, asked, "Harry, did you forget something last night [more audience laughter], like leaving the water running?" An errant roll of film had stopped the drain.

My oversight had ruined thousands of fur coats, and the loss was probably in the millions for the furrier and his insurance company. The Lyric Theatre was shut down for weeks for repairs. Lollar's, one of Birmingham's most successful businesses, was forced to shut down and totally relocate. My fellow employees were now jobless.

However...[with a pause and a hand flair and more laughter], I could escape. A few days later, I enrolled as a freshman here at Auburn. I could pursue my own dream: the fascination of light interacting with matter to capture images; how to record forever a given moment in time, all by shaping glass and photosensitive materials.

In my own mind, Birmingham never fully recovered from that tragic day. But, somehow, I did...and it raises the question of is irony always fair? No.

That failure is but one of many in my own life; some are a lot worse than that one. Each of you will fail many times. Leap over them. You will need every GRAM of enthusiasm, by LOVING WHAT YOU DO [audience clapping] for you to generate the ultimate success you want, and that we all want for you.

Plow through your failures. Dig into the fertile successes that you richly deserve.

I want to thank you for these few moments of your warm and wonderful attention. I will forever cherish this moment.[85]

The commencement speech may have entertained, but its advice was well worn and proven for Harry. Harry certainly did not equate money with happiness, although there often was joy in giving it away. However, Harry theorized that, if one pursued what he or she loved, the money would follow anyway. "Kids wonder what to do with their lives," Harry said in 1999. "They say, 'I want to make a lot of money.' What are you going to do with a lot of money? You can't eat it, you can't sleep with it—you can't buy happiness. But, boy, if you do what you like, you'll make out okay, probably better than okay, financially; and, more importantly, you'll live a life that you're proud of."[86]

Harry basking in the glory of his beloved Auburn's national championship, 2011

Harry's work brought him true success because, through all the challenges and failures, Harry always loved what he did—whether inventing from good science, building an efficient production line, or encouraging learning. Although he had not learned to love and value his relationships with his children until late in his life, he now counted fatherhood as another source of happiness. Harry could not wait to see what else life would teach him.

Epilogue

Genius in America

(2010)

As Harry looked around the buzzing banquet room the evening of April 27, 2010, his heart swelled with emotion. Here, a little more than a mile from Metrologic's now near-decimated Blackwood headquarters, at the Auletto Caterers' venue in Deptford, New Jersey, were gathered almost 300 of Harry's ex-colleagues—former and current employees (and their spouses) of Metrologic from the founder's tenure there. The reunion had been Harry-instigated, but the enjoyment was obvious for all as the old manufacturing team reassembled. Production floor workers and engineers hugged and grinned and told war stories. These people were family.

Clad in a faded Metrologic softball league jersey, associate engineer George Kolis, who worked for the company from 1975 until 2010, was there that night, along with others who remembered Metrologic's first converted-bungalow factory at Bellmawr, such as Judy Leason, who had more than 35 years in as a production supervisor, and Kolis' colleagues Bob Blake and David Wilz. Harry saw the many familiar faces and thought of how *all* his former employees in the room had helped shape Metrologic's history.

Throughout the highs and lows of the company's evolution, the employees had respected and trusted Harry. Both Harry and Janet—another eager reunion attendee that night—had been loving, surrogate parents to the entire production floor crew. Kolis had said that, even during bankruptcy, Metrologic acted as a family and a team. Their loyal work ethic and quality products helped revolutionize an industry.

Harry had come into the bar code scanning industry at its relative infancy, leaving an incredibly successful career in semiconductor technology to teach himself how to make lasers. Forming his own company, Metrologic Instruments, Inc., in May 1968, he soon became the world's largest producer of helium-neon lasers. Within months of the grocery trade's first official laser bar code scanning of a pack of Wrigley's Juicy Fruit gum in 1974, Metrologic had designed its first working scanner.

However, Harry envisioned past the standard, over-sized grocery store scanner. Before the smaller retail stores even knew they needed a handheld scanner, Harry invented one. Eventually, as retailers grasped the power of the new scanners for their businesses, handhelds outnumbered the large in-bed scanners ten to one. More than 350 patents later, Harry had changed the market forever. Along the way, he had fought bankruptcy, seemingly endless patent wars in the courts, global markets, investor demands, and technological walls to continuously push the envelope on what was possible.

Many rivals were bigger and made more money. Other companies had a larger share of the market (although Harry was at the front of the pack selling U.S. scanners overseas). But few advanced pure invention in the same way and no auto-ID company had more heart than the scrappy Metrologic. The heartbeat of Metrologic's success, of course, was Harry, who risked everything repeatedly for the sake of his science and his Metrologic family.

At the height of its U.S. presence, Metrologic had more than 700 employees at its 115,000-square-foot Blackwood, New Jersey, manufacturing plant and headquarters. Since Harry's departure and the purchase of Metrologic by, first, Francisco Partners then Honeywell, however, the vehicles parked at the Blackwood employee lot had dwindled to maybe 100 cars on a good workday. Harry had toiled valiantly to get in front of the economic dynamic of losing labor jobs overseas. His strategy had been to keep the controls and creativity in Blackwood while segmenting out specific work for the Suzhou, China, plant. He tried to balance the expectation for ever-increasing profits when his company was public with his personal priorities of his people and their discoveries. Harry felt strongly that locating too much American ingenuity outside the U.S. would only threaten his nation's strength.

In the end, he lost the battle to preserve and even expand Blackwood to the profit-driven needs of his successors. The reality of the numbers—that bottom line of accountants and managers—minus Harry's broader vision resulted in the loss of hundreds of Metrologic jobs. Still, despite Harry's self-imposed guilt, those former employees didn't blame Harry. Here, at this Metrologic reunion, they effused love for one another, especially Harry. After all, their CEO had launched an idea into a company which had provided a livelihood for 1,500 workers worldwide. Employee after employee came to the camera-bearing Harry during the night to thank him for such a caring, rewarding place to work all those years. Following their leader into a world of Harry's own making, Metrologic employees had found their ingenuity constantly challenged and their sense of accomplishment fully sated.

"Harry Knowles shaped an industry," former Metrologic patent prosecutor Tom Perkowski said. "This is a story about a strong individual with the vision to build something from nothing. Metrologic was built from nothing with private money, not public money or high-tech subsidies.

"Metrologic was his laboratory to explore and express himself. He believed in and nurtured individuals, not corporations. He had a sense of faith in [people]. If you failed, you got up. A lot of people benefited. He took all the risks, and he benefited, too. It's the way capitalism is supposed to work."[1]

Harry thought that the ability for a private individual, an entrepreneur, to build a company such as Metrologic was uniquely American.[2] "In the U.S., one guy can get things done," Harry said. "All decision-making has to be tightly contained in one brain—financial, technical capability, marketing, feasibility—not in a corporate committee. The next big thing…takes a tightly focused team. [Bureaucratic corporations] are not able to focus. Everyone starts to hedge their bets. By the time everyone pads their commitment, the costs are too much [and the risks] make no economic sense. Until someone else does it and proves there's a market."[3]

Bravado and risk-taking were prevalent traits of Harry and crucial elements of the Metrologic success story. His breadth of expertise, from semiconductors to lasers, was unique. Harry had little or no money when he began his venture, but his technical know-how was solid. His generation knew advanced mathematics and science. He and his contemporaries came along during a magic era of Bell Labs-style collaboration when brains and opportunity collided and genius in America thrived, and the world envied.

Harry had watched lagging education and deadly bureaucracy hurt entrepreneurship in the U.S. The Knowles Science Teaching Foundation was Harry's hope for future visionaries and for his country. "Harry is a patriot to his core," former Metrologic general counsel Bruce Harrison said. "[KSTF] is as inspired as it is patriotic. One can identify other successful entrepreneurs who get behind causes that are intended to make the world a better place. Harry wants to make America a better place and maintain its historic position in the world."[4]

"I've been very lucky," Harry said, "leaning on people like the B.J. Zhus, Chic Naylors, Rich Gapins. I didn't do this stuff. I shared the same path, walking down at the same time with so many. There was such a broad range of things we did at Metrologic, it's incredible we survived."[5]

On this April evening in New Jersey blue-collar country, Harry reflected on the innovative history of Metrologic, telling the crowd gathered, "We generated our jobs and our money in a most proud way—we designed and built products that were our own ideas and from our own work....The products were for worldwide usage, and we brought money into the U.S. and into our neighborhoods from all over the world." Harry also highlighted the loyalty of his workforce and sense of family, saying there was "a lot of love, lots of tolerance for each other and with the person running the show—me. And also lots of hard work from all of us. I love you for it."[6]

That love, that distinctly personal touch, distinguished *Harry's* Metrologic from Metrologic the still successful subsidiary of Honeywell. With the absence of the founder's sometimes reckless, but always trail-blazing, courage, Metrologic's corporate personality had been altered profoundly. However, Harry and his Metrologic family's genuine affection for one another had remained. Under the exhilaration of the reunion, Harry felt peace and a deep, fresh hope for the future. While Bruce Harrison feared that Harry was a "vanishing breed" in the U.S., Harry was betting *not* and that, given the opportunity, any young person with an idea and enough knowledge, training, and gumption could become the next genius in America.

Acknowledgments

I first met Harry Knowles Fall 1999 when I interviewed him for a feature story for *Auburn Magazine,* Auburn University's alumni magazine. During that initial visit, I walked the Metrologic floor with Harry at the height of Blackwood's production capabilities. The pride of the sneakers-clad Harry as he excitedly toured me through the plant he created was palpable. Harry's energy was infectious. Without that hallmark energy and Harry's natural ability to inspire, this biography would not exist. He gave selflessly of his time for interviews and science education sessions that morphed from hours to days to years. From the project's beginning, his approach was one of cooperation, not censorship—even when the truths laid bare were difficult. Thank you, Harry, for the resources and faith, as well as your boundless optimism that genius still exists in America. Your foundation is changing this country in remarkable ways.

To my partners in this biography, I am honored to have shared this journey with you and utterly amazed at the depths of your talents: my husband and hero, Sam Hendrix, who always has been a better and faster writer than me and whose input at every level made for a much better product. Designer Mike DeMent combines artistic brilliance with a devotion to elegance and readability of type for which editors dream and rarely get. Mike, working with you again was a joy; your patience knows no bounds. To archivist and records manager Al Barrett, I offer my undying gratitude for swooping in to rescue the plethora of Knowles files from dusty disarray and painstakingly shuffling them into the beautifully organized boxes of documents that now make up the C. Harry Knowles Collection in the Auburn University Department of Special Collections and Archives. Without those rescued files (not to mention the generosity of your wife, Rhonda), the story could not have been completed. My other partner in crime and a true writing kindred spirit, editor-extraordinaire Jacque Kochak, rescued my text many times over with her thoughtful edits, expert proofreading eye, and indexing. All of you have been wonderful company and essential sounding boards.

My thanks to latecomer to the project Jody Hernandez for the Herculean photos assistance under the astute guidance of Al. The brothers team will give Auburn's Digital Collection an amazing treasure trove of historic images. (Kudos to AU Libraries assistant dean Aaron Trehub, digital projects librarian Midge Coates, and web designer Tony Oravet for their support.) Thank you to Chemical Heritage Foundation fellow David Brock for his generous sharing of interview transcripts and amazing historical work on Moore's Law, *Understanding Moore's Law: Four Decades of Innovation.* I depended on his knowledge on the early era of the transistor greatly, as many attributions and endnotes attest. More key context and quotes were gleaned from journalists and historians Rob Walker of Stanford University's Silicon Genesis Project, Ronald Kessler, Diana Lasseter, Anthony Birritteri, Jane Bergen, and Susan Goodwillie, to name a few.

I am grateful to other professionals who gave unselfishly of their expertise, including Tom Perkowski; Bill Rulon-Miller; Bruce Harrison; publisher Rich Donnell; Auburn University head archivist Dwayne Cox (who answered every plea with cheer and efficiency) and his team; and the late Sam Lowther, whose acute comprehension of Auburn's historical statistics provided crucial context for Chapter 2. Much appreciation for historic images is extended to archivist Drew Davis of Motorola Solutions Heritage Services and Archives, Ed Eckert of Alcatel-Lucent USA, George Kupczak of AT&T Archives, Jack Ward of the Transistor Museum, Nancy A. Blair-DeLeon of IEEE, and the team at AU Photographic Services.

Thank you also to the many others whose encouragement and work brought this project to fruition. From writers and dear friends Mike Jernigan, Angie Lowry, and Leah Atkins who told me early on I could not only do this, but do it well, to the family (husband Sam, daughter Kelsey, parents Bill and Mary Hughes, and sister Kathleen Watson) and friends (Tim and Amy Eden, Vickie Jernigan, Steve and Susan Baum, Betty DeMent, Kelly and Shanna Jolley, and others) who read along and never failed to prop me up, I can only say how humbled I am to have such love poured on me. To the rest of the gang (family and friends) who weren't burdened with a sneak preview, I now entrust this story to you.

Notes

Due to the fact that several members of the Knowles family were interviewed, the entire name is specified for those endnote entries. At the risk of repetition and sacrifice of space, clarity was deemed preferable for research purposes. Please note that sources specified as "Metrologic files" may be found in the Auburn University Ralph Brown Draughon Library's Department of Special Collections and Archives under "C. Harry Knowles Collection." A chronological assembly of papers from Dr. Knowles' life, the collection was organized during the course of the writing of this biography. In addition, thousands of supporting photos are being processed; many of those images are finding a home (see diglib.auburn.edu/collections/chk) at Auburn University Libraries.

CHAPTER 1
BIRMINGHAM BOY
1928-1945

1. William W. Penn, Jr., interview by author, November 27, 2007.
2. Leah Rawls Atkins, *The Valley and the Hills: An Illustrated History of Birmingham and Jefferson County* (Woodland Hills, CA: Windsor Publications, 1981), 130.
3. Ibid., 177.
4. Ibid., 142-44.
5. William W. Penn, Jr., interview by author, November 27, 2007.
6. Ibid.
7. C. Harry Knowles, interview by author, February 13, 2008.
8. C. Harry Knowles, interview by author, November 29, 2007.
9. William W. Penn, Jr., interview by author, November 27, 2007.
10. C. Harry Knowles, interview by author, November 29, 2007.
11. William W. Penn, Jr., interview by author, November 27, 2007.
12. Virginia Knowles Hufbauer, comp., *Descendants of Richard Knowles, 1637-1973* (San Diego: Ventures International, 1974), 639.
13. Susan Goodwillie, *Now Hear This: The Life of Hugh S. Knowles, Acoustical Engineer and Entrepreneur* (Washington, DC: Francis Press, 1999), 1-5.
14. Ibid., 5-6.
15. Hufbauer, *Descendants of Richard Knowles*, 641.
16. Goodwillie, *Now Hear This*, 15.
17. Hufbauer, *Descendants of Richard Knowles*, 641.
18. Goodwillie, *Now Hear This*, 22.
19. Ibid., 33-35.
20. Ibid., 39, 43-44.
21. C. Harry Knowles, interview by author, November 29, 2007.
22. Ibid.

23. William W. Penn, Jr., interview by author, November 27, 2007.
24. Ibid.
25. C. Harry Knowles, interview by author, November 29, 2007.
26. William W. Penn, Jr., interview by author, November 27, 2007.
27. Ibid.
28. C. Harry Knowles, interview by author, November 29, 2007.
29. William W. Penn, Jr., interview by author, November 27, 2007.
30. Ibid.
31. William W. Penn, Jr., interview by author, January 16, 2008.
32. C. Harry Knowles, interview by author, November 29, 2007.
33. Hufbauer, *Descendants of Richard Knowles*, 639.
34. William W. Penn, Jr., interview by author, November 27, 2007.
35. C. Harry Knowles, interview by author, February 13, 2008.
36. Goodwillie, *Now Hear This*, 57.
37. William W. Penn, Jr., interviews by author, November 27, 2007, and January 16, 2008.
38. C. Harry Knowles, interview by author, November 29, 2007.
39. Ibid.
40. Goodwillie, *Now Hear This*, 84.
41. Ibid., 113-26.
42. Ibid., 102.
43. Ibid., xiii.
44. Ibid., 90.
45. C. Harry Knowles, interview by author, November 29, 2007.
46. Goodwillie, *Now Hear This*, 90-91.
47. C. Harry Knowles, interview by author, November 29, 2007.
48. Ibid.
49. Hufbauer, *Descendants of Richard Knowles*, 639.
50. Jim and Ruth Ramsey, interview by author, November 28, 2007.
51. C. Harry Knowles, interview by author, November 29, 2007.
52. William W. Penn, Jr., interview by author, November 27, 2007.
53. C. Harry Knowles, interview by author, November 29, 2007.
54. C. Harry Knowles, interview by author, February 15, 2008.
55. Jim and Ruth Ramsey, interview by author, November 28, 2007.
56. Atkins, *The Valley and the Hills*, 144-45.
57. Kenneth C. Davis, *Don't Know Much About History: Everything You Need to Know about American History but Never Learned* (New York: Avon Books, 1990), 294-98.
58. Atkins, *The Valley and the Hills*, 147.
59. William W. Penn, Jr., interviews by author, November 27, 2007, and January 16, 2008.
60. C. Harry Knowles, interview by author, February 13, 2008.
61. William W. Penn, Jr., interview by author, November 27, 2007.
62. C. Harry Knowles, interview by author, November 29, 2007.
63. Jim and Ruth Ramsey, interview by author, November 28, 2007.
64. C. Harry Knowles, interview by author, November 29, 2007.
65. Jim and Ruth Ramsey, interview by author, November 28, 2007.
66. Ruth Ramsey, interview by author, January 18, 2008.

67. Jim and Ruth Ramsey, interview by author, November 28, 2007.
68. Ibid.
69. C. Harry Knowles, interview by author, November 29, 2007.
70. Jim and Ruth Ramsey, interview by author, November 28, 2007.
71. Ibid.
72. C. Harry Knowles, interview by author, November 29, 2007.
73. Ibid.
74. Jim and Ruth Ramsey, interview by author, November 28, 2007.
75. C. Harry Knowles, interview by author, November 29, 2007; and Jim Ramsey, interview by author, November 28, 2007.
76. C. Harry Knowles, interview by author, November 29, 2007.
77. C. Harry Knowles, interview by author, February 15, 2008.
78. C. Harry Knowles, interview by author, November 29, 2007.
79. Get Downtown Birmingham, Lyric Theatre, http://www.getdowntown.info/Lyric_Theatre.html
80. C. Harry Knowles, interview by author, November 29, 2007.
81. Jim and Ruth Ramsey, interview by author, November 28, 2007.
82. C. Harry Knowles, interview by author, November 29, 2007.
83. C. Harry Knowles, interviews by author, February 13 and 15, 2008.
84. C. Harry Knowles, interview by author, November 29, 2007.

CHAPTER 2
AUBURN
1945-1953

1. Historical Enrollment Records, Auburn University Office of Institutional Research and Assessment, 1945-1946.
2. Mickey Logue and Jack Simms, *Auburn: A Pictorial History of the Loveliest Village*, rev. ed. (Auburn, AL, 1996), 12, 166.
3. Alabama Polytechnic Institute, *Glomerata*, vol. 49, ed. Mildred Jean Woodham (Auburn, AL: Student Body of Alabama Polytechnic Institute, 1946), 4-7.
4. Historical Enrollment Records, 1945-1946.
5. C. Harry Knowles, interview by author, February 13, 2008.
6. Goodwillie, *Now Hear This*, 46-49.
7. Alabama Polytechnic Institute, *Glomerata*, vol. 49, 19.
8. Birmingham (AL) Public Library, Local Databases, Alabama Inventors, http://bpldb.bplonline.org/db/inventors
9. C. Harry Knowles, interview by author, February 13, 2008.
10. William Penn, interview by author, November 27, 2007.
11. C. Harry Knowles, interview by author, February 13, 2008.
12. Ibid.
13. William Penn, interview by author, November 27, 2007.
14. C. Harry Knowles, interview by author, February 13, 2008.
15. Historical Enrollment Records, 1945-1946.
16. Alabama Polytechnic Institute, *Glomerata*, vol. 49.
17. C. Harry Knowles, interview by author, February 13, 2008.
18. C. Harry Knowles, interview by author, February 15, 2008.
19. Jim Ramsey, interview by author, November 28, 2007.

20. C. Harry Knowles, interview by author, February 13, 2008.
21. Ibid.
22. William Penn, interview by author, November 27, 2007.
23. C. Harry Knowles, interview by author, February 13, 2008.
24. C. Harry Knowles, interview by author, July 26, 2007.
25. Marine Corps Recruiting Depot, MCRD Parris Island, Visitor Information, About Parris Island, Parris Island Geography and History, https://www.mcrdpi.usmc.mil/SitePages/About%20Parris%20Island.aspx
26. Marine Corps Historical Reference Series, no. 8, "A Brief History of the Marine Corps Recruit Depot, Parris Island, South Carolina, 1891-1962" (Washington, DC, Headquarters: U.S. Marine Corps, rev. 1962), 11-12, http://www.au.af.mil/au/awc/awcgate/usmchist/parris.txt
27. Jim Ramsey, interview by author, November 28, 2007.
28. C. Harry Knowles, interview by author, February 13, 2008.
29. GlobalSecurity.org, Military Facilities, Marine Corps Camps, Henderson Hall, http://www.globalsecurity.org/military/facility/henderson-hall.htm
30. C. Harry Knowles, interview by author, February 13, 2008.
31. Jim Ramsey, interview by author, November 28, 2007.
32. C. Harry Knowles, interview by author, February 13, 2008.
33. C. Harry Knowles, interview by author, November 29, 2007.
34. C. Harry Knowles, interview by author, February 13, 2008.
35. Ibid.
36. Alabama Polytechnic Institute, *Glomerata*, vol. 52, ed. Hugh Gaston (Auburn, AL: Student Body of Alabama Polytechnic Institute, 1949), 16.
37. Physics Department Records, Auburn University Special Collections and Archives, Record Group 551, Accession Number 97-050 (9/28/81), Box 3, R.B. Draughon File 3-26, 1948.
38. Auburn University, Office of Communications and Marketing, Presidential Installation, Past Presidents, http://ocm.auburn.edu/presidential_installation/pastpresidents.html
39. Alabama Polytechnic Institute, *Glomerata*, vol. 52, 22.
40. C. Harry Knowles, interview by author, February 13, 2008.
41. Alabama Polytechnic Institute, *Glomerata*, vol. 52, 22.
42. C. Harry Knowles, interview by author, February 15, 2008.
43. C. Harry Knowles, interview by author, February 13, 2008.
44. Howard Carr to Fred Allison, August 26, 1948, Physics Department Records, Auburn University Special Collections and Archives, Record Group 551, Accession Number 97-050 (9/28/81), Box 4, Howard Carr File.
45. Auburn University News Bureau press release, August 19, 1977, Physics Department Records.
46. American Physical Society Southeastern Section Survey, Alabama Polytechnic Institute statistics, Physics Department Records.
47. Physics Department Records Introduction.
48. C. Harry Knowles, interview by author, February 13, 2008.
49. Alabama Polytechnic Institute, *Glomerata*, vol. 52.
50. Alabama Polytechnic Institute, *Glomerata*, vol. 54, ed. C. Harry Knowles (Auburn, AL: Student Body of Alabama Polytechnic Institute, 1951).
51. Mary Ellen Hendrix, "Between the Lines," *Auburn Magazine*, Winter 2000 (Auburn, AL: Auburn University, 2000), 19.

52. Fred Allison to Charles F. Mercer, April 15, 1941, Fred Allison Papers, Auburn University Special Collections and Archives, Record Group 433, Accession Number 03-058 (4/30/04), Box 1, Howard Carr File 24.

53. C. Harry Knowles, interview by author, February 13, 2008.

54. Hendrix, "Between the Lines," *Auburn Magazine*, 19.

55. C. Harry Knowles, interview by author, February 13, 2008.

56. Ibid.

57. Alabama Polytechnic Institute, *Glomerata*, vol. 53, ed. Harry Golemon (Auburn, AL: Student Body of Alabama Polytechnic Institute, 1950).

58. C. Harry Knowles, interview by author, February 13, 2008.

59. Alabama Polytechnic Institute, *Glomerata*, vol. 53, 54.

60. C. Harry Knowles, interview by author, February 13, 2008.

61. Physics Department Records Introduction, Auburn University Special Collections and Archives, Record Group 551, Accession Number 97-050 (9/28/81).

62. Alabama Polytechnic Institute, *Glomerata*, vol. 54, 337.

63. C. Harry Knowles, interview by author, February 13, 2008.

64. Alabama Polytechnic Institute, *Glomerata*, vol. 53.

65. Alabama Polytechnic Institute, *Glomerata*, vol. 54, 312.

66. C. Harry Knowles, interview by author, February 13, 2008.

67. William W. Penn, Jr., interview by author, November 27, 2007.

68. C. Harry Knowles, interview by author, February 14, 2008.

69. Charles Mathews, e-mail message to author, May 16, 2008.

70. 1950 Atlantic Hurricane Season, Wikipedia, http://en.wikipedia.org/wiki/1950_Atlantic_hurricane_season

71. Mathews, e-mail message to author, May 16, 2008.

72. C. Harry Knowles, interview by author, February 14, 2008.

73. 1950 Atlantic Hurricane Season.

74. Mathews, e-mail message to author, May 16, 2008.

75. C. Harry Knowles, interview by author, February 14-15, 2008.

76. C. Harry Knowles, interview by author, February 13, 2008.

77. Ibid.

78. C. Harry Knowles, interview by author, February 13-15, 2008.

79. Ibid.

80. Howard Carr to Bell Telephone Laboratories, September 21, 1953, Physics Department Records, Box 4, File 4-19.

81. C. Harry Knowles, interview by author, February 14, 2008.

82. C. Harry Knowles, interview by author, February 15, 2008.

83. C. Harry Knowles, interview by author, February 13, 2008.

84. Howard Carr to G.M. Almay, March 10, 1954, Physics Department Records, Box 4, File 4-23.

85. C. Harry Knowles, interview by author, February 15, 2008.

86. C. Harry Knowles, interview by author, February 14, 2008.

87. Ibid.

88. C. Harry Knowles, interview by author, February 15, 2008.

89. Ibid.

90. Ibid.

91. Jim and Ruth Ramsey, interview by author, November 28, 2007.
92. C. Harry Knowles, interview by author, February 15, 2008.
93. Ibid.
94. Robert T. Lagemann and C. Harry Knowles, "Velocity of Compressional Waves in Liquid Hydrogen Fluoride and Some Thermodynamic Properties Derived Therefrom," *Journal of Chemical Physics* 32, no. 2 (1960), http://jcp.aip.org/resource/1/jcpsa6/v32/i2?&page=2
95. Harry H. Knowles to Howard E. Carr, July 3, 1953, Physics Department Records, Box 4, File 4-20.

CHAPTER 3
BELL LABS
1953-1958

1. Jeremy Bernstein, *Three Degrees Above Zero, Bell Labs in the Information Age* (New York: Charles Scribner's Sons, 1984), 1-2, 8-9.
2. Edward A. Sharpe, "In Memoriam...Kenneth D. Smith, 1905-1990," Southwest Museum of Engineering, Communications and Computation (Glendale, AZ: SMECC), reprinted from *Vintage Electrics* 2, no. 1, http://www.smecc.org/k_d__smith.htm
3. James M. Early, "K.D. Smith Memories," Southwest Museum of Engineering, Communications and Computation (SMECC, 1990), http://www.smecc.org/k_d__smith_memories_by_j_m__early.htm
4. Dave Smith, "K.D. Smith," SMECC, http://www.smecc.org/k_d__smith_by_dave_smith.htm
5. Early, "K.D. Smith Memories."
6. Ibid.
7. C. Harry Knowles, interview by author, May 21, 2008.
8. Phil T. Porter, interview by author, January 27, 2009.
9. Alcatel-Lucent, Bell Labs History, Presidents, "Mervin J. Kelly," http://www.alcatel-lucent.com
10. C. Harry Knowles, interview by author, May 21, 2008.
11. "Dr. Mervin J. Kelly Dies at 77," *New York Times*, March 20, 1971, http://www.nytimes.com/
12. PBS Online, History of the Transistor, "Transistorized!" (ScienCentral, Inc., and the American Institute of Physics, 1999), http://www.pbs.org/transistor/album1/addlbios/kelly.html
13. Ronald Kessler, "Absent at the Creation: How One Scientist Made Off with the Biggest Invention since the Light Bulb," *Washington Post Magazine*, April 6, 1997, http://www1.hollins.edu/faculty/richter/327/AbsentCreation.htm
14. Ibid.
15. PBS Online, History of the Transistor, "Transistorized!"
16. Inventor Biographies, William Shockley Biography, http://www.madehow.com/inventorbios/12/William-Shockley.html
17. "Dr. Mervin J. Kelly Dies at 77," *New York Times*.
18. PBS Online, History of the Transistor, "Transistorized!"
19. Kessler, "Absent at the Creation."
20. David C. Brock, *Understanding Moore's Law: Four Decades of Innovation* (Philadelphia: Chemical Heritage Press, 2006), 8-9.

21. Ibid.

22. Kessler, "Absent at the Creation."

23. Mervin J. Kelly, "The First Five Years of the Transistor," *Bell Telephone Magazine*, Summer 1953 (New York: American Telephone and Telegraph Company, 1953).

24. Kessler, "Absent at the Creation."

25. Ibid.

26. Kelly, "The First Five Years of the Transistor."

27. Brock, *Understanding Moore's Law*, 10-11.

28. Ibid.

29. "The Story of the Transistor: Ten Years of Progress" (Bell Telephone Laboratories Inc., 1958), 8.

30. Kelly, "The First Five Years of the Transistor."

31. "The Story of the Transistor," 8; and Brock, *Understanding Moore's Law*, 11.

32. Brock, *Understanding Moore's Law*, 11-12.

33. Frederick Seitz and Norman G. Einspruch, *Electronic Genie: The Tangled History of Silicon* (University of Illinois, 1998), 171.

34. C. Harry Knowles, interview by author, February 15, 2008.

35. C. Harry Knowles, interview by author, May 22, 2008.

36. Phil T. Porter, interview by author, January 27, 2009.

37. Ibid.

38. Solar Cells, Wikipedia, http://en.wikipedia.org/wiki/Solar_cell

39. "Arthur Leonard Schawlow," *A Dictionary of Scientists* (Oxford University Press, 1993, 1999, 2003) Answers.com, http://www.answers.com/topic/arthur-leonard-schawlow

40. David F. Salisbury, "Memorial Service May 20 for Arthur Schawlow, Laser Co-inventor," *Stanford Online Report*, May 5, 1999, http://news-service.stanford.edu/news/1999/may5/schawlowobit-55-a.html

41. C. Harry Knowles, interview by author, November 6, 2008.

42. Institute of Electrical and Electronics Engineers, "A Brief History of the IEEE" (New York: IEEE, 2008), http://www.ieee.org/web/aboutus/history/index.html

43. C. Harry Knowles, interviews by author, May 22, 2008, and November 6, 2008.

44. C. Harry Knowles, interview by author, November 6, 2008.

45. Bernstein, *Three Degrees Above Zero*, 96-97.

46. Brock, *Understanding Moore's Law*, 11-13.

47. C. Harry Knowles, interview by author, May 22, 2008.

48. C. Harry Knowles, interview by author, November 6, 2008.

49. C. Harry Knowles, interview by author, May 22, 2008.

50. C. Harry Knowles, interview by author, May 21, 2008.

51. C. Harry Knowles, interviews by author, February 15, 2008, and May 22, 2008.

52. Michael Riordan, "How Bell Labs Missed the Microchip," *IEEE Spectrum*, December 2006, http://spectrum.ieee.org/dec06/4749

53. C. Harry Knowles, interview by author, May 21, 2008.

54. C. Harry Knowles, interview by David C. Brock, September 18, 2007, tape 1, transcript, 20.

55. C. Harry Knowles, interview by author, May 22, 2008.

56. Ibid.

57. C. Harry Knowles, interview by Brock, September 18, 2007, tape 1, transcript, 21.

58. C. Harry Knowles, interview by author, November 6, 2008.

59. C. Harry Knowles, interview by Brock, September 18, 2007, tape 1, transcript, 21.
60. C. Harry Knowles, interview by author, July 26, 2007.
61. C. Harry Knowles, interview by Brock, September 18, 2007, tape 1, transcript, 23.
62. C. Harry Knowles, interview by author, May 22, 2008.
63. C. Harry Knowles, interview by Brock, September 18, 2007, tape 1, transcript, 23.
64. C. Harry Knowles, interview by author, May 21, 2008.
65. C. Harry Knowles, interview by author, November 5, 2008.
66. C. Harry Knowles, interview by author, November 6, 2008.
67. C. Harry Knowles, interview by author, May 21, 2008.
68. C. Harry Knowles, interview by Brock, September 18, 2007, tape 1, transcript, 24.
69. C. Harry Knowles, interview by author, November 6, 2008.
70. C. Harry Knowles, interview by author, May 22, 2008.
71. C. Harry Knowles, interview by author, November 6, 2008.
72. C. Harry Knowles, interview by author, May 21, 2008.

CHAPTER 4
PHOEBE
1953-1958

1. C. Harry Knowles, interview by author, February 15, 2008.
2. Philip T. Porter, interview by author, January 27, 2009.
3. Ibid.
4. Phoebe Barrett Knowles, interview by author, July 27, 2008.
5. Philip T. Porter, interview by author, January 27, 2009.
6. C. Harry Knowles, interview by author, May 21, 2008.
7. Phoebe Barrett Knowles, interview by author, July 27, 2008.
8. C. Harry Knowles, interview by author, May 21, 2008.
9. Phoebe Barrett Knowles, interview by author, July 27, 2008.
10. Philip T. Porter, interview by author, January 27, 2009.
11. C. Harry Knowles, e-mail message to author, July 10, 2011.
12. C. Harry Knowles to Phoebe Barrett Knowles and v.v., July 1955, Knowles personal files.
13. Phoebe Barrett Knowles, interview by author, July 27, 2008.
14. C. Harry Knowles, interview by author, May 21, 2008.
15. Ibid.
16. Jim Ramsey, interview by author, November 28, 2007.
17. William W. Penn, Jr., interview by author, November 27, 2007.
18. C. Harry Knowles, interview by author, May 21, 2008.
19. Phoebe Barrett Knowles, interview by author, July 27, 2008.
20. Phoebe Barrett Knowles, private journal, circa 1955, Knowles personal files.
21. C. Harry Knowles, interview by author, May 22, 2008.
22. C. Harry Knowles, interview by author, February 14, 2008.
23. C. Harry Knowles to Dr. Kinley, January 22, 1956, Knowles personal files.
24. Phoebe Barrett Knowles, interview by author, July 27, 2008.
25. C. Harry Knowles to Dr. Kinley.
26. Ibid.
27. Phoebe Barrett Knowles to C. Harry Knowles, February 7, 1956, Knowles personal files.
28. C. Harry Knowles to Josephine Knowles, 1956, Knowles personal files.

29. C. Harry Knowles, interview by author, May 21, 2008.
30. Ibid.
31. C. Harry Knowles, interview by author, November 6, 2008.
32. C. Harry Knowles, interview by author, May 22, 2008.
33. Brock, *Understanding Moore's Law*, 13-15.
34. C. Harry Knowles, interview by author, May 21, 2008.
35. Phoebe Barrett Knowles, interview by author, July 27, 2008.
36. C. Harry Knowles, interview by author, November 6, 2008.
37. C. Harry Knowles, e-mail message to author, October 10, 2011.

CHAPTER 5
MOTOROLA
1958-1962

1. Phoebe Barrett Knowles, interview by author, July 27, 2008.
2. Dude Hubka, Motorola, Inc., Information Service news release, [February 1958?], Motorola Heritage Services and Archives, Form No. 248-96.
3. C. Harry Knowles, interview by David C. Brock, September 18, 2007, tape 1, transcript, 25.
4. C. Harry Knowles, interview by author, May 21, 2008.
5. C. Harry Knowles, interview by Brock, September 18, 2007, tape 1, transcript, 25-26.
6. Ibid.
7. C. Harry Knowles, interview by author, May 22, 2008.
8. "C. Lester Hogan, Physicist Who Fought Motorola, Dies at 88," *New York Times*, August 16, 2008, http://www.nytimes.com/
9. C. Lester Hogan, interview by Rob Walker, Stanford University Silicon Genesis Project, January 24, 1995, http://www-sul.stanford.edu/depts/hasrg/histsci/silicongenesis/hogan-ntb.html
10. Ibid.
11. Motorola, Inc., About Motorola, History, Timeline, 1930, 1940, http://www.motorola.com/staticfiles/Business/Corporate/US-EN/history/timeline.html
12. Hogan, interview by Walker.
13. Ibid.
14. C. Harry Knowles, interview by Brock, November 19, 2007, tape 2, transcript, 7-8.
15. Hogan, interview by Walker.
16. C. Harry Knowles, interview by Brock, November 19, 2007, tape 2, transcript, 6-7.
17. Hogan, interview by Walker.
18. Motorola Annual Report, 1957 (Chicago: Motorola, Inc., 1957).
19. Motorola Annual Report, 1958, 6-7.
20. Motorola Annual Report, 1959, 11.
21. C. Harry Knowles, interview by Brock, November 19, 2007, tape 2, transcript, 7.
22. Motorola Annual Report, 1958, 6.
23. Motorola Annual Report, 1959, 10.
24. Hogan, interview by Walker.
25. C.H. Knowles, "New Transistor Design—The 'Mesa'!," *Electronics Industries* 17, no. 8 (August 1958): 55-60.
26. C. Harry Knowles, interview by Brock, November 19, 2007, tape 2, transcript, 8; and C. Harry Knowles, interview by author, October 20, 2011.
27. C. Harry Knowles, interview by author, November 6, 2008.

28. C. Harry Knowles, interview by author, May 21, 2008.
29. Brock, *Understanding Moore's Law*, 13.
30. C. Harry Knowles, interview by Brock, November 19, 2007, tape 2, transcript, 12.
31. C. Harry Knowles, interviews by author, September 22, 2011, and November 6, 2008; and C. Harry Knowles, interview by Brock, September 18, 2007, tape 1, transcript, 27.
32. C. Harry Knowles, interview by Brock, September 18, 2007, tape 1, transcript, 28-29.
33. C. Harry Knowles, interview by author, November 6, 2008.
34. C. Harry Knowles, interview by Brock, September 18, 2007, tape 1, transcript, 29.
35. C. Harry Knowles, interview by author, November 6, 2008.
36. C. Harry Knowles, interview by Brock, September 18, 2007, tape 1, transcript, 29.
37. C. Harry Knowles, interview by author, May 22, 2008.
38. C. Harry Knowles, interview by Brock, November 19, 2007, tape 2, transcript, 12.
39. C. Harry Knowles, interview by author, May 22, 2008.
40. C. Harry Knowles, interview by author, May 21-22, 2008.
41. National Park Service, History, Minuteman Missile, Section I: The Cold War and National Armament, Chapter 3, "Minuteman and the Next Generation: 1960s-Present," November 19, 2003, http://www.nps.gov/history/history/online_books/mimi/hrs1-3a.htm
42. C. Harry Knowles, interview by Brock, November 19, 2007, tape 2, transcript, 9.
43. Ibid., 16.
44. C. Harry Knowles, interview by Brock, September 18, 2007, tape 1, transcript, 29.
45. Motorola Annual Report, 1959, 11.
46. C. Harry Knowles, interview by author, November 6, 2008.
47. C. Harry Knowles, interview by Brock, September 18, 2007, tape 1, transcript, 29.
48. C. Harry Knowles, interview by author, November 6, 2008.
49. Ibid.
50. C. Harry Knowles, interview by Brock, September 18, 2007, tape 1, transcript, 27.
51. Phoebe Barrett Knowles, interview by author, July 27, 2008.
52. C. Harry and Phoebe Knowles personal financial records, 1959-1961.
53. Phoebe Barrett Knowles, interview by author, July 27, 2008; and C. Harry Knowles, e-mail message to author, July 10, 2011.
54. Phoebe Barrett Knowles, interview by author, July 27, 2008.
55. Thelma Knowles to Charles S. Knowles, August 1, 1960, Knowles personal files.
56. C. Harry Knowles, interview by author, May 22, 2008.
57. Thelma Knowles to Charles S. Knowles, August 1, 1960, Knowles personal files.
58. C. Harry Knowles, interview by author, May 22, 2008.
59. Paul Davis, interview by Jacque Kochak as told to author, January 2011.
60. Thelma Knowles to Charles S. Knowles, August 1, 1960, Knowles personal files.
61. Harry Holmes Knowles State of Alabama Death Certificate, Bureau of Vital Statistics, Alabama Department of Health, issued March 16, 1962.
62. C. Harry Knowles, interview by author, May 22, 2008.
63. Ibid.
64. C. Harry Knowles, interview by author, May 21, 2008.
65. Phoebe Barrett Knowles, interview by author, July 27, 2008.
66. C. Harry Knowles, interview by author, February 14, 2008.
67. William W. Penn, Jr., interview by author, November 27, 2007.
68. Brock, *Understanding Moore's Law*, 15.

69. Computer History Museum, The Silicon Engine, "1958: Silicon Mesa Transistors Enter Commercial Production," 2007, http://www.computerhistory.org/semiconductor/timeline/1958-Mesa.html

70. Brock, *Understanding Moore's Law*, 18-19.

71. C. Harry Knowles, interview by author, September 22, 2011.

72. Brock, *Understanding Moore's Law*, 18-19.

73. PBS Online, History of the Transistor, "Transistorized!" (ScienCentral, Inc., and the American Institute of Physics, 1999), http://www.pbs.org/transistor/background1/events/icinv.html

74. Ibid.

75. Computer History Museum, The Silicon Engine, "1959: Practical Monolithic Integrated Circuit Concept Patented," 2007, http://www.computerhistory.org/semiconductor/timeline/1959-Noyce.html

76. C. Harry Knowles, e-mail message to author, July 10, 2011.

77. C. Harry Knowles, interview by author, November 6, 2008.

78. George Scalise, interview by Rob Walker, Stanford University Silicon Genesis Project, October 3, 2003, http://silicongenesis.stanford.edu/transcripts/scalise.htm

79. Ibid.

80. C. Harry Knowles, interview by author, May 21, 2008.

81. Hogan, interview by Walker.

82. Motorola Annual Report, 1960, 3, 8-9.

83. Ibid.

84. C. Harry Knowles, interview by author, September 22, 2011.

85. Motorola Annual Report, 1960, 4.

86. Computer History Museum, The Silicon Engine, "1960: Epitaxial Deposition Process Enhances Transistor Performance," 2007, http://www.computerhistory.org/semiconductor/timeline/1960-Epitaxial.html

87. C. Harry Knowles, interview by author, May 21, 2008.

88. C. Harry Knowles, interview by Brock, November 19, 2007, tape 2, transcript, 26.

89. Wilf Corrigan, interview by Rob Walker, Stanford University Silicon Genesis Project, October 17, 1998, http://silicongenesis.stanford.edu/transcripts/corrigan.html

90. Ibid.

91. C. Harry Knowles, interview by author, May 22, 2008.

92. C. Harry Knowles, interview by Brock, November 19, 2007, tape 2, transcript, 26-27.

93. C. Harry Knowles, interview by author, November 6, 2008.

94. C. Harry Knowles, interview by author, May 22, 2008.

95. Carl Harry Knowles, "Transistor Comprising Prong-Shaped Emitter Electrode," U.S. Patent 3,214,652, filed March 19, 1962, and issued October 26, 1965.

96. Ibid.

97. C. Harry Knowles, interview by author, May 22, 2008.

98. Jack Ward, "Curator's Introduction," John C. Haenichen Oral History, The Transistor Museum, 2007, http://semiconductormuseum.com/Transistors/Motorola/Haenichen/Haenichen_Index.htm

99. Motorola Annual Report, 1961, 11.

100. Motorola Annual Report, 1962, 10.

101. John C. Haenichen Oral History, interview by Jack Ward, The Transistor Museum.

102. C. Harry Knowles, interview by author, May 22, 2008.
103. C.H. Knowles to C.L. Hogan, June 28, 1962, Knowles files.
104. C. Harry Knowles, interview by author, May 21, 2008.

CHAPTER 6
WESTINGHOUSE
1962-1968

1. C. Harry Knowles, interview by author, November 6, 2008.
2. C. Harry Knowles, interview by author, May 22, 2008.
3. Ibid.
4. Computer History Museum, The Silicon Engine: A Timeline of Semiconductors in Computers, "Companies—Westinghouse Electric," 2007, http://www.computerhistory.org/semiconductor/companies.html#uz
5. Ibid.
6. Ed Sack, interview by author (via e-mail), February 27, 2010.
7. Computer History Museum, "Companies—Westinghouse Electric."
8. Westinghouse Electric Corporation, "Forum: Electronic Components and Specialty Products for Automotive Application," Westinghouse forum itinerary, [1964?], Knowles files.
9. C. Harry Knowles, interview by author, May 21, 2008.
10. C. Harry Knowles, interview by David C. Brock, September 18, 2007, tape 1, transcript, 49.
11. Sack, interview by author (via e-mail), February 27, 2010.
12. C. Harry Knowles, e-mail message to author, October 23, 2011.
13. C. Harry Knowles, interview by author, November 6, 2008.
14. C. Harry Knowles, interview by Brock, September 18, 2007, tape 1, transcript, 54-56; and C. Harry Knowles, interview by author, October 24, 2011.
15. C. Harry Knowles, interview by Brock, September 18, 2007, tape 1, transcript, 54-56.
16. C. Harry Knowles, interview by author, October 24, 2011.
17. C. Harry Knowles, e-mail message to author, October 23, 2011.
18. George McCarthy, interview by author, February 2, 2009.
19. C. Harry Knowles, e-mail message to author, July 9, 2011.
20. McCarthy, interview by author, February 2, 2009.
21. C. Harry Knowles, interview by Brock, November 19, 2007, tape 2, transcript, 20-23.
22. Sack, interview by author, February 27, 2010.
23. C. Harry Knowles, e-mail message to author, July 9, 2011.
24. Ibid.
25. C. Harry Knowles, interview by Brock, November 19, 2007, tape 2, transcript, 20-23; and C. Harry Knowles, e-mail message to author, October 23, 2011.
26. Sack, interview by author, February 27, 2010.
27. C. Harry Knowles, interview by author, May 21, 2008.
28. C. Harry Knowles, interview by author, November 6, 2008.
29. Fairchild Semiconductor, "A History of Innovation—Fairchild Company History, 1957," 2011, http://www.fairchildsemi.com/company/history/#
30. Brock, *Understanding Moore's Law,* 19.

31. Ibid., 26.
32. Ibid., 29.
33. C. Harry Knowles, interview by Brock, September 18, 2007, tape 1, transcript, 52.
34. C. Harry Knowles, interview by Brock, November 19, 2007, tape 2, transcript, 34-35.
35. C. Harry Knowles, interview by author, October 24, 2011.
36. Brock, *Understanding Moore's Law*, 31.
37. Ibid.
38. C. Harry Knowles, "Research and Development in Integrated Circuits," *IEEE Spectrum*, 1964, 78.
39. C. Harry Knowles, interview by author, November 6, 2008.
40. Brock, *Understanding Moore's Law*, 31, 33.
41. Ibid., 33-34.
42. C. Harry Knowles, interview by Brock, September 18, 2007, tape 1, transcript, 59.
43. C. Harry Knowles, interview by author, September 28, 2009.
44. Brock, *Understanding Moore's Law*, 35-37.
45. Gordon E. Moore, "Cramming More Components Onto Integrated Circuits," *Electronics* 38:8 (April 19, 1965): 114-117.
46. Computer History Museum, "1965—'Moore's Law' Predicts the Future of Integrated Circuits," http://www.computerhistory.org/semiconductor/timeline/1965-Moore.html
47. Brock, *Understanding Moore's Law*, 69-70.
48. Ibid.
49. Ibid., 34.
50. Ibid., 33-34.
51. Ibid.
52. Gordon E. Moore, "Progress in Digital Integrated Electronics," *Technical Digest*, IEEE International Electron Devices Meeting 21 (1975): 11-13.
53. Computer History Museum, The Silicon Engine: A Timeline of Semiconductors in Computers.
54. C. Harry Knowles, interview by author, August 29, 2008.
55. C. Harry Knowles, interview by Brock, September 18, 2007, tape 1, transcript, 61.
56. C. Harry Knowles, e-mail message to author, October 23, 2011.
57. C. Harry Knowles, interview by author, August 29, 2008.
58. C. Harry Knowles, Westinghouse 1965 correspondence files.
59. Ibid.
60. C. Harry Knowles, interview by author, May 21, 2008.
61. C. Harry Knowles, interview by author, July 26, 2007.
62. C. Harry Knowles, interview by author, February 12, 2013.
63. Robert H. Knowles, interview by author, July 27, 2008.
64. Phoebe Knowles, interview by author, July 27, 2008.
65. C. Harry Knowles, e-mail message to author, October 23, 2011.
66. "Knowles Wins Final Series to Take Bay Sailing Regatta," *Baltimore Sun*, July 26, 1965.
67. Robert H. Knowles, interview by author, July 27, 2008.
68. C. Harry Knowles, interview by author, May 21, 2008.
69. C. Harry Knowles, interview by author, May 22, 2008.
70. Robert H. Knowles, interview by author, July 27, 2008.

71. "Separation Agreement Between Carl Harry Knowles and Phoebe Barrett Knowles," March 28, 1967, Knowles personal files.

72. "Judicial Power of the State of Chihuahua, Certified Copy of Divorce Decree," File Number 6113/967, Copy Number 249737, First Civil Court, Bravos District, Ciudad Juarez, State of Chihuahua, United Mexican States, June 13, 1967, Knowles personal files.

73. Phoebe Knowles, interview by author, July 27, 2008.

74. C. Harry Knowles, e-mail message to author, July 9, 2011.

75. Phoebe Knowles, interview by author, July 27, 2008.

76. C. Harry Knowles, interview by author, May 21, 2008.

77. Computer History Museum, "Companies—Westinghouse Electric."

78. C. Harry Knowles, e-mail message to author, October 23, 2011.

79. C. Harry Knowles, interview by author, July 26, 2007.

CHAPTER 7
METROLOGIC EARLY YEARS
1968-1976

1. C. Harry Knowles, interview by author, August 29-31, 2008.

2. C. Harry Knowles, interview by author, July 26, 2007.

3. C. Harry Knowles, e-mail message to Thomas J. Perkowski, May 7, 2010.

4. "Arthur Leonard Schawlow," *A Dictionary of Scientists*, Answers.com.

5. C. Harry Knowles, e-mail message to author, July 5, 2011.

6. Michael W. Davidson, "Laser Fundamentals: Introduction to Lasers," Molecular Expressions Optical Microscopy Primer (Florida State University, 1998-2010), http://micro.magnet.fsu.edu/primer/ightandcolor/laserhome.html

7. C. Harry Knowles, e-mail message to author, July 5, 2011.

8. C. Harry Knowles, interview by author, August 29-31, 2008.

9. C. Harry Knowles, e-mail message to Perkowski, May 7, 2010.

10. C. Harry Knowles, e-mail message to author, July 5, 2011.

11. C. Harry Knowles, interview by author, August 29-31, 2008.

12. C. Harry Knowles, interview by author, July 26, 2007.

13. C. Harry Knowles, e-mail message to author, July 14, 2011.

14. C. Harry Knowles, interview by author, August 29-31, 2008.

15. Ibid.

16. Davis, *Don't Know Much About History*, 378-79.

17. C. Harry Knowles, interview by author, August 29-31, 2008.

18. C. Harry Knowles, interview by author, May 22, 2008.

19. C. Harry Knowles, interview by author, July 26, 2007.

20. "History of Metrologic," April 1973, Metrologic Instruments, Inc., files.

21. C. Harry Knowles, e-mail message to author, July 5, 2011.

22. C. Harry Knowles, interview by author, August 29-31, 2008.

23. "History of Metrologic," September 1972, Metrologic files.

24. C. Harry Knowles, e-mail message to Perkowski, May 7, 2010.

25. C. Harry Knowles, interview by author, August 29-31, 2008.

26. C. Harry Knowles, e-mail message to Perkowski, May 7, 2010.

27. C. Harry Knowles, interview by author, August 29-31, 2008.

28. "Metrologic Sales Billed by Year, 1969-1974," 1969-1978 Financials, Metrologic files; and "Operations, 1971," 1971-1979 Financials.

29. C. Harry Knowles, interview by author, August 29-31, 2008.

30. C. Harry Knowles, e-mail message to author, October 9, 2009.

31. C. Harry Knowles, interview by author, August 29-31, 2008.

32. L.D. Adams to J.W. Christie, January 11, 1973, Metrologic files.

33. C. Harry Knowles, e-mail message to Perkowski, May 9, 2010.

34. C. Harry Knowles, e-mail message to author, February 3, 2009.

35. C. Harry Knowles, e-mail message to author, July 5, 2011.

36. C. Harry Knowles, e-mail message to author, February 3, 2009.

37. C. Harry Knowles, interview by author, August 29-31, 2008.

38. C. Harry Knowles, interview by author, May 22, 2008.

39. Robert H. Knowles, interview by author, July 27, 2008.

40. C. Harry Knowles, e-mail message to author, August 11, 2008.

41. Robert H. Knowles, interview by author, July 27, 2008.

42. Marjorie B. Knowles to C. Harry Knowles, March 20-21, 2008, Knowles personal files.

43. Robert H. Knowles, interview by author, July 27, 2008.

44. C. Harry Knowles, interview by author, May 22, 2008.

45. Robert H. Knowles, interview by author, July 27, 2008.

46. C. Harry Knowles, interview by author, May 22, 2008.

47. "Tropical Storm Carrie, August 29-September 5," 1972 Atlantic Hurricane Season, National Hurricane Center Archive, National Oceanic and Atmospheric Administration, *Monthly Weather Review* 101, no. 4: 332, http://www.nhc.noaa.gov/archive/storm_wallets/atlantic/atl1972-prelim/carrie/prelim01.gif

48. C. Harry Knowles, interview by author, May 22, 2008.

49. C. Harry Knowles, e-mail message to author, August 11, 2008; and C. Harry Knowles, interview by author, May 22, 2008.

50. C. Harry Knowles, interview by author, August 31, 2012.

51. C. Harry Knowles, e-mail message to author, August 11, 2008.

52. Robert H. Knowles, interview by author, July 27, 2008.

53. C. Harry Knowles, e-mail message to author, August 11, 2008.

54. Marjorie B. Knowles to C. Harry Knowles, March 20-21, 2008, Knowles personal files.

55. Robert H. Knowles, interview by author, July 27, 2008.

56. 35th Anniversary presentation, 2003, Metrologic Instruments, Metrologic files.

57. "History of Metrologic," September 1972, Metrologic files.

58. "Operations, 1972," 1971-1979 Financials, Metrologic files.

59. "GS1 Timeline," 2010, http://www.gs1.org/about/media_centre/timeline; and Steve Bass, Lisa Miller, and Bryan Nylin, "The Uniform Code Council" in *HIPAA Compliance Solutions* (Microsoft Press, 2001), http://www.microsoft.com/mspress/books/sampchap/5583b.aspx

60. George J. Laurer, "Development of the UPC Symbol," 2001, http://www.laurerupc.com/

61. Vineet Garg, Charles Jones and Christopher Sheedy, *17 Billion Reasons to Say Thanks: The 25th Anniversary of the U.P.C. and Its Impact on the Grocery Industry* (Dayton, Ohio: PricewaterhouseCoopers, 1999), 19.

62. Laurer, "Development of the UPC Symbol."

63. Russ Adams, Bar Code 1, "A Short History of Bar Code," 2009, http://www.adams1.com/history.html

64. Ibid.

65. Rebecca Schlofner, *eHow*, "The History of Bar Code Scanning," 2010, http://www.ehow.com/about_6630272_history-bar-code-scanning.html

66. Adams, Bar Code 1, "A Short History of Bar Code."

67. "IBM to Help Retailers Meet Jan.1, 2005 Deadline for Adopting New Global Bar Code Standard," IBM Press Release, 2004, http://www-03.ibm.com/press/us/en/pressrelease/7228.wss

68. "Universal Product Code," *Wikipedia*, 2010, http://en.wikipedia.org/wiki/Universal_Product_Code#cite_note-UMalumni-3

69. GS1, "The Story of the Ad Hoc Committee," 2010, http://www.gs1us.org/about_us/history/ad_hoc_committee

70. "GS1 Timeline."

71. Hendrix, "Between the Lines," *Auburn Magazine*, 18.

72. Rob Cummings, "History of the UPC Bar Code and the Uniform Code Council, Inc.," 2010, http://www.cummingsdesign.com/bar_codes101_UCC_History.htm

73. "Universal Product Code," *Wikipedia*.

74. Tom Reynolds, National Barcode, "History of Barcode Scanners," 2010, http://www.nationalbarcode.com/history-of-barcode-scanners.htm

75. Laurer, "Development of the UPC Symbol."

76. Reynolds, National Barcode, "History of Barcode Scanners."

77. GS1, "Numbers in the History of the Universal Product Code," 2010, http://www.gs1us.org/about_us/numbers_in_the_upc

78. Cummings, "History of the UPC Bar Code and the Uniform Code Council, Inc."

79. C. Harry Knowles, interview by author, August 29-31, 2008.

80. "Operations, 1974," 1971-1979 Financials, Metrologic files.

81. C. Harry Knowles, interview by author, August 29-31, 2008.

82. C. Harry Knowles, interview by author, October 21, 1999.

83. C. Harry Knowles, e-mail message to Perkowski, May 6, 2010.

84. C. Harry Knowles, interview by author, August 29-31, 2008.

85. 35th Anniversary presentation.

86. C. Harry Knowles, e-mail message to Perkowski, May 6, 2010.

87. C. Harry Knowles, interview by author, August 29-31, 2008.

88. Brian Albright, "The UPC Turns 30: The Grocery Industry Celebrates the Birth of the UPC Bar Code at the Site of the First Grocery Scanner Installation," *Frontline Solutions*, September 2004, http://findarticles.com/p/articles/mi_m0DIS/is_9_5/ai_n27801064/

89. "GS1 Timeline."

90. Garg, Jones and Sheedy, *17 Billion Reasons*.

91. C. Harry Knowles, interviews by author, August 29-31, 2008, and October 21, 1999.

92. C. Harry Knowles, e-mail message to Perkowski, May 6, 2010.

93. C. Harry Knowles, e-mail message to Perkowski, May 9, 2010.

94. C. Harry Knowles, interview by author, August 29-31, 2008.

95. C. Harry Knowles, e-mail message to Perkowski, May 6, 2010.

96. Hendrix, "Between the Lines," *Auburn Magazine*.

97. C. Harry Knowles, interview by author, August 29-31, 2008; and C. Harry Knowles, e-mail message to Perkowski, May 6, 2010.

98. "Symbol Technologies, Inc.," Funding Universe Company Histories, http://www.fundinguniverse.com/company-histories/Symbol-Technologies-Inc-Company-History.html

99. C. Harry Knowles, interview by author, October 21, 1999.

100. C. Harry Knowles, interview by author, August 29-31, 2008.

101. C. Harry Knowles, e-mail message to Perkowski, May 6, 2010.

102. Invoices dated June 15, 1976-October 17, 1977, per agreement dated May 25, 1976, between Metrologic and UPC Film Masters, Inc./Symbol Technologies, Inc., Metrologic files.

103. C. Harry Knowles, e-mail message to Perkowski, May 6, 2010.

CHAPTER 8
METROLOGIC STORMS
1975-1993

1. George Kolis, interview by author, April 27, 2010.

2. C. Harry Knowles, e-mail message to author, July 8, 2011.

3. C. Harry Knowles, e-mail message to Thomas J. Perkowski, May 9, 2010.

4. Kolis, interview by author, April 27, 2010.

5. Richard Hamilton, interview by author, April 27, 2010.

6. C. Harry Knowles, e-mail message to author, July 8, 2011.

7. Operations Reports, 1975 and 1976, 1971-1979 Financials, Metrologic files.

8. 35th Anniversary presentation.

9. Metrologic 1976 Catalog, 8, http://www.repairfaq.org/sam/brochures/Metrologic1976Catalog/

10. Ibid., 24.

11. C. Harry Knowles, interview by author, November 3, 2011.

12. Metrologic 1976 Catalog, 22.

13. C. Harry Knowles, e-mail message to author, July 8, 2011.

14. 35th Anniversary presentation.

15. C. Harry Knowles, e-mail message to author, July 8, 2011.

16. Metrologic 1979-1980 Catalog and Laser Handbook, 2, 32, http://www.repairfaq.org/sam/brochures/Metrologic19791980Catalog/

17. C. Harry Knowles, interview by author, December 14, 2011.

18. Metrologic 1979-1980 Catalog, 8.

19. Ibid., 34-40.

20. Craig R. Smith, "Jimmy Carter—A National Disgrace," World Net Daily, August 21, 2006, http://www.wnd.com/news/article.asp?ARTICLE_ID=51612

21. David Rubel, *Scholastic Encyclopedia of the Presidents and Their Times* (New York: Scholastic Inc., 1994), 190, 192.

22. "Operations, 1979," 1971-1979 Financials, Metrologic files.

23. Stephen J. Andriole, "C. Harry Knowles & Metrologic Instruments," Final Expert Report, 2010, 14, Metrologic files.

24. C. Harry Knowles, interview by author, November 3, 2011.

25. C. Harry Knowles, interview by author, August 29-31, 2008.

26. C. Harry Knowles, interview by author, November 3, 2011.

27. George B. Rockstein, David M. Wilz, Sr., David P. Bubnoski, and Carl H. Knowles, "Portable Bar Code Symbol Reading Device with Bar Code Symbol Detection

Circuit for Activating Microprocessor Implemented Bar Code Symbol Decoder," U.S. Patent 5424525, filed November 4, 1993, and issued June 13, 1995.

28. C. Harry Knowles, interview by author, August 29-31, 2008.

29. "Employment Contract," between Metrologic Instruments, Inc., and Michael L. Sanyour, April 8, 1982, 1-2, 6, 13.

30. C. Harry Knowles, interview by author, August 29-31, 2008.

31. "Metrologic Instruments, Inc.: Proposed Plan of Reorganization," U.S. Bankruptcy Court for the District of New Jersey, January 7, 1986, 8.

32. C. Harry Knowles, e-mail message to author, October 15, 2010.

33. *Symbol Technologies, Inc. v. Metrologic Instruments, Inc. and C. Harry Knowles,* Civil Action No. 88-0461, U.S. District Court for the District of New Jersey, August 8, 1991.

34. C. Harry Knowles, e-mail message to Perkowski, May 6, 2010.

35. "Symbol Technologies Company History," Answers.com, http://www. answers.com/topic/symbol-technologies

36. C. Harry Knowles, interview by author, December 14, 2011.

37. *Symbol Technologies v. Metrologic Instruments,* 1991.

38. Ibid.

39. *Symbol Technologies, Inc. v. Opticon, Inc. and Opto Electronics,* No. 90-1409, U.S. Federal Circuit Court of Appeals, June 14, 1991.

40. Ibid.

41. *Symbol Technologies, Inc. v. Opticon, Inc. and Opto Electronics,* No. 86CV8736, U.S. District Court for the Southern District of New York, May 3, 1990.

42. *Symbol Technologies v. Metrologic Instruments,* 1991.

43. 35th Anniversary presentation.

44. C. Harry Knowles, interview by author, August 29-31, 2008.

45. "Form S-1 Registration Statement under the Securities Act of 1933, Metrologic Instruments, Inc.," U.S. Securities and Exchange Commission, filed June 10, 1987 (IRS No. 221866172), Metrologic files.

46. Reed Abelson, "Celebrating a 'Coming Out,'" *Philadelphia Business Journal* 4, no. 51 (March 3-9, 1986): 1, 36-37.

47. Metrologic Proposed Plan of Reorganization, 9-10.

48. Chris W. Biddle, "Failing Firm Succeeds in Finding New Success," *Burlington County Times,* August 6, 1987.

49. C. Harry Knowles, interview by author, August 29-31, 2008.

50. Abelson, "Celebrating a 'Coming Out,'" 37.

51. C. Harry Knowles, interview by author, August 29-31, 2008.

52. Abelson, "Celebrating a 'Coming Out,'" 36.

53. C. Harry Knowles, interview by author, August 29-31, 2008.

54. Kolis, interview by author, April 27, 2010.

55. *Symbol Technologies v. Metrologic Instruments,* 1991.

56. C. Harry Knowles, interview by author, August 29-31, 2008.

57. "Annual Average Unemployment Rate," U.S. Department of Labor, Bureau of Labor Statistics, 2011, http://www.bls.gov/cps/prev_yrs.htm

58. Rubel, *Scholastic Encyclopedia,* 196.

59. Albright, "The UPC Turns 30."

60. Adams, Bar Code 1, "A Short History of Bar Code."

61. C. Harry Knowles, interview by author, August 29-31, 2008.
62. "Form S-1 Registration Statement," Metrologic, 1987.
63. C. Harry Knowles, interview by author, August 29-31, 2008.
64. *Symbol Technologies, Inc. v. Opticon, Inc.*, 1990.
65. C. Harry Knowles, interview by author, August 29-31, 2008.
66. *Symbol Technologies v. Metrologic Instruments*, 1991.
67. Biddle, "Failing Firm Succeeds."
68. *Symbol Technologies v. Metrologic Instruments*, 1991.
69. Hendrix, "Between the Lines," *Auburn Magazine*.
70. "A Brief History of the Patent Law of the United States," Ladas & Parry, LLP, Intellectual Property Law, 2009, http://www.ladas.com/Patents/USPatentHistory.html
71. C. Harry Knowles, interview by author, March 1, 2010.
72. USPTO Patent Full-Text and Image Database, U.S. Patent Collection, "Knowles and Metrologic Instruments Inc.," Records 453-456, http://patft.uspto.gov
73. C. Harry Knowles, e-mail message to author, September 25, 2009.
74. Goodwillie, *Now Hear This*, 170.
75. C. Harry Knowles, e-mail message to author, December 15, 2011.
76. *Symbol Technologies, Inc. v. Opticon, Inc.*, 1990.
77. Ibid.
78. *Symbol Technologies v. Metrologic Instruments*, 1991.
79. Mrs. Ruby Genevieve K. Carson obituary, *Birmingham News*, May 17, 1989.
80. William W. Penn, Jr., interview by author, November 27, 2007.
81. Ruby Carson obituary, *Birmingham News*.
82. William W. Penn, Jr., interview by author, November 27, 2007.
83. *Symbol Technologies, Inc. v. Opticon, Inc.*, 1991.
84. Thomas J. Perkowski, e-mail message to author, May 3, 2010.
85. *Symbol Technologies, Inc. v. Opticon, Inc.*, 1990.
86. C. Harry Knowles, e-mail message to Perkowski, May 6, 2010.
87. Ibid.
88. C. Harry Knowles, e-mail message to author, November 2, 2011.
89. C. Harry Knowles, e-mail message to Perkowski, May 6, 2010.
90. *Symbol Technologies, Inc. v. Opticon, Inc.*, 1990.
91. Ibid.
92. C. Harry Knowles, e-mail message to author, November 4, 2011.
93. *Symbol Technologies, Inc. v. Opticon, Inc.*, 1990.
94. *Symbol Technologies, Inc. v. Opticon, Inc.*, 1991.
95. C. Harry Knowles, e-mail message to author, November 4, 2011.
96. C. Harry Knowles, e-mail message to Perkowski, May 6, 2010.
97. *Symbol Technologies, Inc. v. Opticon, Inc.*, 1990.
98. *Symbol Technologies, Inc. v. Opticon, Inc.*, 1991.
99. Thomas J. Perkowski, interviews by author, February 26, 2010, and April 28, 2010.
100. Hendrix, "Between the Lines," *Auburn Magazine;* and C. Harry Knowles, e-mail message to author, July 8, 2011.
101. "Metrologic Instruments, Inc., December 31, 1990," Gold, Meltzer, Plasky & Wise, Certified Public Accountants, Financial Report, 1991, 4, Metrologic files.

102. 35th Anniversary presentation; and C. Harry Knowles Memo to All Employees, March 29, 1990, Metrologic files.

103. C. Harry Knowles, interview by author, August 29-31, 2008.

104. Perkowski, interviews by author, February 26, 2010.

105. Perkowski, interview by author, April 28, 2010.

106. "Symbol LS9208 Hands-free Omni-directional Presentation Scanner" Specification Sheet, Motorola General Purpose Bar Code Scanners, LS9208, 2007, http://www.motorola.com/web/Business/Products/Bar%20 Code%20 Scanning/Bar%20Code%20Scanners/General%20Purpose%20Scanners/ LS9208/_Documents/Static%20Files/LS9208_New.pdf

107. "Metrologic MS700i Series" Specification Sheet, Fixed Projection Scanners, 1998, Metrologic product files.

108. Perkowski, interview by author, April 28, 2010.

109. C. Harry Knowles, Metrologic Memo to All Employees, September 17, 1991, Metrologic files.

110. Perkowski, interview by author, April 28, 2010.

111. C. Harry Knowles, interview by author, November 18, 2011.

112. Ibid.

113. *Symbol Technologies v. Metrologic Instruments,* 1991.

114. Ibid.

115. C. Harry Knowles, e-mail message to Perkowski, May 6, 2010.

116. C. Harry Knowles, interview by author, August 29-31, 2008.

117. Bernie Weisenfeld, "Metrologic Sales Surging," *Courier-Post,* July 8, 1993.

CHAPTER 9
METROLOGIC MODERN
1993-2001

1. Metrologic Instruments, Inc., "1997 SEC Annual Report for Year Ending December 1996," U.S. Securities and Exchange Commission Form 10-K (filed March 31, 1997), Item 1, http://www.sec.gov/cgi-bin/browse-edgar?action=get company&CIK=0000815910&type=10-K&dateb=&owner=exclude&count=40

2. C. Harry Knowles, e-mail message to author, December 13, 2011.

3. "1997 SEC Annual Report," Item 6.

4. Ibid., Item 15.

5. C. Harry Knowles, interview by author, August 29-31, 2008.

6. C. Harry Knowles, interview by author, October 21, 1999; and Hendrix, "Between the Lines," *Auburn Magazine.*

7. C. Harry Knowles to William W. Penn, Jr., and Cathy Penn, June 5, 1993, Knowles personal files.

8. "Metrologic Instruments, Inc. Adds Investment Banker to Board," Metrologic press release, March 5, 1998, http://web.archive.org/web/20011121042254/http:// www.metrologic.com/corporate/pressrel.htm

9. C. Harry Knowles, interview by author, August 29-31, 2008.

10. William L. Rulon-Miller, interview by author, September 27, 2011.

11. Ibid.

12. Anthony Birritteri, "Meet NJBIA's Trustees: Thomas E. Mills, IV," *New Jersey Business,* July 1, 2004, http://www.allbusiness.com/north-america/united-states-new-jersey/1065562-1.html

13. "1997 SEC Annual Report," Item 4.
14. C. Harry Knowles, interview by author, August 29-31, 2008.
15. Ginger Ramsey Grippe, interview by author, December 27, 2008.
16. Ibid.
17. "Billboard Reveals the 2012 Power 100," *Billboard*, January 28, 2011, http://www.billboard.biz/bbbiz/industry/record-labels/billboard-reveals-the-2012-power-100-1005969352.story
18. "1997 SEC Annual Report," Item 6.
19. Metrologic Instruments Corporate Profile, *Business Wire*, October 6, 1995, http://www.allbusiness.com/company-activities-management/company-structures/7173267-1.html
20. USPTO Patent Full-Text and Image Database, U.S. Patent Collection, "Knowles and Metrologic Instruments Inc.," Records 355-379, http://patft.uspto.gov; and "1997 SEC Annual Report," Item 6.
21. Metrologic Instruments Corporate Profile.
22. "Metrologic Selected for Second Presidential Award," Metrologic press release, August 8, 1995.
23. Diana G. Lasseter, "A Bar-Code Breakthrough," *BUSINESS News New Jersey* 10, no. 15 (May 19, 1997): 1.
24. "Carl H. (C. Harry) Knowles," 1995 Award Winners, Inventors of the Year, New Jersey Inventors Hall of Fame, http://www.stevens.edu/njinvent/awards/Awards1995.html
25. "1997 SEC Annual Report," Item 1.
26. C. Harry Knowles, e-mail message to Thomas J. Perkowski, November 12, 2008.
27. Thomas J. Perkowski, interviews by author, February 26, 2010.
28. "1997 SEC Annual Report," Item 1.
29. C. Harry Knowles, e-mail message to author, December 13, 2011.
30. "1997 SEC Annual Report," Item 1.
31. C. Harry Knowles, interview by author, August 29-31, 2008.
32. C. Harry Knowles, interview by author, October 21, 2011.
33. Ibid.
34. C. Harry Knowles, e-mail message to Tim Good, April 29, 2010; and e-mail message to author, July 2, 2012.
35. C. Harry Knowles, "UPS Visit," memo to Board of Directors, Officers, December 17, 1994, Metrologic files.
36. C. Harry Knowles, interview by author, August 29-31, 2008; and "Domestic Tech Series Opportunities," [December 1994?], Metrologic files.
37. Perkowski, interview by author, April 28, 2010.
38. C. Harry Knowles, e-mail message to author, July 2, 2012.
39. C. Harry Knowles, e-mail message to author, October 23, 2011.
40. C. Harry Knowles, interview by author, October 21, 2011.
41. "Metrologic Instruments, Inc. Announces Order from UPS," press release, September 8, 1995.
42. C. Harry Knowles, "UPS Visit," memo.
43. "Ken Lacy Appointed UPS CIO; Frank Erbrick to Retire," *Business Wire*, November 6, 1996, http://www.thefreelibrary.com/Ken+Lacy+appointed+UPS+C IO%3B+Frank+Erbrick+to+retire.-a018836633
44. C. Harry Knowles, interview by author, October 21, 2011; and C. Harry Knowles to Frank Erbrick, October 7, 1996, Metrologic files.

45. Mark Harrington, "Fugitive Ex-CEO Faces $90 Million Civil Penalty," *Newsday*, October 6, 2011, Long Island region edition, Business sec., http://www.newsday.com/business/fugitive-ex-ceo-faces-90m-civil-penalty-1.3228303

46. "No Criminal Complaint Filed Against Symbol Technologies," Symbol press release, June 3, 2004, http://www.symbol.com/news/pressreleases/misc_no criminal_complaint.html

47. C. Harry Knowles, interviews by author, August 29-31, 2008, and October 21, 2011.

48. "1997 SEC Annual Report," Item 6.

49. Ibid., Item 7.

50. Lasseter, "A Bar-Code Breakthrough."

51. "Interview with C. Harry Knowles," *Wall Street Reporter Magazine*, November 18, 1999, http://www.wallstreetreporter.com/client/nov/mtlg.htm

52. Ibid.

53. Perkowski, interview by author, April 28, 2010.

54. C. Harry Knowles, interviews by author, August 29-31, 2008, and October 21, 2011.

55. "1997 SEC Annual Report," Item 1; and "1998 SEC Annual Report," Item 1.

56. Perkowski, interviews by author, February 26, 2010.

57. Lasseter, "A Bar-Code Breakthrough."

58. "Metrologic Instruments Reports Fourth Quarter and Year-End Results," press release, February 20, 1997.

59. "Metrologic Instruments Reports Record Sales for Fourth Quarter and Year-End," press release, February 26, 1998.

60. July 24, 1997, and September 8, 1997, Metrologic press releases.

61. "Entrepreneurs Honored in Philadelphia," PR Newswire, June 27, 1997.

62. C. Harry Knowles, e-mail message to author, October 21, 2007.

63. "Life After Breast Cancer: A Survivor Speaks," *eHealth Connection*, October 2007, http://www.cooperhealth.org/content/ehealth_2007_10_01.htm

64. Maryann Brinley, "Generosa Grana's Journey," *UMDNJ Magazine*, Fall/Winter 2008, http://www.umdnj.edu/umcweb/marketing_and_communications/publications/umdnj_magazine/fall2008/10.htm

65. "Life After Breast Cancer."

66. Ibid.

67. C. Harry Knowles, e-mail message to author, October 21, 2007.

68. "Life After Breast Cancer."

69. C. Harry Knowles, e-mail message to William W. Penn, Jr., and Cathy Penn, May 20, 1998.

70. Andriole, Final Expert Report, 5, Metrologic files.

71. C. Harry Knowles, interview by author, August 29-31, 2008.

72. "Metrologic Instruments Names Chief Operating Officer," press release, April 22, 1998.

73. Metrologic Instruments, "1999 SEC Annual Report for Year Ending December 1998," Form 10-K (filed March 31, 1999), Item 1.

74. C. Harry Knowles, e-mail message to William W. Penn, Jr., and Cathy Penn, May 20, 1998.

75. C. Harry Knowles, interview by author, July 6, 2012.

76. C. Harry Knowles, e-mail message to author, December 13, 2011.

77. William J. Cromie, "New Telescope Graces Roof of Science Center," *Harvard University Gazette*, May 28, 1998, http://news.harvard.edu/gazette/

78. "1999 SEC Annual Report," Item 6.
79. Ibid., Item 1.
80. Ibid.
81. "Metrologic Instruments, Inc. Introduces Orbit," press release, June 17, 1998.
82. C. Harry Knowles, e-mail message to author, July 2, 2012.
83. Perkowski, interview by author, April 28, 2010.
84. Perkowski, interviews by author, February 26, 2010.
85. C. Harry Knowles, interview by author, November 6, 2008.
86. "Metrologic Instruments, Inc. Announces Formation of Metrologic do Brasil Ltda," press release, March 17, 1998.
87. "Metrologic Instruments, Inc. Announces New Scan Engine," press release, September 15, 1998.
88. "Emery Worldwide Deploys HoloTrak Scanners," Metrologic press release, October 22, 1998.
89. Metrologic Instruments, "2000 SEC Annual Report for Year Ending December 1999," Form 10-K (filed March 30, 2000), Items 6-7.
90. "2000 SEC Annual Report," Item 1.
91. C. Harry Knowles, interview by author and Metrologic reunion event speech, April 27, 2010.
92. "Metrologic Announces Opening of a Research and Development and Manufacturing Facility in China," press release, October 4, 1999.
93. C. Harry Knowles, interview by author, July 6, 2012.
94. "Metrologic Announces Opening in China."
95. Ibid.
96. C. Harry Knowles, e-mail message to author, July 2, 2012.
97. Andriole, Final Expert Report, 13.
98. "Interview with C. Harry Knowles," *Wall Street Reporter Magazine.*
99. Andriole, Final Expert Report, 14.
100. C. Harry Knowles, e-mail message to Jeffrey Kralik, August 19, 2007.
101. Ibid.
102. "The Knowles Foundation and the Retreat Concept, Preliminary Draft," 1998, Knowles personal files.
103. C. Harry Knowles, e-mail message to Kralik, August 19, 2007.
104. "Angelo Collins Vita," Knowles personal files.
105. "KSTF Today," KSTF History, http://kstf.org/about/history.html
106. "Metrologic Promotes Key Executives in Marketing and Manufacturing," press release, November 17, 1999.
107. "Metrologic Instruments, Inc. Adds Chief Operating Officer to Board," press release, March 31, 1999.
108. "Metrologic Instruments, Inc. Adds Three Outside Directors to Board," press release, October 11, 1999.
109. "First Patent Issued for Metrologic's HoloTrak Scanner Technology," press release, September 30, 1999.
110. "Metrologic's HoloTunnel Set to Feature at ScanTech USA '99," press release, September 20, 1999.
111. "First Patent Issued for HoloTrak."
112. "Metrologic Files Suit Against PSC Inc. for Patent Infringement," press release, October 13, 1999.

113. Perkowski, interviews by author, February 26, 2010.
114. C. Harry Knowles, e-mail message to author, July 2, 2012.
115. Perkowski, interviews by author, February 26, 2010.
116. C. Harry Knowles, e-mail message to author, February 19, 2008.
117. Metrologic Instruments, "2001 SEC Annual Report for Year Ending December 2000," Form 10-K (filed April 2, 2001), Items 1, 6.
118. "Metrologic Instruments, Inc. to be Inducted into the New Jersey Inventors Hall of Fame," press release, December 22, 1999.
119. "Metrologic Names New President," press release, February 9, 2000.
120. C. Harry Knowles, interview by author, August 29-31, 2008.
121. "Metrologic Names New President."
122. "Metrologic Announces Combined Sales Management for the Americas," press release, July 28, 2000.
123. "Metrologic Introduces Three New Products at NRF Trade Show," press release, January 17, 2000.
124. Ibid.
125. Perkowski, interview by author, April 28, 2010.
126. Andriole, Final Expert Report, 13.
127. "The U.S. Postal Service and Lockheed Martin Purchase Metrologic Scanners," press release, April 13, 2000.
128. "Purolator Courier Selects Metrologic's HoloTunnel," press release, May 4, 2000.
129. "2001 SEC Annual Report," Item 1.
130. "Metrologic Acquires Vision-Based Technology Subsidiary of United Technologies," press release, December 22, 2000.
131. Ibid.
132. Perkowski, interview by author, April 28, 2010.
133. Metrologic Instruments, "2002 SEC Annual Report for Year Ending December 2001," Form 10-K (filed April 16, 2002), Items 1, 6.
134. Thomas E. Mills, IV, e-mail message to C. Harry Knowles, September 17, 2012.
135. C. Harry Knowles, e-mail message to Thomas E. Mills, IV, September 17, 2012.
136. Mills, e-mail message to C. Harry Knowles, September 17, 2012.
137. "2002 SEC Annual Report," Item 6.
138. "Metrologic Instruments, Inc. Reports Financial Results," press release, February 22, 2001.
139. Ibid.
140. "Metrologic and AOA Introduce iQ," press release, February 12, 2001.
141. "Metrologic Renews Its Licensing Agreement for Bar Code Reading Software," press release, October 1, 2001.
142. C. Harry Knowles, interview by author, July 3, 2012.
143. "Metrologic Expands Its Retail Product Line," press release, November 6, 2001.
144. "2002 SEC Annual Report," Item 1.
145. C. Harry Knowles, e-mail message to author, July 2, 2012.
146. "Metrologic Signs Agreement," press release, October 5, 2001.
147. "Metrologic Receives Order," press release, September 27, 2001.
148. "Metrologic Equips Littlewoods," press release, November 13, 2001.
149. "2002 SEC Annual Report," Item 1.
150. "Metrologic Announces Promotion of Key Executives," press release, February 7, 2001.

151. "AOA Delivers Wavefront Sensor," Metrologic press release, December 21, 2001.
152. C. Harry Knowles, e-mail message to author, July 2, 2012.

CHAPTER 10
MONEY MATTERS
2000-2004

1. Metrologic Instruments, Inc., "2003 SEC Annual Report for Year Ending December 2002," U.S. Securities and Exchange Commission Form 10-K (filed March 26, 2003), Item 7, http://www.sec.gov/cgi-bin/browse-edgar?action=getcompany&CIK=0000815910&type=10K&dateb=&owner=exclude&count=40
2. C. Harry Knowles, interview by author, December 16, 2011.
3. "2003 SEC Annual Report," Items 7-8.
4. "2001 SEC Annual Report," Item 8.
5. C. Harry Knowles, interview by author, December 16, 2011.
6. "2003 SEC Annual Report," Item 7.
7. "Metrologic Reaches Agreement with Banks and Executes Amended Credit Facility," Metrologic press release, July 11, 2002, http://web.archive.org/web/20030807214340/http://metrologic.com/corporate/prel_mn.htm
8. William L. Rulon-Miller, interview by author, September 27, 2011.
9. "2003 SEC Annual Report," Item 7.
10. "Metrologic Restructures Bank Debt; Bank Agreement Provides for More Flexible Financing and Reduced Interest Costs," press release, January 31, 2003.
11. "2003 SEC Annual Report," Items 1, 8.
12. Ibid.
13. "Metrologic Unveils Two New Products at NRF Trade Show in New York," press release, January 14, 2002.
14. "2003 SEC Annual Report," Item 1.
15. Ibid.
16. "Metrologic's VoyagerCG Bar Code Scanners Selected by Burlington Coat Factory," press release, May 3, 2002.
17. "Metrologic Awarded $1.9 Million Contract for iQ-180 Parcel Scanning, Dimensioning, and Tracking System by Fortune 500 Company," press release, March 19, 2002.
18. Metrologic 2002 press releases.
19. "Lockheed Martin to Use Metrologic Technology on Automated Package Processing System for U.S. Postal Service Project," press release, November 1, 2002.
20. "Metrologic Receives Order for Approximately $1.5 Million from One of Largest Retail Department Store Chains in North America," press release, May 2, 2002.
21. "Metrologic Receives Order for Approximately $2.4 Million," press release, December 3, 2002.
22. "Metrologic Receives $1.4+ Million Order from RedDotNet," press release, September 4, 2002.
23. "New Chief Financial Officer Appointed by Metrologic," press release, August 6, 2002.
24. "Metrologic Promotes Key Executive to Vice President, General Counsel," press release, March 20, 2002.

25. "Metrologic Announces Key Executive Appointment to Head Industrial Business," press release, March 21, 2002.
26. "2003 SEC Annual Report," Item 7.
27. Metrologic Instruments, "2004 SEC Annual Report for Year Ending December 2003," Form 10-K (filed March 16, 2004), Item 7.
28. "Metrologic and United Technologies Enter Early Payment Agreement," press release, January 31, 2003.
29. Thomas J. Perkowski, interviews by author, February 26, 2010.
30. "2003 SEC Annual Report," Item 2.
31. Perkowski, interviews by author, February 26, 2010.
32. Rulon-Miller, interview by author, September 27, 2011.
33. "Metrologic Addresses New Markets with Introduction of Five New Products at National Retail Federation Trade Show," press release, January 13, 2003.
34. "Metrologic's AOA Subsidiary Addresses New Markets with the Introduction of Three New Industrial iQ Products," press release, February 10, 2003.
35. "Metrologic Announces Record Financial Results for First Quarter," press release, April 29, 2003.
36. "2004 SEC Annual Report," Item 6.
37. "Metrologic Opens New Office in Moscow," press release, June 30, 2003.
38. "2004 SEC Annual Report," Items 1, 6.
39. "Metrologic Celebrates Its 35th Year in Business," press release, May 2, 2003.
40. C. Harry Knowles, e-mail message to Rulon-Miller and 43 others, January 1, 2003, Metrologic files.
41. "2004 SEC Annual Report," Item 7.
42. C. Harry Knowles, e-mail message to author, June 27, 2012.
43. Wendy Tanaka, "Scanner-maker Has Paid Price for Success," *Philadelphia Inquirer,* August 11, 2003, City D edition, C01.
44. "2004 SEC Annual Report," Item 1.
45. C. Harry Knowles, e-mail message to Rulon-Miller and 14 others, April 13, 2003, Metrologic files.
46. "2004 SEC Annual Report," Item 2.
47. C. Harry Knowles, e-mail message to author, July 2, 2012.
48. C. Harry Knowles, Metrologic reunion event speech, April 27, 2010.
49. C. Harry Knowles, e-mail message to Kevin Bratton and 10 others, July 24, 2003, Metrologic files.
50. "Metrologic Instruments Announces Proposed Public Offering of Common Stock," press release, August 4, 2003, and "Metrologic Instruments Intends to File Amendment to Registration Statement," press release, September 9, 2003, http://web.archive.org/web/20070814211531/http://www.metrologic.com/corporate/pressrel2003.htm
51. "2004 SEC Annual Report," Item 5.
52. "Metrologic Announces Pricing of Follow-on Public Offering of Common Stock," press release, October 1, 2003.
53. C. Harry Knowles, e-mail message to Benny Noens and 38 others, July 13, 2003, Metrologic files.
54. "Metrologic's Board Authorizes Stock Split," press release, June 9, 2003.
55. "Metrologic Instruments Added to Russell 2000 and 3000 Indexes," press release, July 9, 2003.

56. C. Harry Knowles, e-mail message to Noens and 38 others, July 13, 2003, Metrologic files.

57. "Metrologic Instruments, Inc., Board of Directors Meeting, June 19, 2003," minutes and notes, Metrologic files.

58. C. Harry Knowles, e-mail message to Kevin Bratton and 10 others, June 29, 2003, Metrologic files.

59. Scott Goldstein, "Shaping Up, Not Shipping Out," *NJBIZ* 17, no. 6 (February 9, 2004): 16.

60. "2004 SEC Annual Report," Item 7.

61. "Metrologic's Board Authorizes Stock Split," press release, October 7, 2003.

62. Peter Benesh, "Age 75, He Still Drives Scanning Firm's Gains," *Investor's Business Daily,* December 1, 2003.

63. "Metrologic Receives a $3.7 Million Contract Award from United Airlines," press release, November 19, 2003.

64. "Metrologic Continues to Gain Market Share in Major Retail Accounts," press release, November 17, 2003.

65. "2004 SEC Annual Report," Item 1.

66. "Retail Cosmetics Chain Chooses Metrologic's Hand-Held Scanners," press release, October 21, 2003.

67. "Metrologic Receives Contract to Provide Optical System for NASA's James Webb Space Telescope," press release, December 4, 2003.

68. "Metrologic Receives Order from Major U.S. Airline," press release, November 20, 2003.

69. "Metrologic Receives $2.2 Million Field Service Contract from a Fortune 500 Company," press release, August 6, 2003.

70. "Metrologic's Voyager Scanners Help Improve Patient Care and Safety," press release, August 26, 2003.

71. "HHS Announces New Requirement for Bar Codes on Drugs and Blood to Reduce Risks of Medication Errors," U.S. Department of Health and Human Services press release, February 25, 2004, http://archive.hhs.gov/news/press/2004pres/20040225.html

72. Benesh, "Age 75, He Still Drives."

73. Tanaka, "Scanner-maker Has Paid Price."

74. "2004 SEC Annual Report," Item 3.

75. C. Harry Knowles, interview by author, August 29-31, 2008.

76. Rulon-Miller, interview by author, September 27, 2011.

77. Ibid.

78. Bruce L. Harrison, interview by author, April 29, 2010.

79. Goldstein, "Shaping Up, Not Shipping Out."

80. "Metrologic Announces the Departure of Tom Mills, President," press release, February 10, 2004, http://web.archive.org/web/20070814162039/http://www.metrologic.com/corporate/pressrel2004.htm

81. "2004 SEC Annual Report," Item 4.

82. "Metrologic Announces Departure of Tom Mills," press release.

83. C. Harry Knowles, interview by author, August 29-31, 2008.

84. Anthony Birritteri, "Meet NJBIA's Trustees: Thomas E. Mills, IV," *New Jersey Business,* July 1, 2004, http://www.allbusiness.com/north-america/united-states-new-jersey/1065562-1.html

85. "Gichner Systems Group, Inc., Executive Profile, Tom Mills, IV," Bloomberg Businessweek, http://investing.businessweek.com/research/stocks/private/person.asp?personId=338291

Chapter 11
Endings
2004-2009

1. Benesh, "Age 75, He Still Drives."
2. "Metrologic Announces Promotion of Several Key Executives," Metrologic press release, March 19, 2004, http://web.archive.org/web/20070814162039/http://www.metrologic.com/corporate/pressrel2004.htm
3. C. Harry Knowles, e-mail message to Justin Klein and 16 others, May 16, 2004, Metrologic files.
4. "Metrologic Instruments, Inc., Board of Directors Meeting Agenda," May 19, 2004, and "Project Meteor Discussion Materials," May 18, 2004.
5. "Shareholders Meeting Questions and Suggestions," May 27, 2004, Metrologic files.
6. C. Harry Knowles, e-mail message to Bill Rulon-Miller and 16 others, May 1, 2004, Metrologic files.
7. Metrologic Instruments, Inc., Board of Directors Meeting materials, May 27, 2004, Metrologic files.
8. C. Harry Knowles, e-mail message to Rulon-Miller and 16 others, May 1, 2004.
9. "Metrologic Subsidiary, AOA, Awarded an Additional Contract," press release, February 12, 2004.
10. "Metrologic Introduces the IS-3480 QuantumE," press release, April 27, 2004.
11. "Metrologic Introduces QuantumT," press release, October 18, 2004.
12. Metrologic Instruments, Inc., "2005 SEC Annual Report for Year Ending December 2004," U.S. Securities and Exchange Commission Form 10-K (filed March 16, 2005), Item 1, http://www.sec.gov/cgi-bin/browse-edgar?action=get company&CIK=0000815910&type=10-K&dateb=&owner=exclude&count=40
13. "Metrologic's Expanding Patent Portfolio Reaches Milestone," press release, November 16, 2004.
14. "2005 SEC Annual Report," Item 1.
15. Ibid., Items 1, 6.
16. "Metrologic Opens Three New Sales Offices," press release, June 21, 2004.
17. C. Harry Knowles, interview by author, August 29-31, 2008.
18. "Metrologic Names Benny Noens as New CEO and President," press release, June 22, 2004.
19. Bruce L. Harrison, interview by author, April 29, 2010.
20. "Metrologic Names Mark Ryan as Director, EMEA Sales," press release, June 24, 2004.
21. "Metrologic Names Benny Noens," press release.
22. William L. Rulon-Miller, interview by author, September 27, 2011.
23. C. Harry Knowles, interview by author, August 29-31, 2008.
24. "Metrologic's Chairman and CEO Gifts Shares," press release, April 21, 2004.
25. C. Harry Knowles, interview by author, August 29-31, 2008.
26. "Metrologic Sells Its Education Laser Product Line," press release, November 10, 2004.

27. "Metrologic Acquires Imaging Software Company, Omniplanar, Inc.," press release, September 27, 2004.
28. "Garrett Russell Named General Manager of Omniplanar, Inc.," press release, October 4, 2004.
29. "Metrologic's Subsidiary Licenses SwiftDecoder Software to Adobe Systems," press release, April 28, 2005, http://web.archive.org/web/20070814162809/http://www.metrologic.com/corporate/pressrel2005.htm
30. "Metrologic Instruments, Inc. CEO to Open the NASDAQ Stock Market," press release, September 26, 2004.
31. Metrologic Instruments, "2006 SEC Annual Report for Year Ending December 2005," Form 10-K (filed March 15, 2006), Item 1.
32. "2006 SEC Annual Report," Items 3, 5, 7.
33. "Metrologic Receives Ruling in Arbitration with Symbol Technologies," press release, August 29, 2005.
34. "2006 SEC Annual Report," Item 3.
35. "Metrologic Accused of Patent Infringement," press release, September 29, 2005.
36. Rulon-Miller, interview by author, September 27, 2011.
37. "Metrologic and PSC Announce Settlement of Patent Lawsuits," press release, August 30, 2005.
38. "Metrologic Joins Intermec RFID Rapid Start Licensing Program," press release, September 7, 2005.
39. "Metrologic Introduces Focus," press release, January 17, 2005.
40. Thomas J. Perkowski, interview by author, April 28, 2010.
41. C. Harry Knowles, e-mail message to Rulon-Miller and 42 others, April 20, 2003, Metrologic files.
42. "Metrologic Expands Its Stratos Bi-Optic Scanner Product Line," press release, June 13, 2005.
43. "Tesco Stores Ltd. Selects Metrologic's MS-2320 Stratos Bi-optic Scanner," press release, July 22, 2005.
44. "Tesco Stores Ltd. Orders Additional Metrologic Stratos Bi-optic Scanners," press release, January 19, 2006; and "Metrologic to Supply Its StratosS Bi-Optic Scanner/Scale Solution to Tesco Stores," press release, March 20, 2006, http://web.archive.org/web/20061016044540/http://www.metrologic.com/corporate/pressrel.htm
45. "Metrologic Adds the OptimusS to Its Line of Mobile Computers," press release, September 8, 2005.
46. "Metrologic Formalizes Agreement with Target Corporation," press release, August 9, 2005.
47. "Metrologic Negotiates $25 Million Subcontract," press release, September 28, 2005; and Metrologic 2005 press releases.
48. "PG Elections Improving Canada's Electoral Process," press release, October 27, 2005; and "Metrologic Wins Major Order," press release, July 20, 2005.
49. "2006 SEC Annual Report," Item 7.
50. "Metrologic Revises its Full Year 2005 Guidance," press release, June 16, 2005.
51. "Metrologic Adds Corporate Development Function," press release, September 22, 2005.
52. "2006 SEC Annual Report," Items 1, 2, 7.
53. Metrologic Instruments, Inc., Board of Directors Meeting materials, Facility

Space Report, November 21, 2006; and Public Lenders' Presentation, November 29, 2006, Metrologic files.

54. "Metrologic Introduces FocusBT," press release, February 13, 2006.

55. "Metrologic Enters Agreement with Healthcare Integrator Enovatelt," press release, February 9, 2006; and "Metrologic and Spacelabs Medical Enter Into a Worldwide Agreement," press release, March 10, 2006.

56. "Metrologic and Intelli-Check, Inc. Announce Strategic Partner Agreement," press release, March 23, 2006.

57. "Metrologic Announces Scanner Rollout with Systeme U," press release, April 11, 2006.

58. "Metrologic Chairman of the Board to Modify Existing Plan to Sell Shares," press release, February 16, 2006.

59. "2006 SEC Annual Report," Item 4.

60. Harrison, interview by author, April 29, 2010.

61. C. Harry Knowles, interview by author, March 1, 2010.

62. Rulon-Miller, interview by author, September 27, 2011.

63. "Metrologic Announces Organizational Changes," press release, April 20, 2006.

64. Rulon-Miller, interview by author, September 27, 2011.

65. Jane M. Von Bergen, "Metrologic Stock Falls 14 Percent After CEO Resigns," *Philadelphia Inquirer,* April 22, 2006, http://articles.philly.com/2006-04-22/business/25394442_1_metrologic-instruments-benny-noens-joseph-sawitsky

66. Benjamin Y. Lowe, "Metrologic Shares Fall on Reforecast," *Philadelphia Inquirer,* May 11, 2006, http://articles.philly.com/2006-05-11/business/25401779_1_metrologic-instruments-benny-noens-revenue-outlook

67. C. Harry Knowles, interview by author, August 29-31, 2008.

68. Rulon-Miller, interview by author, September 27, 2011.

69. "Metrologic Instruments, Inc. Goes Private," MCG Capital Corp., *Transactions* 9, no. 4 (November 2006): 3-4, http://www.mcgcapital.com/downloads/MCG_Transactions_Nov_06.pdf

70. C. Harry Knowles, interview by author, August 29-31, 2008.

71. "Metrologic Goes Private," *Transactions.*

72. "Metrologic to Be Acquired by Investor Group Led by Francisco Partners," press release, September 12, 2006.

73. Harrison, interview by author, April 29, 2010.

74. "Metrologic to Be Acquired by Investor Group," press release.

75. Rulon-Miller, interview by author, September 27, 2011.

76. "Metrologic Announces Completion of Acquisition by Investor Group Led by Francisco Partners," press release, December 21, 2006, http://www.sec.gov/Archives/edgar/data/815910/000110465906083603/a06-26249_2ex99da6.htm

77. "Metrologic and Essex Corp. Close Sale Transaction of AOA," press release, October 2, 2006, and "Metrologic and Essex Corp. Enter into Purchase Agreement for Sale of AOA," press release, September 20, 2006.

78. "Metrologic Announces Financial Results for the Second Quarter 2006," press release, July 25, 2006.

79. "Metrologic Acquires RFID Technology Company, Visible-RF," press release, May 8, 2006.

80. "Metrologic Introduces RFID Readers for Supply-Chain Automation," press release, May 1, 2006.

81. "Omniplanar Launches New Image-Processing Software," press release, May 16, 2006.

82. "Metrologic Introduces Newest Omni-directional Scanner," press release, October 6, 2006.

83. "Metrologic Scanners Ranked #1 in VSR Survey," press release, July 27, 2006.

84. "Hall of Fame, C. Harry Knowles, Metrologic Instruments, Inc.," *NJ Biz* Business of the Year 2006 Awards, www.njbiz.com

85. "Metrologic Accused of Patent Infringement by PSC," press release, May 16, 2006.

86. "Metrologic Wins Judgment Against Symbol Technologies," press release, June 28, 2006.

87. Harrison, interview by author, April 29, 2010.

88. C. Harry Knowles, Metrologic reunion event speech, April 27, 2010.

89. "Metrologic Names Darius Adamczyk as New Chief Executive Officer," press release, March 26, 2007, http://web.archive.org/web/20071222113126/http://www.metrologic.com/corporate/pressrel.htm

90. Harrison, interview by author, April 29, 2010.

91. C. Harry Knowles, interview by author, August 29-31, 2008.

92. C. Harry Knowles, e-mail message to author, October 10, 2008.

93. Harrison, interview by author, April 29, 2010.

94. Rulon-Miller, interview by author, September 27, 2011.

95. "Francisco Partners Agrees to Sell Metrologic Instruments to Honeywell International," press release, April 28, 2008, http://web.archive.org/web/20080430152933/http://www.metrologic.com/corporate/pressrel.htm

96. Harrison, interview by author, April 29, 2010.

97. Perkowski, interview by author, April 28, 2010.

98. C. Harry Knowles, interview by author, March 1, 2010.

99. Brody Mullins, "Equity Firms Try to Repair Image," *Wall Street Journal*, November 2, 2012.

100. "Honeywell Acquires Metrologic Instruments," Metrologic/Honeywell press release, July 2, 2008, http://news.thomasnet.com/companystory/Honeywell-Acquires-Metrologic-Instruments-Expands-Growing-Laser-Imaging-and-Enterprise-Mobility-Business-818401

101. Harrison, interview by author, April 29, 2010.

102. Perkowski, interview by author, April 28, 2010.

103. C. Harry Knowles, interview by author, March 1, 2010.

104. C. Harry Knowles, e-mail message to author, June 20, 2007.

Chapter 12
Beginnings
2007-2012

1. Knowles Science Teaching Foundation, "KSTF 2007 Annual Report," 19, http://www.kstf.org/wp-content/uploads/2013/07/kstf_AR_2007.pdf

2. C. Harry Knowles, e-mail message to Phil Porter, August 8, 2007.

3. Ibid.

4. C. Harry Knowles, e-mail message to author, February 4, 2007.

5. "Scholarship and Professorship Honor Late Howard E. Carr," Auburn University COSAM News, November 2003, http://www.auburn.edu/academic/science_math/cosam/news/archive/03/11/carr.html

6. C. Harry Knowles, interviews by author, February 13-14, 2008.

7. "Scholarship and Professorship Honor Carr."

8. Martha G. Barker, "Donating His 'Share' to Science Education," Auburn University College of Sciences and Mathematics, *Journey*, 2005: 16.

9. C. Harry Knowles, e-mail message to Porter, August 8, 2007.

10. C. Harry Knowles, e-mail message to author, January 5, 2008.

11. Hendrix, "Between the Lines," *Auburn Magazine*, 21.

12. C. Harry Knowles, e-mail message to Porter, August 8, 2007.

13. C. Harry Knowles, e-mail message to David Steerman, June 18, 2007.

14. C. Harry Knowles, e-mail message to author, June 27, 2007.

15. "Angelo Collins Vita," Knowles personal files.

16. "KSTF Today," KSTF History, http://kstf.org/about/history.html

17. "KSTF 2007 Annual Report," 15.

18. KSTF, "2007 Summer Teaching Fellows Meeting, July 26-28, 2007," meeting program, 23-26.

19. Angelo Collins, interview by author, July 26, 2007.

20. "KSTF 2007 Annual Report," 2.

21. Jennifer Barchie, interview by author, July 27, 2007.

22. Benjamin Buehler and Lisa Sitek, interviews by author, July 27, 2007.

23. Lisa Sitek, "Reflections on KSTF" (submission to KSTF, September 27, 2007).

24. Collins, interview by author, July 26, 2007.

25. Benjamin Buehler, "Thank You KSTF" (presentation to KSTF, April 20, 2007).

26. C. Harry Knowles, e-mail message to author, May 8, 2007; and C. Harry Knowles, e-mail message to William Penn, James Ramsey, and Ginger Grippe, as shared with author, April 22, 2007.

27. C. Harry Knowles, e-mail message to Penn, Ramsey, and Grippe, as shared with author, April 22, 2007.

28. Steve DeAngelis, interview by author, July 26, 2007.

29. "KSTF 2007 Annual Report," 7.

30. Buehler, "Thank You KSTF."

31. C. Harry Knowles, e-mail message to author, July 12, 2012.

32. "KSTF 2007 Annual Report," 19.

33. "KSTF Business Meeting" (session, KSTF Summer Teaching Fellows Meeting, Chicago, July 28, 2007).

34. C. Harry Knowles, interview by author, July 26, 2007.

35. C. Harry Knowles, interview by author, July 28, 2007.

36. Collins, interview by author, July 26, 2007.

37. C. Harry Knowles, e-mail message to Phil Porter, November 10, 2007.

38. C. Harry Knowles, interview by author, November 18, 2011.

39. "Edward D. Viner, M.D., Presented with Highest Honor from Philadelphia County Medical Society," *Inside Cooper,* Cooper University Hospital blog, July 2, 2012, http://blogs.cooperhealth.org/news/2012/07/edward-d-viner-md-presented-with-highest-honor-from-philadelphia-county-medical-society/

40. C. Harry Knowles, e-mail message to Jeffrey Kralik, August 19, 2007.

41. Scott McVay, interview by author, July 27, 2007.

42. C. Harry Knowles, interview by author, September 28, 2009.

43. Thomas J. Perkowski, interview by author, February 26, 2010.

44. Dawn Kawamoto, "Dow Jones Decline Rate Mimics Great Depression," CNET

News, Business Tech, March 2, 2009, http://news.cnet.com/8301-1001_3-10185559-92.html

45. 2007-2012 Global Financial Crisis, Wikipedia, http://en.wikipedia.org/wiki/2007-2012_global_financial_crisis
46. "KSTF Annual Reports," http://www.kstf.org/about/annual_reports.html
47. William L. Rulon-Miller, interview by author, September 27, 2011.
48. Rulon-Miller, e-mail message to author, September 2, 2012.
49. Alicia Marchena, e-mail message to author, September 10, 2012.
50. "KSTF Teaching Fellowships," http://www.kstf.org/programs/teaching.html
51. "A Message from C. Harry Knowles," KSTF, http://www.kstf.org/about/message.html
52. Dina Portnoy, interview by author, July 26, 2012.
53. "KSTF 2011 Annual Report," http://kstf.org/about/reports/KSTF_AnnualReport_2011.pdf
54. C. Harry Knowles, e-mail message to author, February 14, 2012.
55. Nicole Gillespie, interview by author, July 28, 2012.
56. Ibid.
57. C. Harry Knowles, KSTF Summer Meeting, dinner speech, July 26, 2012.
58. C. Harry Knowles, e-mail message to Ed Viner, June 17, 2007.
59. C. Harry Knowles, e-mail message to Steerman, June 18, 2007.
60. C. Harry Knowles, e-mail message to Viner, June 23, 2007.
61. C. Harry Knowles, e-mail message to author, August 27-28, 2007.
62. C. Harry Knowles, e-mail message to Porter, August 8, 2007.
63. C. Harry Knowles, e-mail message to author, November 4, 2007.
64. C. Harry Knowles, e-mail message to author, September 13, 2007.
65. Robert H. Knowles, interview by author, July 27, 2008.
66. Ibid.
67. C. Harry Knowles, interview by author, February 14, 2008.
68. Bruce L. Harrison, e-mail message to author, May 5, 2010.
69. C. Harry Knowles, e-mail message to author, October 9, 2007.
70. C. Harry Knowles, e-mail message to Porter, November 10, 2007; and C. Harry Knowles, e-mail message to author, September 30, 2007.
71. C. Harry Knowles, e-mail message to author, November 4, 2007.
72. C. Harry Knowles, e-mail message to author, January 5, 2008.
73. C. Harry Knowles, e-mail message to Porter, November 10, 2007.
74. C. Harry Knowles, e-mail message to author, January 19, 2010.
75. C. Harry Knowles, e-mail message to author, March 8, 2008.
76. C. Harry Knowles, e-mail message to author, March 16, 2008.
77. C. Harry Knowles, e-mail message to author, May 12, 2008.
78. Robert H. Knowles, interview by author, July 27, 2008.
79. Andriole, Final Expert Report, 11-12.
80. Perkowski, interviews by author, February 26, 2010.
81. William W. Penn, Jr., interview by author, November 27, 2007.
82. James E. Ramsey, interview by author, November 28, 2007.
83. Rulon-Miller, interview by author, September 27, 2011.
84. C. Harry Knowles, Auburn University commencement speech, May 10, 2008.
85. Ibid.
86. Hendrix, "Between the Lines," *Auburn Magazine*, 21.

EPILOGUE
GENIUS IN AMERICA
2010

1. Thomas J. Perkowski, interview by author, February 26, 2010.
2. C. Harry Knowles, interview by author, March 1, 2010.
3. C. Harry Knowles, interview by author, October 21, 2011.
4. Bruce L. Harrison, e-mail message to author, May 5, 2010.
5. C. Harry Knowles, interview by author, May 11, 2012.
6. C. Harry Knowles, Metrologic reunion event speech, April 27, 2010.

Selected Bibliography

Since the source notes (beginning on page 335) contain exhaustive reference details, the reader is not burdened with a full repeat in the bibliography. However, sources are categorized below for a quick overview of much of the research. Omitted from the bibliography are most e-mail message sources, personal/non-retrievable files, court cases, and various one-time-accessed web addresses (although all of these are specified in the notes section). Researchers are reminded that a significant portion of documentation can be found in the Auburn University Library's Department of Special Collections and Archives under "C. Harry Knowles Collection."

BOOKS

Atkins, Leah Rawls. *The Valley and the Hills: An Illustrated History of Birmingham and Jefferson County.* Woodland Hills, CA: Windsor Publications, 1981.

Bass, Steve, Lisa Miller, and Bryan Nylin. "The Uniform Code Council" in *HIPAA Compliance Solutions.* Microsoft Press, 2001.

Bernstein, Jeremy. *Three Degrees Above Zero, Bell Labs in the Information Age.* New York: Charles Scribner's Sons, 1984.

Brock, David C. *Understanding Moore's Law: Four Decades of Innovation.* Philadelphia: Chemical Heritage Press, 2006.

Davis, Kenneth C. *Don't Know Much About History: Everything You Need to Know about American History but Never Learned.* New York: Avon Books, 1990.

Garg, Vineet, Charles Jones and Christopher Sheedy. *17 Billion Reasons to Say Thanks: The 25ᵗʰ Anniversary of the U.P.C. and Its Impact on the Grocery Industry.* Dayton, Ohio: PricewaterhouseCoopers, 1999.

Goodwillie, Susan. *Now Hear This: The Life of Hugh S. Knowles, Acoustical Engineer and Entrepreneur.* Washington, DC: Francis Press, 1999.

Hufbauer, Virginia Knowles, comp. *Descendants of Richard Knowles, 1637-1973.* San Diego: Ventures International, 1974.

Logue, Mickey and Jack Simms. *Auburn: A Pictorial History of the Loveliest Village,* rev. ed. Auburn, AL, 1996.

Rubel, David. *Scholastic Encyclopedia of the Presidents and Their Times.* New York: Scholastic Inc., 1994.

Seitz, Frederick and Norman G. Einspruch. *Electronic Genie: The Tangled History of Silicon.* University of Illinois, 1998.

COLLECTIONS AT AUBURN UNIVERSITY SPECIAL COLLECTIONS AND ARCHIVES

Alabama Polytechnic Institute *Glomerata,* vols. 49, 52, 53, and 54.

C. Harry Knowles Collection.

Fred Allison Papers.

Physics Department Records.

Cited Interviews Conducted by Author

Barchie, Jennifer. July 27, 2007.
Buehler, Benjamin. July 27, 2007.
Collins, Angelo. July 26, 2007.
DeAngelis, Steve. July 26, 2007.
Gillespie, Nicole. July 28, 2012.
Grippe, Ginger Ramsey. December 27, 2008.
Hamilton, Richard. April 27, 2010.
Harrison, Bruce L. April 29, 2010.
Knowles, C. Harry.
   October 21, 1999.
   July 26, 2007.
   July 28, 2007.
   November 29, 2007.
   February 13-15, 2008.
   May 21-22, 2008.
   August 29-31, 2008.
   November 5-6, 2008.
   September 28, 2009.
   March 1, 2010.
   April 27, 2010.
   September 22, 2011.
   October 20-21, 2011.
   October 24, 2011.
   November 3, 2011.
   November 18, 2011.
   December 14, 2011.
   December 16, 2011.
   May 11, 2012.
   July 3, 2012.
   July 6, 2012.
   August 31, 2012.
   February 12, 2013.
Knowles, Phoebe Barrett. July 27, 2008.
Knowles, Robert H. July 27, 2008.
Kolis, George. April 27, 2010.
McCarthy, George. February 2, 2009.
McVay, Scott. July 27, 2007.
Penn, Jr., William W. November 27, 2007, and January 16, 2008.
Perkowski, Thomas J. February 26, 2010, and April 28, 2010.
Porter, Phil T. January 27, 2009.
Portnoy, Dina. July 26, 2012.
Ramsey, Jim and Ruth (dual). November 28, 2007.
Ramsey, Jim. November 28, 2007.
Ramsey, Ruth. January 18, 2008.
Rulon-Miller, William L. September 27, 2011.
Sack, Ed (via e-mail). February 27, 2010.
Sitek, Lisa. July 27, 2007.

INTERVIEWS BY OTHERS/SPEECHES

Brock, David C. Interviews with C. Harry Knowles (transcripts). September 18, 2007, and November 19, 2007.

Knowles, C. Harry. Auburn University commencement speech, May 10, 2008.

Kochak, Jacque. Interview with Paul Davis (as told to author, January 2011).

Walker, Rob. Stanford University Silicon Genesis Project. http://silicongenesis. stanford.edu/complete_listing.html. Interview with C. Lester Hogan. January 24, 1995.

———. Interview with George Scalise. October 3, 2003.

———. Interview with Wilf Corrigan. October 17, 1998.

Ward, Jack. "John C. Haenichen Oral History." The Transistor Museum. http:// semiconductormuseum.com/Museum_Index.htm.

ARTICLES

Abelson, Reed. "Celebrating a 'Coming Out.'" *Philadelphia Business Journal* 4, no. 51 (March 3-9, 1986): 1, 36-37.

Albright, Brian. "The UPC Turns 30: The Grocery Industry Celebrates the Birth of the UPC Bar Code at the Site of the First Grocery Scanner Installation." *Frontline Solutions*, September 2004.

Barker, Martha G. "Donating His 'Share' to Science Education." Auburn University College of Sciences and Mathematics, *Journey*, 2005: 16.

Benesh, Peter. "Age 75, He Still Drives Scanning Firm's Gains." *Investor's Business Daily*, December 1, 2003.

Biddle, Chris W. "Failing Firm Succeeds in Finding New Success." *Burlington County Times*, August 6, 1987.

Birritteri, Anthony. "Meet NJBIA's Trustees: Thomas E. Mills, IV." *New Jersey Business*, July 1, 2004.

Brinley, Maryann. "Generosa Grana's Journey." *UMDNJ Magazine*, Fall/Winter 2008.

"C. Lester Hogan, Physicist Who Fought Motorola, Dies at 88." *New York Times*, August 16, 2008.

Cromie, William J. "New Telescope Graces Roof of Science Center." *Harvard University Gazette*, May 28, 1998.

"Dr. Mervin J. Kelly Dies at 77." *New York Times*, March 20, 1971.

Goldstein, Scott. "Shaping Up, Not Shipping Out." *NJBIZ* 17, no. 6 (February 9, 2004): 16.

Harrington, Mark. "Fugitive Ex-CEO Faces $90 Million Civil Penalty." *Newsday*, October 6, 2011.

Hendrix, Mary Ellen. "Between the Lines." *Auburn Magazine*, Winter 2000.

"Interview with C. Harry Knowles." *Wall Street Reporter Magazine*, November 18, 1999.

Kelly, Mervin J. "The First Five Years of the Transistor." *Bell Telephone Magazine*, Summer 1953.

Kessler, Ronald. "Absent at the Creation: How One Scientist Made Off with the Biggest Invention since the Light Bulb." *Washington Post Magazine*, April 6, 1997.

Knowles, C.H. "New Transistor Design—The 'Mesa'!" *Electronics Industries* 17, no. 8 (August 1958): 55-60.

Knowles, C. Harry. "Research and Development in Integrated Circuits." *IEEE Spectrum*, June 1964, 77.

"Knowles Wins Final Series to Take Bay Sailing Regatta." *Baltimore Sun,* July 26, 1965.

Lagemann, Robert T. and C. Harry Knowles. "Velocity of Compressional Waves in Liquid Hydrogen Fluoride and Some Thermodynamic Properties Derived Therefrom." *Journal of Chemical Physics* 32, no. 2 (1960).

Lasseter, Diana G. "A Bar-Code Breakthrough." *BUSINESS News New Jersey* 10, no. 15 (May 19, 1997): 1.

Lowe, Benjamin Y. "Metrologic Shares Fall on Reforecast." *Philadelphia Inquirer,* May 11, 2006.

Moore, Gordon E. "Cramming More Components Onto Integrated Circuits." *Electronics* 38:8 (April 19, 1965): 114-117.

Moore, Gordon E. "Progress in Digital Integrated Electronics." *Technical Digest,* IEEE International Electron Devices Meeting 21 (1975): 11-13.

"Mrs. Ruby Genevieve K. Carson" obituary. *Birmingham News,* May 17, 1989.

Mullins, Brody. "Equity Firms Try to Repair Image." *Wall Street Journal,* November 2, 2012.

Riordan, Michael. "How Bell Labs Missed the Microchip." *IEEE Spectrum,* December 2006.

"Story of the Transistor: Ten Years of Progress." Bell Telephone Laboratories Inc., 1958.

Tanaka, Wendy. "Scanner-maker Has Paid Price for Success." *Philadelphia Inquirer,* August 11, 2003.

Von Bergen, Jane M. "Metrologic Stock Falls 14 Percent After CEO Resigns." *Philadelphia Inquirer,* April 22, 2006.

Weisenfeld, Bernie. "Metrologic Sales Surging." *Courier-Post,* July 8, 1993.

CORPORATE MATERIALS
(from C. Harry Knowles Collection unless otherwise indicated)

Bell Telephone Laboratories.

Bell Telephone Laboratories History, Presidents. "Mervin J. Kelly." http://www.alcatel-lucent.com.

Knowles Science Teaching Foundation.

KSTF Annual Reports. http://www.kstf.org.

Metrologic Catalogs, 1976, 1979-1980. http://www.repairfaq.org/sam/brochures/ Metrologic.

Metrologic Instruments, Inc.

Metrologic Instruments, Inc. U.S. Securities and Exchange Commission Annual Reports. http://www.sec.gov/cgi-bin/browse-edgar?action=getcompany&CIK=0000 815910&type=10-K&dateb=&owner=exclude&count=40.

Metrologic Press Releases. Way Back Machine, http://archive.org/web/web.php.

Motorola Heritage Services and Archives. Annual Reports, 1957-1962. http://www. motorolasolutions.com/US-EN/About/Company+Overview/History. Motorola, Inc.

Westinghouse Electric Corporation.

ONLINE SOURCES

Adams, Russ. "A Short History of Bar Code." 2009. http://www.adams1.com/history. html.

"Arthur Leonard Schawlow," *A Dictionary of Scientists*. Oxford University Press, 2003. http://www.answers.com/topic/arthur-leonard-schawlow.

Auburn University Past Presidents. Office of Communications and Marketing. http://ocm.auburn.edu/presidential_installation/pastpresidents.html.

Birmingham (AL) Public Library Alabama Inventors. http://bpldb.bplonline.org/db/inventors.

"Brief History of the Marine Corps Recruit Depot, Parris Island, South Carolina, 1891-1962." http://www.au.af.mil/au/awc/awcgate/usmchist/parris.txt.

"Brief History of the Patent Law of the United States." Ladas & Parry, LLP, 2009. http://www.ladas.com/Patents/USPatentHistory.html.

"Carl H. (C. Harry) Knowles, 1995 Award Winners, Inventors of the Year." New Jersey Inventors Hall of Fame. http://www.stevens.edu/njinvent/awards/Awards1995.html.

Computer History Museum, The Silicon Engine. http://www.computerhistory.org/semiconductor.

Cummings, Rob. "History of the UPC Bar Code and the Uniform Code Council, Inc." 2010. http://www.cummingsdesign.com/bar_codes101_UCC_History.htm.

Davidson, Michael W. "Laser Fundamentals: Introduction to Lasers." Molecular Expressions Optical Microscopy Primer. Florida State University, 1998-2010. http://micro.magnet.fsu.edu/primer/lightandcolor/laserhome.html.

Early, James M. "K.D. Smith Memories." SMECC, 1990. http://www.smecc.org/k_d__smith_memories_by_j_m__early.htm.

Fairchild Semiconductor. "A History of Innovation—Fairchild Company History, 1957." 2011. http://www.fairchildsemi.com/company/history/#.

Get Downtown Birmingham, Lyric Theatre. http://www.getdowntown.info/Lyric_Theatre.html.

GS1. "Numbers in the History of the Universal Product Code." 2010. http://www.gs1us.org/about_us/numbers_in_the_upc.

GS1. "The Story of the Ad Hoc Committee." 2010. http://www.gs1us.org/about_us/history/ad_hoc_committee.

"Hall of Fame, C. Harry Knowles, Metrologic Instruments, Inc." *NJ Biz* Business of the Year 2006 Awards. www.njbiz.com.

Historical Enrollment Records, Auburn University Office of Institutional Research and Assessment. https://oira.auburn.edu.

Institute of Electrical and Electronics Engineers. "A Brief History of the IEEE." 2008. http://www.ieee.org/web/aboutus/history/index.html.

Inventor Biographies. William Shockley Biography. http://www.madehow.com/inventorbios/12/William-Shockley.html.

Laurer, George J. "Development of the UPC Symbol." 2001. http://www.laurerupc.com/.

"Life After Breast Cancer: A Survivor Speaks." *eHealth Connection*, October 2007. http://www.cooperhealth.org/content/ehealth_2007_10_01.htm.

Marine Corps Camps, Henderson Hall. http://www.globalsecurity.org/military/facility/henderson-hall.htm.

Marine Corps Recruiting Depot, Parris Island. https://www.mcrdpi.usmc.mil/SitePages/About%20Parris%20Island.aspx.

"Metrologic Instruments, Inc. Goes Private." MCG Capital Corp., *Transactions* 9, no. 4 (November 2006): 3-4. http://www.mcgcapital.com/downloads/MCG_Transactions_Nov_06.pdf.

"Minuteman and the Next Generation: 1960s-Present," National Park Service, November 19, 2003. http://www.nps.gov/history/history/online_books/mimi/hrs1-3a.htm.

Motorola History, 1930, 1940. http://www.motorola.com/staticfiles/Business/Corporate/US-EN/history/timeline.html

PBS Online. "Transistorized!" http://www.pbs.org/transistor/album1/addlbios/kelly.html.

Reynolds, Tom. "History of Barcode Scanners." 2010. http://www.nationalbarcode.com/history-of-barcode-scanners.htm.

Salisbury, David F. "Memorial Service May 20 for Arthur Schawlow, Laser Co-inventor." *Stanford Online Report,* May 5, 1999. http://news-service.stanford.edu/news/1999/may5/schawlowobit-55-a.html.

Schlofner, Rebecca. "The History of Bar Code Scanning." 2010. http://www.ehow.com/about_6630272_history-bar-code-scanning.html.

"Scholarship and Professorship Honor Late Howard E. Carr." Auburn University COSAM News, November 2003. http://www.auburn.edu/academic/science_math/cosam/news/archive/03/11/carr.html.

Sharpe, Edward A. "In Memoriam...Kenneth D. Smith, 1905-1990." Southwest Museum of Engineering, Communications and Computation. http://www.smecc.org/k_d__smith.htm.

Smith, Dave. "K.D. Smith." SMECC, http://www.smecc.org/k_d__smith_by_dave_smith.htm.

Solar Cells. Wikipedia. http://en.wikipedia.org/wiki/Solar_cell.

"Symbol Technologies, Inc." http://www.fundinguniverse.com/company-histories/Symbol-Technologies-Inc-Company-History.html.

"Universal Product Code." *Wikipedia*, 2010. http://en.wikipedia.org/wiki/Universal_Product_Code#cite_note-UMalumni-3.

U.S. Patent and Trademark Office. http://patft.uspto.gov.

Index

**THE
DONNELL
GROUP**